W. Kolbe, R. Bussmann, F. Winter

Agriculture and Food

The Ploughman (1945) Gerhard Marcks

Gerhard Marcks (1889—1981) has lived since 1950 in Cologne-Müngersdorf where he has practised the sculptor's art for three decades. His wood engraving "The Ploughman" which dates from 1945, a time when people in Europe also went hungry, symbolizes the importance of agriculture as the primary source of our food.

W. Kolbe, R. Bussmann,
F. Winter

# Agriculture and Food

Selected conversations and radio reports
(1963—1983)

Rheinischer Landwirtschafts-Verlag G.m.b.H., Bonn

With 155 illustrations and a four-page facsimile reproduction

English translation: Charlton & Wilkesmann, Cologne

Deutsche Bibliothek Cataloguing in Publication Data

Kolbe, Wilhelm:
Agriculture and Food / by Wilhelm Kolbe,
Rolf Bussmann and Franz Winter
Bonn: Rheinischer Landwirtschafts-Verlag 1985

ISBN: 3-924683-42-5

NE: Bussmann, Rolf
Winter, Franz



German title of the book: „Landbau und Ernährung"
1st German Edition 1983
2nd German Edition 1984

---

The reports originally broadcast as part of the radio agricultural service are published here with the kind permission of Westdeutscher Rundfunk, Cologne.

Printing and distribution: Rheinischer Landwirtschafts-Verlag G.m.b.H., Bonn

## Preface

Agriculture, for thousands of years a primary source of food in all continents and countries of the earth, has been practised by many generations of man. No matter what scientific and technical advances we achieve in our present age, we shall still need to cultivate the earth. Only plants, with the aid of the sun's energy, the carbon dioxide in the air and the nutrient solutions absorbed through their roots, are able to synthesize in their cells all year round the materials essential for life, such as carbohydrates, protein, fat and vitamins. Early in his history, man therefore attempted not only to collect the edible parts of plants, but also to cultivate those found to be useful. Evolution, the development of many different species of plants from wild to cultivated varieties, is one of man's inventive activities which began as long ago as the Stone Age and which continues to sustain our life on earth. World trade in antiquity and particularly in the modern era led to many plants being rediscovered and exchanged as a means of widening the range of available food. After the discovery of America, the potato and maize became new staple foods in many parts of Europe. In 19th century Germany "acclimatization associations" were formed to promote the establishment of new cultivated plants.

While in the European Community we now for the first time have a situation where agricultural and horticultural production not only meets the demands of the populace, but in which, as a result of good harvest years and agricultural policies, surpluses are being generated, there are many countries throughout the world where, either because of economic policy or for climatic reasons, less food is harvested than is needed. Increasing international trade in cereals and other agricultural produce is an eloquent testimony to this fact.

The conversations and radio reports collected in the present volume represent an attempt to promote an understanding of these relationships in the context of man's civilized history, giving particular emphasis to agriculture as the basic source of food as the life sustaining element of multiplying mankind.

The interdependence and overall relationships between all economic and political processes do not stop when it comes to agriculture. Like other social activities, agriculture is integrated into the prevailing economic systems. Over the last few decades, technical advances together with rural depopulation have brought about radical changes in crop growing and harvesting methods. The farmer and horticulturist must come to terms with this revolution in equipment and working methods if he wishes to run his enterprise efficiently and profitably. These changes are given attention in our talks.

There is strong competition for the products of man's crop growing endeavours. Many species of animal and other damaging organisms prefer to draw their sustenance from the crops cultivated by man. Hence man's endeavours from the very outset to protect the plants grown for his own consumption from attack by pests and from attendant harvest losses. Futurological studies repeatedly warn us that the increasing world population of the next 20, 50 or 100 years cannot be adequately fed unless food production is drastically increased. One of the themes of our commentaries is to demonstrate that technical progress, in the absence of economic and political obstacles, can undoubtedly provide the basis for improving harvests by extending cultivation and raising yields. While climate continues to exert major influence on annual harvests throughout the world, the most essential precondition for successful agriculture remains world peace.

The following words written by Bruno Wehnelt in 1934 provide an appropriate introduction to this book:

*History teaches us with many examples*
*that the finest fruit of wisdom is humility.*
*As old as tribulation*
*is the inventiveness of the hard-pressed.*
*Exploring our way backwards*
*again and again we find testimony to this ancient wisdom,*
*surprising only to those who believe*
*that their own age dictates the course of worlds,*
*that its discoveries are new and its works are eternal.*

Awareness of historical processes and an understanding of their interplay are the most important prerequisites for discussion in the present day.

The Authors

# Contents

Page



## Topics of discussion (1963—1983)

## Foreword

Concern for our daily bread has been a preoccupation since the dawn of man. In all periods of our history, lack of food has claimed as many victims as old age and disease, when corn rotted on the stem or when war prevented crops being tilled. Whereas in antiquity famines were limited in duration and extent, in medieval times from the eighth to the fourteenth century hunger became a permanent condition in all the countries of Europe.

12th century Germany, for example, suffered five protracted famines, and 13th century England underwent 15 such periods, truly 100-year wars of man to secure his daily nourishment. For these people, hunger did not have technical, but rather supernatural origins. Eclipes of the sun and moon ushered in famine and flood and hailstorms destroyed harvests as a divine punishment. In the chronicles of Gembloux, hunger is compared to the "ram", the siege machine of the Romans. Like the ram crashing against the city walls, hunger brings down the houses of rich and poor alike. Attempts to relieve famine by means of emergency measures are rarely found in the Middle Ages. One of the few such initiatives was taken by Charlemagne (768—814 A. D.), who forbade exports of cereals, issued an edict regulating maximum prices, decreed an emergency tax and established commissary distribution centres for the poor. These unfortunates crowded into the refectories where they received three meals per day.

This plight of the starving masses contrasts sharply with the descriptions we have received of courtly life. Need never afflicts the members of a given society to an equal degree, writes Prentice in his book on the influence of hunger on man's history. In situations where all should work together to relieve hardship, many continue to live in affluence. In the Middle Ages, many princely courts were indeed oases of opulence. Pictures from this time show lords and ladies clothed in costly garments. The courtly splendour also extends to the banqueting hall; spectacular dishes are served, such as castles with gardens of meat and pastry. Not only the cooks, but also the "culinary sculptors" had been at work. So for example in times of war, the winter siege of a fortified city was presented, with frozen moats modelled in confectionery, siege engines of sugar and fishponds of gelatin. The bread so desperately needed by the populace was present here in abundance. More than twenty types of bread are described in the 12th and 13th century, bread served only to nobles, bread meant only for servants and finally the "pain de boulanger" eaten only by the common people. Crowds of beggars jostled at the doors of the rich hoping to receive some of the discarded tablecloths which at that time were made of bread dough. One of the strangest customs of the Middle Ages perhaps, but explicable in view of the lack of linen tablecloths. On these dough "cloths" the meat was cut and, at the end of the meal, splashed with fat and wine, were eaten from the ends of the table or, following a more Christian custom, distributed to the poor waiting outside.

Extravagance was however not unknown in other classes. In the city of Augsburg, for example, an artisan family which had come into wealth ran through an entire fortune in a single week, after inviting 700 guests to a wedding. These excesses were practised against the sombre background of the time. The bread for which peasants and townsfolk clamoured in the long periods of famine, was regarded as sacred. Many manners and customs, legends and fairy tales which still persist today among the people, make reference to the sacred nature of bread, quite apart from its religious significance in the Christian Mass. Many ancient stories deal with the wanton misuse of bread. The city of Vineta sank into the Baltic Sea because its impious inhabitants stopped the holes in the city walls with bread.

Ezekiel (6th century B. C.) was instructed how to eke out one's bread in times of want: "Take wheat, barley, beans, lentils, millet and spelt, put all into a barrel and make bread thereof". The starving masses of Europe in the Middle Ages also resorted to many kinds of substitute foods: acorn bread, bread made from common marram grass, medusohead and reed was baked, as was bread made from straw and the bark of trees. Others, driven by hunger, could not wait and took to the fields. The chronicler reports: Like cattle they devoured raw herbs and perished from dysentery. Hunger, referred to by Homer (8th century B. C.) as the "degrader of mankind" drove men to extremes in an attempt to relieve their distress.

Yet even worse was to come. In Europe around 1300, hunger was joined by its grim fellow, the plague. While in ancient times hunger and plague had been limited both in duration and extent, both now spread throughout Europe in the wake of increasing world trade. Originating in India, the plague spread in succession to Sicily, Italy, France, England, Germany and Russia. The first wave lasted for four years. After a brief respite, further waves were to come. Like a vast earthquake, the twin evils of pestilence and hunger devastated the western world. In the years around 1350, four million of the eight million inhabitants of England were wiped out by starvation and disease. Many cities of Northern Europe appear to have lost 90 per cent of their inhabitants at this time. Of the 100 million Europeans alive during the Middle Ages, 25 million were carried off by starvation coupled with plague. Villages and towns alike were depopulated.

Despite all the progress achieved by our civilization over the last hundred years, the world in which we are now living faces the worst food crisis in its history. The enormous growth in population has left us with almost insuperable food supply problems. 40 million people starve to death every year. Only one in three eats his fill. Forecasts tell us that in twenty years the world population will have grown from the present four and a half to six thousand million. For the first time, however, hunger in the world, as a humanitarian scandal, is not simply being ignored but researched as a social phenomenon and taken seriously as a political problem.

Although we Europeans have known famine for a hundred years, relatively speaking a short period, only as a consequence of wars and revolutions but not as a result of harvest failures, today's areas of food scarcity lie within a broad belt around the equator in the tropical and subtropical zones, in Southern Asia, the Middle East, Africa and Latin America. These are agrarian economies whose outdated farming methods produce insufficient food for their increased population. International, national, religious and private organizations are engaged in trying to provide assistance and bring about improvements by raising yields in the starving countries and by delivering grain from the surplus-producing countries such as the USA and Canada. Peace in the world depends on solving the food supply problem and eradicating hunger. The significance of these measures in terms of world politics is tellingly expressed by the celebrated proverb of Solomon (965—926 B. C.): If thy enemy hungers, feed him with bread.

## Introduction

Information on specialized or technical subjects is communicated through the spoken and written word. The coming of radio, which broadcast its first programme in Germany in 1923, opened up new and formerly unsuspected dimensions in the dissemination of information and knowledge.

As long ago as August 11, 1924, Hamburg Radio included the "Farmer's Hour" in its broadcasting schedule. Around this time, special radio programmes such as the "Doctor's Hour" or the "Solicitor's Hour" were also being developed for other professional groups. Of all these, only the "Agricultural and Farming Programme" has survived, together with the "Economics Programme" and "Schools Radio", since these programmes are of interest not only to specialists but also the general listener.

At the International Agricultural Congress in Dresden in 1939, Morales y Fraile, the Spanish member of the Central Committee of the International Association of Agricultural Broadcasting, reported that agricultural radio programmes were being broadcast in 44 countries throughout the world. The transmission times he quoted ranged from six hours per day to 15 minutes per week.

In the early days of agricultural broadcasting in Germany, programmes consisted of market and price bulletins, weather forecasts, business advice and technical information, the latter taking the form of specialized lectures on topics from horticulture and animal husbandry. The introduction of the "walking microphone" ushered in the age of on-the-spot outside broadcasting. Popular series such as "From a Westphalian Farm" and "In a Winery on the Rhine" broadcast in 1929 by the West German Broadcasting Corporation, in which reports were relayed directly from the scene of the action, gave birth to a new form of broadcasting, namely reportage or the reportage series.

The importance of radio can be judged from the number of subscribers, that is the number of radio licences which have been issued: In Germany, this number reached 100,000 as early as 1924, rose to one million in 1926, eight million in 1936 and a total of ten million in 1939. The Federal Republic of Germany currently has more than twenty million licensed radio subscribers and in the European Community of the Ten more than 100 million radio licences have been issued. In the USA, more than 400 million radio sets are at present in use.

Reporting and information services in radio and particularly in agricultural broadcasting draw on established journalistic and instructional techniques. Besides reportage, in which the reporter gives a more personal view of current events or trends in a specialized field or, if delivered in the form of interview reportage, relays the opinions of the people interviewed, the dialogue, a conversation between two or more persons, continues to be cultivated and used as a form of scientific, literary or practical discussion within the framework of reportage.

In Classical Antiquity and the Middle Ages, the dialogue was used to present scientific problems not only through the medium of didactic verbal exchange, but also in book form, for instance in the epic or the philosophical disputation.

In the field of agriculture, the Birckmann publishing house in Cologne issued "Rei Rusticae Libri Quatuor", the "Four Books on Agriculture" by Konrad Heresbach (2. 8. 1496—14. 10. 1576 A. D.), who for four decades farmed Lorward Estate near the town of Wesel in the Lower Rhine District, and who in this work presented his observations, experience and principles. This conversational form also served as the basis for the dialogue technique used in the agricultural works "Rerum Rusticarum Libri III" by Marcus Terrentius Varro (116—27 B. C.), an important writer of ancient Rome.

The continued relevance of the problems of agriculture and crop growing experienced in antiquity is apparent from the "conversation" included in this volume, which is taken from the first book "On Agriculture" by Heresbach, which appeared for the first time in German translation in 1970. Topics discussed in this work include technical cultivation problems relating to cereal crops towards the end of the Middle Ages. It is evident from the 400-year old "technical discussion" or "reportage" that the problems of tillage, sowing and seed treatment, weed control, harvesting and stored product protection faced by farmers so long ago are very similar to those which concern us today.

Following this introduction and the discussion dating from 1570 between Konrad Heresbach and his friend Rigo, who receives instruction about the problems of arable farming in this period, a number of radio talks and reportages, broadcast over the last two decades, are presented, which are concerned with the problems of agriculture as a basic means of production and supplier of food to the world's population. These discussions and reportages are the product of cooperation both on a technical and personal level between authors who have been active for many years as agricultural journalists, technical advisors, scientists and farm managers.

During these twenty years, agriculture has undergone fundamental changes worldwide, particularly in the industrialized countries. In the age of Konrad Heresbach, the invention of the clock as an instrument for measuring time and the introduction of the horse as a draught animal revolutionized the Middle Ages. These developments are paralleled in our own age by advances in soil and crop cultivation methods, plant breeding, agrochemistry and traffic engineering, which have led to an increase in agricultural and horticultural yields and intensified world trade in agricultural produce. An improved supply of food to the world's population has been the result.

Over the past two decades, the authors have held 365 radio talks and reportages in the agricultural programme of the West German Broadcasting Corporation (WDR) alone. This book presents a selection, arranged under ten major headings, of talks and reportages which highlight characteristic trends in agriculture over this period. The statistical data provided have been updated, chiefly to facilitate comparison. As an aid to comprehension, each section is preceded by an introduction to the respective topic.

## Conversation about agriculture from the year 1570

A didactic dialogue from the year 1570 between the landowner Konrad Heresbach, of Lorward estate, Lower Rhine, and his friend Rigo, who visits him at home in the country, seeking advice about topical farming problems of the time.

*The sky is sunny and bright, it beckons me forth to take a walk in the open air and view your estate. Please tell me something about the nature of your farmland and how it is worked.*

First let me tell you about the soil for growing cereals. The best place for farming is on a southwards-inclined plane at the foot of a mountain. In cold regions, the farmland should lie to the south or east. In hot regions, a northerly position is best.

*It is said that one should attempt to sense out the quality of the ground one wishes to farm.*

The nature of a piece of land is easier to recognize than the character of a man. It does not attempt to conceal its true self, but presents itself openly and plainly for all to see. To judge the quality of the earth, Xenophon (430—354 B. C.) said that one should first look at the plants and trees which grow there. And one should not attempt to cultivate anything which cannot withstand the climate. The climate therefore has the greatest influence on the quality of the soil, because neither the sky nor the air are constant in all regions.

*The local climate doubtless exerts a very great influence on the fertility of the soil. I have noticed myself that soil of the selfsame quality produces richer or poorer yields depending on its location.*

Herodotus (484—424 B. C.) writes that Babylon ist so fertile that wheat there gives a 200- and 300-fold yield. Pliny (23—79 A. D.) says that the harvest produces a 50-fold, and for more industrious farmers even a 100-fold interest. Italy is so fertile that Varro (116—27 B. C.) refers to it as an orchard, so abundant are the crops.

*I have heard that Germany and France were formerly not so fertile, whereas now they produce everything one could need and are surpassed by no other country. Which wine from anywhere in the world could now be thought better than that from Southern Germany or the Rhineland?*

In our region too (the Lower Rhine) fields giving new yields each year are no rarity. For example, after a single sowing rape-seed often grows back in two successive years without re-sowing and cultivation.

*Since the soil does not contain such a fruitful mixture in every place, what does one do when faced with poor and infertile soil? Is it possible to improve such soils artificially and to make them fertile?*

Various methods can be used, but the most effective are fertilization and careful cultivation. For this purpose we keep the dung which I showed you recently. Among the various other methods of enriching the soil, in Germany we also spread rich and fat earth (marl) on the land instead of manure, as if to strengthen the marrow of the earth. Marl is obtained from ditches dug deep in the earth. In other areas, the mud is collected from pools and rivers and makes the land extremely fertile. In many areas with poor soil, the land can be made fertile again with lime. In Upper Italy ash is so highly prized for this purpose that it is preferred to manure.

*Now we have heard of the various methods of fertilization, I should like to hear something about ploughing, tilling the earth and sowing.*

Ploughing and preparing the soil for sowing is extremely important. Above all, the weeds which enrich the earth like manure are ploughed in and prevented from sprouting before the seed germinates.

*Can one also plough at night?*

Certainly! In warmer climes, in summer one starts ploughing in the evening and works the whole night through until sunrise. The advantage of this is that, in the shadow, the moisture and the fat soil remain under the clod and the draught animals do not suffer in the hot sun and become ill.

*But can one plough and sow the same earth continuously every year?*

There are some regions where annual sowing is possible. Otherwise, the old country proverb should be followed: Do not cheat the seed of its fruit, which means do not cultivate the land until nothing more will grow. In other words, depending on the nature of the soil, the land should either be left fallow every second year or sown with lighter seed, for instance lupin seed, which places less of a burden on the soil and does not drain the strength from the land. Beans and the other legumes enrich the soil in which they grow and serve as fertilizer.

*Now you have shown how the land is prepared for sowing, could you now explain what kinds of seed there are and how they should be planted in the earth?*

Pliny speaks of two kinds of crop: cereals which have ears and legumes which have husks. When sowing seeds brought from another country, it is important that they be planted in a richer soil than before. One should also make sure that the seed has not been damaged by mice, birds or ants. To improve the seed, it should be sprinkled with houseleek before sowing. To protect the seed from birds, add hellebore in large amounts to the grain which is sown. Sowing evenly with a steady hand is also an art to be learned. Wheat, rye, barley, oats and some others are sown by the handful, but turnip seed should be sown with only three fingers. Heavy soil like that in the Rhineland needs more, and a lighter earth less seed.

After sowing is finished, harrowing must be performed. This is done by drawing toothed wickerwork over the field, which breaks up the clods and covers the seeds. This is known as harrowing in.

As regards the best time for sowing and the amounts of seed to be sown per acre, some people observe certain rules, but these apply only for the special climatic conditions and the nature of the soil in their own region.

When the seed form the first nodules, the weeds are pulled from the ground, which admits more air to the roots, which are then separated from the clumps of grass.

When the weather becomes warmer, a stem shoots from the centre on whose fourth or third nodule the ear forms. Wheat flowers at about the same time as the vine, and thus the two noblest crops come to fruition side by side. After flowering, the ear becomes thick and ripens within 40 days.

The awn is a kind of needle on the ear of wheat and barley by means of which the plant protects its artfully arranged fruit from attack by birds.

*What method do you use for mowing?*

In our area we use three kinds of sickling methods for mowing: a crescent-shaped sickle is held in the right hand with which the stems are cut above the ground, while the cut wheat is gathered into sheaves with a long hook held in the left hand. If the stems are rather long, they are cut off in the middle so that they can be collected and threshed more easily.

The straw which remains is either burned or left on the ground to rot and fertilize the soils.

After cutting, the grain should not be stored immediately in the barn, but must first be allowed to dry for a time appropriate to the variety of grain or legume. Wheat however can be put into storage sooner than other crops, unless it is heavily interspersed with weeds, since then it takes longer to dry.

The mown and dried grain however is stored either in granaries or field barns and then later in the winter time is either threshed out by the cattle or with flails and cleaned with the aid of winnows.

Because of the weeds, the land must be ploughed directly after the harvest; this also makes it more receptive for future sowing.

*When the grains have been threshed out, how are they stored to make them safe from grain weevils?*

The granaries in which the threshed and cleaned grain is stored must be high structured so that the wind can blow through them. No moist air from the neighbourhood must be allowed to touch them. The best possible storage conditions for grain should be both as cold and as dry as possible. In our region, both grapes and grain are also stored underground. Since grain is also exposed to the threat of decimation by grain weevils and similar creatures, it is quickly destroyed if it is not stored properly. The walls should therefore be coated with clay to which hair is added instead of chaff, and should then be coated inside and outside with white clay. Finally, the roots and leaves of the wild cucumber are softened in water for two days and the water is added to a mortar mixture of lime and sand, which is used to coat the inside of the granary. Often cattle urine is mixed with the lime, as this is believed to kill vermin. The leaves of houseleek, wormwood or hops, and particularly — if available — oil foam are also effective for killing these pests. Many use instead the brine from pickled herring. When the walls and the floor have been treated in this way and have dried, it is believed that the grain can then be stored free from the threat of grain weevils and similar harmful insects. Many farmers spread half-cooled elecampane underneath the corn. Strabo (63 B. C.—23 A. D.) writes that grain is preserved by an admixture of chalcidic earth. Others consider the surest method to expose the grain repeatedly to draughts on the threshing floor and allowing it to cool a little, although Columella (1st century A. D.) assures us that this method is incorrect, since in this way the harmful insects are not driven out but rather spread throughout the entire heap whereas, if it is not moved, they attack only the surface. Experience however teaches us that there is no more effective means of expelling the grain weevil than by frequently moving and airing the grain, particularly in summer.

But surely I must be tiring you with this long walk around the estate. If you are agreeable let us now return home.

*As you like! However it has been a great pleasure to walk with you and to hear your interesting opinions about farming.*

*As you have presented it, farming is certainly a wide-ranging science which demands diligence and continuous care.*

Dr. Konrad Heresbach (1496—1576)
Statesman and farmer
Farmed Lorward estate in the Lower Rhinland from 1536 to 1576 and wrote the first book on German agriculture.

Konrad Heresbach was born in 1496 at Heresbach farm in Mettmann-Hahnenfurth. The estate, with buildings dating from the 15th century, is still in the family's possession.

This stone inlaid by Konrad Heresbach into the wall of his farmhouse at Lorward in 1538 bears the following inscription (in translation): This is the stone discarded by the builders, which has been made a cornerstone and in none other is salvation. Petri 2,7 Acts of the Apostles. Dedicated to the Host of the Saviour by the married couple Jurist Conrad Heresbach and Mechtild von Dunen on June 1, 1538.

Lorward estate was later re-named Ryswickshof. View of Ryswickshof in Mehr (Haffen-Mehr) 50 years ago.

Where once fields were farmed for many centuries on Lorward estate and later at Ryswickshof, we now find an artificial lake in a disused gravel quarry.

At Höfchen Experimental Station in Burscheid, the talks were held which led to the compilation of this book of selected radio reports. View of the timber-framed farmhouse in the slate-hung Bergischer style built early last century.

## Topics of discussion (1963—1983)

# I. World food supply and the limits of food production

The struggle against hunger is man's major problem in our present age. Even now, half of all the inhabitants of the developing countries are inadequately nourished: one tenth are suffering from hunger. The economic inequality of peoples is the most serious cause of tension in today's world. Every day, thousands are dying from hunger and its effects. In India alone one fifth and in Africa about one third of all children less than one year old suffer this fate. Many initiatives have now been taken to provide urgent remedies for this situation.

By the year 2000, statisticians have calculated, mankind which now numbers more than 4,700 million will have increased to more than 6,000 million, without food production in the countries threatened by the population explosion having increased accordingly.

To keep pace with this ominous rise in the world population, another 1.25 million tons of food would have to be produced each year. Unhappily, the available food is distributed unequally around the globe. No less than 70 per cent of all humanity inhabit the developing countries of Africa, Asia and South America. However, these countries produce only about 45 per cent of all food supplies. In the year 2000, these countries will account for 80 per cent of the world population. Even now, 30 to 40 million tons of grain have to be sent each year to these hunger-stricken countries. Although at the moment this is often the only effective means of providing assistance, many efforts are being undertaken to improve the agricultural structure and harvest yields in the affected countries.

The danger of threatening world famine will have to be met in two ways: firstly by curbing the population increase, and secondly by increasing food production. Since worldwide birth control cannot be expected to play a decisive role in preventing increasing food shortages in the coming decades, harvest quantities will have to be substantially increased if the more than 6,000 million people expected to populate the earth by the year 2000 are to have enough to eat.

The central task in preventing world famine will be to achieve in the developing countries most acutely threatened by hunger that which has been possible in America, Europe and particularly in the European Community, namely to increase yields per unit area.

At the start of the previous century, these yields were as low in our countries as they are now in most developing countries, that is 800 kg grain per hectare. Today's wheat yields in the Federal Republic of Germany, Denmark, the Netherlands and Great Britain, but also in parts of France and Italy, run at about 5 to 6 tons per hectare, and in favourable locations and with intensive cropping even much higher.

Hunger is the basic problem which lies at the root of many difficulties throughout the world. The United Nations Food and Agriculture Organization (FAO) is endeavouring to improve the cultivation methods of all crops in terms of soil tillage, mechanization, fertilization, selection of cultivars and crop protection in all the crisis areas of the world.

Depending on the climatic zone, losses caused by pests, diseases and weeds reach 25 to 35 per cent and more. Crop protection is thus the most important factor in world agriculture for achieving increased yields and securing harvests.

According to the Food and Agriculture Organization (FAO), control programmes to combat pests, diseases and weeds in agricultural production could become the decisive factor in the fight against malnutrition.

Only about 35 per cent of the earth's surface are suitable for agricultural use. Furthermore, large parts of this are lost each year due to soil erosion and urbanization of the countryside. To compensate for this diminution in area, which can scarcely be compensated by land recovery, it will be necessary to increase agricultural yields.

On average, the potential world harvest of grain would be 25 per cent higher than the actual harvest of more than 1.6 thousand million tons. The other 400 million tons are lost each year due to the absence or inadequate application of measures to protect crops and stored products.

Consistently high yields are for example achievable for cereals such as wheat and barley, particularly in regions of moderate climate. In the farming regions of the continental climatic zone, especially in dry regions or in drought years and in regions with early or protracted winter, yields are repeatedly subject to negative influences which can result in considerable variations and losses of yield. Whatever the region, however, crops growing in adverse or favourable climates must be protected from losses by means of crop protection.

Especially in the developing countries, loss-free storage of harvests must be ensured, since protection of stored products is a major priority in hot countries because of the high rate at which pests breed.

Agricultural production must therefore be increased in the future if the growing world population is to be adequately fed. Political upheavals in hunger-stricken areas with worldwide repercussions will be the result if we are unsuccessful in reconciling the production and demand for food.

## *1. World cereal balance*

*Regular and adequate supply of the population with cereal products is the most important task in world politics. A decisive factor in achieving this aim is to stockpile production in years of ample harvests as a security for years of crop failure. How large is the total cereal cultivation area of the world?*

The total world cropping area for cereals is 740 million hectares, and world cereal production is 1.6 thousand million tons. Apart from the cereals produced by the different countries for domestic consumption, the quantity of grain offered on the world market by the exporting countries is also very important.

*Which are the major grain exporting countries on the world market?*

World trade in grain currently amounts to 200 million tons. North America is more and more becoming the granary of the world. Since 1970, grain exports from the USA and Canada have increased from 65 million tons to a present 140 million tons. Grain exports are a major source of foreign exchange for these countries.

*What are the reasons for this?*

The USA has the largest continuous land mass of fertile soil with favourable climate and suitable cropping conditions for cereal production in the world. After meeting domestic demands, about 60 per cent of wheat and rice, about half of the soybean crop, one quarter of the sorghum and over 20 per cent of maize production are available for export to the rest of the world. The largest cereal growing region of the earth, the wheat belt in the Midwest of the USA, produces the world's largest grain harvest every year, even though in some years yields are reduced in periods of drought and extreme heat. From one harvest to the next, that is from year to year, the vast multitude of hundreds of millions of people in the world continues to multiply, whose demand for food can be met only by grain imports from the United States and Canada and from other grain exporting countries.

*Were not grain exports formerly also important for the balance of payments in many countries?*

Even before the Second World War, in all the major geographical units of the earth with the exception of Western Europe, more cereals were grown than were consumed. Now, however, of the 115 countries for which reliable foreign trade statistics are available, only a few countries like the USA, Canada, France, Australia and Argentina export more grain than they import. Countries which have to import more than half their grain requirement include Japan, Senegal, Lybia, Saudi Arabia, Venezuela, Lebanon, Algeria and Switzerland.

*The biggest grain importer on the world market must be the Soviet Union at about 30 million tons. What is the reason for this large demand?*

The reason lies in Russia's high annual bread consumption of 150 kg per head of population, whereas in the Federal Republic of Germany only 60 to 70 kg, and in the USA 50 kg, are consumed. The production deficits in the USSR are due to the crop failures which occur in certain areas due to unfavourable climatic influences such as drought or early onset of winter, which frequently occur in these latitudes. The agricultural structure of this country also tends to exacerbate the consequences of harvest failures caused by bad weather.

*The inadequate grain supply in almost all countries of the world would seem to justify the question as to what can be done in terms of production methods to remedy this situation?*

Cereal production can be increased both by enlarging cultivation areas, and also by increasing yields per unit area. Since the world's available cropping areas are generally subject to limitations, increased grain production can be achieved only by improving area yields.

*What are the most important means of achieving this?*

In addition to soil cultivation, fertilization, farming and harvesting techniques as well as selection of varieties and provision of healthy seed, it is without doubt crop protection which will be able to permanently boost yields. In addition to the control of insect pests and fungal diseases, another important factor in increasing yields worldwide is weed control. We must also not forget the need to protect stored products, since much food is lost to man due to the depredations of stored product pests such as grain weevils and rats, which destroy large quantities of grain after it has been harvested.

## 2. *Food supply on the European market*

*The European Common Market serves more than 270 million consumers in the ten EC countries Federal Republic of Germany, France, Greece, Italy, the Netherlands, Luxemburg, Great Britain, Ireland and Denmark. The European Community thus has more consumers than the USA or Soviet Union. The borders between these countries are no longer barred by customs tariffs or import quota restrictions. Food and other important produce can now pass unhindered from one country to another. What are the practical consequences of this situation?*

The advantage of the Common Market lies in the improvement of trade relations. The area ultimately available to the consumer to obtain the necessities of life at favourable prices is greatly increased. The larger the market becomes, the stronger will be the market position of those producers who, for reasons of climate or because of other natural advantages, can produce more cheaply than their competitors. This leads to considerable distortions in the competitive structure, which may manifest themselves as advantages or disadvantages for the producer and/or consumer.

*Has the nature of the food supply changed?*

The range of foods on offer each day has indeed improved dramatically over the last few years. This is apparent even from the wide choice offered by the grocer and greengrocer with his many new products coming for example from France, Italy, the Netherlands or Belgium, and also from non-EC countries. Fresh vegetables of all kinds from different areas of the EC are available almost all year round, irrespective of the season. Depending on the climate or latitude, deliveries are made successively throughout the year. Autumn and spring are the most important seasons for production in Italy and Southern France. In summer, however, production in these regions is relatively much lower because of the protracted hot and dry weather, sometimes lasting for several months. It is during these very periods that domestic vegetable production reaches its peak. These supplies are completed by greenhouse crops, a form of cultivation which so far has been pursued intensively only in the Netherlands. In this country, cultivation and harvesting are controlled in such a way that the different varieties of vegetable come onto the market when field crops are not or no longer available, or only in insufficient quantities.

*What level of self-sufficiency has now been achieved by the European Community?*

At present there are some six million agricultural enterprises in the European Community, including horticultural production. These produce about 90 to 95 per cent of the food requirement of the European population. Only 5 to 10 per cent of our food is imported from third countries.

*Agriculture must certainly have undergone some changes?*

The structure of agriculture has certainly changed considerably. Today, less than half as many farmers on a somewhat reduced area produce more than twice as much food as in 1950. To achieve this, they have increased their investment fivefold. The productivity of each worker is four to five times higher in terms of quantity and eight times higher in financial terms.

*This must have major consequences?*

Further basic changes in the structure of agriculture and horticulture are to be expected. The latest technological knowledge is now being applied. For reasons of rationalization, as in industry, these advances are compelling the introduction of mass production methods to achieve the highest possible production output per person, area and animal. Now and in future, much more capital will be needed than before. An associated trend however is a decrease in the need for manpower. In this way, an increase in per capita income can be achieved. As production and marketing units become ever more efficient, the complex relationships between production and marketing proliferate. The pressure on the many small agricultural enterprises whose competitiveness is declining more and more, is becoming inescapable. Also to be considered in this respect are the social problems arising from the shedding of labour in rural areas as result of technical advances.

*Apart from this change in traditional agricultural production methods, there must be many enterprises which hope to obtain new consumer outlets by cultivating new products such as sweet corn, crisp lettuce, cress and aubergines which are not yet so familiar in this country?*

These attempts derive from the recognition that, in the long term, saturation of the market will preclude a further quantitative increase in food consumption. Rather, it will tend quite markedly to promote a more discriminating choice of products for more demanding tastes. With decreasing per capita consumption, the less selective eating habits of former times will be replaced by a more health-conscious approach. Quality will become more important than quantity, and quality produce of the highest standard will displace the anonymous, cheap, but not always first class mass-produced products from the market. Quality produce can be offered to satisfy individual taste and can be sold directly, particularly around large towns. The consumer however will have to pay higher prices for this improved service.

*Surely there will be considerable differences here too?*

Eating habits are extremely varied within the different regions of the European Community. They are based on custom, climatic conditions and also on influences originating from the great differences in income level. Naturally, price differences or more precisely the price relations between the individual foods are significant in this respect. Also to be remembered is the interplay between consumption and production and vice versa which is determined to a great extent by tradition. In traditional vine-growing regions, for example, much more wine will be consumed than in regions where vines do not flourish.

*Can you illustrate this difference with another example?*

As a general rule, we can say that in the cooler zones of the European Community, more concentrated foods with a higher fat and protein content are consumed than in the southerly zones. Conversely, in the warmer latitudes we frequently find that a lighter diet is favoured, for instance more vegetables than potatoes and often also more fruit. To this extent the climate is also a decisive factor, since in countries subject to high temperatures, easily perishable foods are not so much in demand.

*Perhaps it would be helpful to quote some figures to illustrate this?*

The consumption of cereals calculated in terms of flour per year and per head of population varies from 130 kg in Italy to 65 kg in Germany, Denmark and the Netherlands. By contrast, Italy with 30 kg per capita consumes the least amount of potatoes and Ireland the most with 130 kg. As regards sugar consumption, the last few years have shown a considerable assimilation trend, so that consumption now varies only between 35 and 45 kg. Vegetable consumption is highest in Italy with 150 kg and lowest in Denmark with 50 kg. Finally, the consumption of fruit is highest in the Federal Republic of Germany at 120 kg per capita and lowest in Ireland at 40 kg.

*The great variety of agricultural produce and of consumer habits is a conspicuous feature of the European Community. At the same time, it is one of the Community's greatest assets. Producers can grow and market the widest varieties of food at many different times throughout the year. This in turn allows consumers to satisfy their more discerning tastes.*

## 3. The importance of bread in the world food supply

(Some thoughts on the occasion of the harvest thanksgiving festival)

*As has always been the case, bread continues to be a staple element of our daily food. The importance which all peoples have attached and continue to attach to bread is demonstrated by its symbolic significance in world religion. Bread is sacred to all peoples, bread is a symbol of peace and friendship. To trample on a cornfield, to throw bread away, has been counted a sin for thousands of years. Even though grain for bread is harvested in every season throughout the world, we still retain the custom of expressing harvest thanksgiving on the first Sunday after Michaelmas. After all, a good or a poor harvest formerly decided, as indeed it does today, whether people go hungry or can be adequately provided with bread. What in fact is bread?*

Bread is baked from flour, water and salt with addition of raising agents. Dough is formed through the combination of flour and water. A raising or fermenting agent swells the dough. The traditional raising agent is sourdough whose bacteria and yeasts cause fermentation. Sourdough is used for baking rye-bread; for wheat bread, yeast is used. The breads most frequently on offer in this country have been baked with yeast, which is a quicker method and presents fewer problems. The taste of bread also depends on the crust. Crusty breads generally have a richer taste than those without crust.

*What are the origins of bread?*

The art of baking bread, as far as we know, was invented by the Egyptians about 5000 years ago. The oldest description of a bakery dates from the time of Ramses III (1188—1157 B. C.). At that period in history, bread was not only a food but also a currency. For example, a peasant would receive three loaves as his daily wage. In the Iron Age around 800 B. C., bread was already generally known among the Germans; this was rye-bread. The baker's trade as such came into being in this country in the 13th and 14th century A. D.

*How does bread consumption in former times compare to that today?*

Around 1800 our bread consumption was 300 kg per person and year, whereas now, because of the wide variety of foods available, it has declined to 60 to 70 kg. Nevertheless, bread still accounts for 40 per cent of our total food requirement. Cereal products provide more than one third of our protein intake and half of our carbohydrate consumption.

*What life-sustaining materials does bread contain?*

Our commonest bread contains six to ten per cent protein, about 50 per cent carbohydrates and one per cent fat. The minerals are usually one per cent common salt and up to one per cent other minerals with one per cent fibre. The water content of bread is about 40 per cent. The composition is subject to great variations and very much depends on the type of bread and the chemical composition of the flour which is used.

*What are the most important types of bread grain?*

In our latitudes, bread is made mainly from rye and wheat, although recently wheat has tended to displace rye to a great extent. The importance of wheat also lies in its suitability for other froms of baked products and the other cereal products of the food industry, such as semolina or noodles. In all other parts of the world, bread is baked not only from wheat and rye but also from all other varieties of grain.

*How is the flour prepared?*

Flour is produced by grinding the cereal grains. Different degrees of grinding are performed. Light grinding removes the outer parts of the grain which are used as bran for cattle food. The different types of flour are identified with numbers as such as 405 or 1150. The number states the content of non-combustible constituents, that is of life sustaining minerals. Type 405 for example indicates that 100 grams of flour yield 0.405 grams of ash on combustion.

*Which flour is used to bake which bread?*

Rye-bread is at present baked mainly from flour Type 1150, and German army bread from pure rye flour of Type 1370, in other words both of these breads are made from flours with a high mineral content. White bread is prepared from light wheat flour of Types 550 and 405, and mixed bread consists primarily of 60 per cent rye flour of Type 1150 and 40 per cent wheat flour of Type 1050. Wholemeal bread contains all parts of the grain including the husk and the seed and is thus particularly nourishing and healthy.

*Bread therefore continues to be an important staple food. Our population can regard their supply of bread as secure; what is the situation in other parts of the world?*

Despite tremendous advances in agriculture, we have not yet succeeded in banishing hunger from the world. Devastating famines occur as a result of crop failures in Africa and many other regions. The Food and Agriculture Organization of UNO, the FAO, has been concerned for years to reduce the incidence of hunger in the developing countries. These endeavours take the form both of direct deliveries of food and development projects aimed at improving harvests in the affected countries.

*Every year, 25 to 35 per cent of the world grain harvest is lost because of pests and diseases. If everything possible were to be done to prevent these losses not only in the industrialized countries but in all other countries by improving cultivation methods and standards of crop protection, the supply of bread could be secured and hunger would be eradicated.*

# II. Food crops in agriculture and horticulture

Although there are many thousands of plant species throughout the world which are used directly for human nourishment, there are only a few which have general importance for mankind in terms of the world economy. These types of plant can be classified into several groups.

The first group consists of all kinds of cereal; secondly, other plants which store carbohydrates such as sugar cane, sugar beet, potatoes and sweet potatoes; and thirdly plants which produce protein. Also known are the oil plants, fibre plants, stimulants and other plants which are the source of semi-luxury products and spice plants. A special category includes vines, exotic and domestic fruits. Finally, the rubber plant, the hop and the medicinal plants should also be mentioned.

One major reason for the importance of some of these plants in the world economy is their high yield, their great adaptability to different climates and soils, and the favourable characteristics of the harvested and processed products in storage and transport.

The cereal varieties wheat, barley, rye, oats and maize are exceptional in that they can be stored for long periods and can be cultivated anywhere in the world. A special position is occupied by rice, whose cultivation as paddy or upland rice is concentrated in the warmer climates of the earth and particularly in South and East Asia. Cereals are our most important source of carbohydrates.

Other species of plants which store carbohydrates also supply us with sugar. Whereas the cultivation of sugar cane is limited to the tropical and subtropical regions, sugar beet is grown in moderate climates.

The potato, which per unit area produces just as much protein and twice as many carbohydrates as cereal, has become very widely grown throughout the world over the last few centuries. Plant varieties which have worldwide importance as protein producers are soybean and other varieties of legume such as beans and peas.

Vegetable fats and oils are of major importance for man's supply of fat. Annual production is about 15 to 16 million tons, and that of animal fats is about 11 million. The cultivation of soybean, ground nuts and sunflowers has risen continuously over the past twenty years. The oil plants are another range of botanical species extending from the annuals such as soybean, sunflower, cotton seed, peanuts and rape to permanent crops such as oil palm and olive tree. There are thus a large number of plant species which are globally important for our food supply. An important precondition for necessary and regular supply is a consistent yield, but the harvest quantity depends each year on the prevailing weather and growing conditions.

Other species of plants are also important in providing us with food. A special position is occupied by the various types of fruit including exotic fruits which are especially important as sources of vitamins and for dietetic reasons. Also to be mentioned are the spice and medicinal plants and the plants used for producing beverages throughout the world, such as grapevine, tea, coffee and cocoa as well as hops and barley and other types of cereal for brewing beer.

The major importance of these plants is due in no small measure to the good transport and storage characteristics of the harvested and processed products. Also important are high yield and extensive cultivation areas.

Crop production methods at their present state of development offer the precondition for high yields per unit area in all climatic zones. Against a background of continuously increasing world population, worldwide agricultural research has so far been successful also in achieving an increase in crop production. Hopefully it will be possible, by means of improved production techniques, to secure food supplies for the world.

The measures necessary to achieve this differ according to each climatic zone. In all regions, however, crop protection is an urgent priority. Whereas in the hot regions the control of insect pests is the primary requirement, in the moderate climates the chemical eradication of weeds is decisive, particularly for crops which develop slowly in their early stages. Halting infection by crop diseases is a worldwide problem for safeguarding yields and maintaining quality.

The conversations presented below discuss the technical problems involved in cultivating a number of important crops.

## *1. Barley*

*Barley occupies a special place among the cereals, being used not only as fodder grain and for many other purposes in the food industry, but also throughout the world as brewing barley for beer production. What is the total cultivation area?*

The total world cultivation area for barley is 80 million hectares. By comparison, 240 million hectares of wheat, 145 million hectares of rice, 134 million hectares of maize, 27 million hectares of oats and 15 million hectares of rye are grown. World cereal cultivation encompasses a total area of 740 million hectares and now supplies the most important staple food for the more than 4.7 thousand million inhabitants of the earth.

*What is the barley cropping area in the Federal Republic of Germany?*

In this country, about two million hectares of barley are grown, of which 0.75 million hectares are spring barley and 1.3 million hectares winter barley. Barley cultivation is not on the increase in the world as a whole, but is increasing in this country, particularly because the cultivation area for winter barley is being extended for economic reasons.

*Why is barley so important?*

Although barley comes a long way behind wheat in the world cereal trade, it can be cultivated in the most extreme conditions. Barley crops extend as far as beyond the Arctic Circle, into the high plateau regions of Asia and deep into the equatorial regions. Barley is thus the most widespread cereal both in the most northerly uplands and in some of the Mediterranean countries. In Northern Europe and in mountainous regions it is used for baking bread, while in the Orient and throughout the Mediterranean it replaces oats as a major source of fodder grain and in other countries serves primarily as raw material for malting, brewing, distilling and for coffee substitute, pot barley and highly digestible fodder concentrate for animal production.

*What is the reason for its widespread cultivation and its multiple uses?*

The great versatility of barley is due not only to the many different varieties within the species, but also to the extreme adaptability of the individual varieties; one important feature is however common to almost all the varieties, namely early ripening and a comparatively low sensitivity to drought and to cold summer weather. Consequently, barley is unaffected both by the early onset of winter in northerly and mountainous regions and by the summer drought in prairie lands. Short-lived spring varieties ripen in three months in the polar circle, and winter cultivars with an extended growing season thrive particularly well during the long, mild autumn of the oceanic climate and in the rainfall of the Mediterranean winter.

*We therefore make a distinction between winter and spring barley?*

Winter barley cultivation is at present on the increase mainly because, after winter wheat, it is the highest-yielding fodder grain cereal. It is used exclusively for fodder grain. Spring barley, on the other hand, is used mainly for brewing and is processed industrially as a raw material for malting, but is also a source of fodder grain.

*What factors must the farmer take into account when growing barley?*

Since it needs little water, barley like wheat throws few roots and is thus highly dependent on good cultivation conditions. On the other hand, its sensitivity to acidic soil reaction and careless soil cultivation is greater. Under favourable conditions, with a good previous crop and fertilization, winter barley gives the highest yield of nutrients of all the main varieties of cereal; moreover, with its early ripening, it fits superbly into the crop rotation. Because of its lower spelt content, spring barley, while giving an equal yield, provides more nutrients than oats. The fodder value of its relatively small amount of straw is not equalled by other types of cereal straw.

*How do the roots of barley develop?*

In terms of extent, depth and performance in the soil, the root network of spring barley is less developed than that of oats. The short growth period of spring barley coupled with its yield capacity indicates that it makes heavy claims on the soil and nutrient supply. High crop density, short stems and minimal root development are typical and genetically conditioned. Spring barley varieties are generally types of barley without winter hardiness but with the characteristics of a long-day plant, which do not till after delayed sowing.

Winter barley on the other hand throws deeper roots; it generally needs thorough pre-winter tillering, since the temperature during the shooting period in spring is very low and thus no re-tillering occurs in spring.

*The most important factor in achieving a high yield of barley is therefore optimal crop density?*

Yes, and this is why the sowing quantity is important particularly for barley. With brewing barley, heavy tillering is undesirable, since this results in double growth and uneven ripening. It should be drilled relatively intensively with 130 to 160 kg per hectare and in a close manner. Flat sowing, that is two to three centimetres deep, is decisive for rapid germination.

*Is the seed depth very important?*

As a general rule, the seed should not be spread in a layer less than three centimetres thick. Seed which is sown too deeply weakens the seedling, delays germination and results in retarded leaf formation and tillering. Depositing seed up to a depth of seven centimetres in a soil which is not very well settled frequently leads to infection of the seedlings with fungal diseases, which can be held in check by seed treatment. It should be noted that in the dry regions of the world barley is sown more deeply to ensure sufficient moisture for germination.

*What is the importance of seed treatment in this context?*

This is an urgent necessity for winter and spring barley, particularly for the control of leaf stripe and loose smut, and is in fact generally practised. Seed treatment is also decisively important for winter barley as a means of controlling snow mould.

*Chemical weed control is therefore also important for early crop development, especially for winter barley?*

Chemical weed control is performed during sowing using soil herbicides specifically approved for the purpose, since weed control is urgently necessary in the autumn to eliminate broad-leaved weeds and grasses from winter barley because of its early sowing. The milder the weather in autumn and winter, the more severely the weeds damage the winter barley crops unless timely weed control is performed in the autumn.

*Winter barley cultivation has increased continuously over the past few years because of its high grain yields. As we have heard, optimal tillering and sowing techniques are an important factor in obtaining high yields. To what can these yields be attributed?*

Yield increases obtained with winter barley can be ascribed to several factors. As well as the breeding of higher-yielding varieties, improved cropping methods and seed treatment, chemical weed control is decisive. No other species of cereal generally suffers such heavy competition from weeds as winter barley.

*What diseases and pests tend to occur?*

Mildew control is most important of all. Barley mildew is very widespread among winter and spring barley and has the effect of reducing both yield and quality. Treatment should be performed at the start of the attack. With heavy infection in varieties susceptible to mildew, a second control operation may be necessary.

The yield increases obtained as result of mildew control in barley cropping range between ten to twenty per cent in the long-term average and are manifested mainly as an increase in the whole grain component. Mildew control is also carried out in the form of seed treatment with special fungicides.

Rust diseases also have adverse effects on barley yield. Reliable control techniques are now also available for these infections.

Attack by insect pests in barley crops varies according to the location. In the autumn, field slugs can cause severe damage; furthermore, aphids spread a virus causing yellow dwarf disease, which severely depresses yields. If performed in good time, aphid control reduces damage.

In the last few years, the yellow mosaic virus has also become widespread in winter barley. This virus disease is propagated by soil fungi. The infection is halted by means of suitable crop rotation, in other words barley should not be grown too often. Moreover, decreases in yield can be prevented only by cultivating resistant varieties, since chemical soil disinfection in barley cropping is not economical.

*After wheat, barley has become the most important cereal in the Federal Republic of Germany in terms of cropping area, and continues to grow in prominence. The fundamental precondition for high yields is an optimal production technique which includes fertilization and crop protection.*

## 2. Wheat

*Wheat is not only the most important bread cereal in the Federal Republic of Germany, but, together with rice and maize, is the most important crop in the world food supply. How has the wheat acreage developed in the Federal Republic of Germany?*

The total cereal acreage in the Federal Republic of Germany is about 5.1 to 5.3 million hectares, 1.6 million hectares of which are occupied by wheat, 90 per cent of which is winter wheat and ten per cent spring wheat. Over the last twenty years, wheat growing has increased by 50 per cent.

*What are the reasons for this extreme increase in wheat growing?*

The increase has resulted both from changes in the agricultural price system and from rising demand coupled with greater scope for sales. Wheat products are more in demand from the discriminating consumer than wholemeal bread and oat flakes.

*How has wheat growing developed in the rest of the world?*

The world wheat cropping area has increased by 20 per cent over the last 25 years. Over the same period, the wheat harvest has risen by 120 per cent to 460 million tons. This means that yield increases on existing cropping areas were much greater than the expansion of acreage.

*What is the explanation for these increased yields?*

There are several reasons for this increase in wheat yields. Chief among these will probably be the successes achieved in breeding new higher-yielding varieties combined with improvements in cultivation techniques, promoted particularly by advances in agricultural engineering and biochemistry.

*What considerations are important for the wheat grower if he wishes to achieve high yields, and what are the factors which influence the yield?*

The first aspect to be considered is sowing. After all, high wheat yields are dependent not only on the weather, the previous crop, soil cultivation and fertilization, but also on the so-called yield-forming components. The yield naturally depends on the crop density, that is on the number of ear-bearing stems, which are themselves determined by the sowing quantity, and the single ear weight which results from the number of grains per ear and the single grain weight.

*Can you give an example to illustrate this?*

Under our own conditions, a yield of 8000 kg per hectare is the product of a crop density of 500 ears per square metre and a single ear yield of 1.6 grams, with a grain number per ear of 32 and a weight per thousand grains of 50 grams.

*Weed control must also be a factor in achieving a high yield?*

Weed control plays a major role in wheat cultivation, due to the low competing ability of wheat against the many different types of weed. Substantial improvements have been achieved in this respect over the past few years, through the development of weed control agents which, when sprayed immediately after the wheat has been drilled, prevent germination of the broad-leaved weeds or grass weeds such as blackgrass, thereby guaranteeing optimal development of the young wheat seedlings.

*Seed dressing must surely have been extremely important for wheat ever since ancient times?*

Even in antiquity, seed dressing was performed as a means of controlling bunt of wheat and seed fertilization was practised to stimulate germination of the seeds.

Bunt of wheat continues to be a major worldwide problem, and in many countries seed dressing for wheat has become a statutory requirement. The wheat bunt fungus prevents grain formation, and instead of the wheat grains, the spores of the fungus, known as bunted kernels, grow inside the diseased ears and burst when the grain is threshed and re-infect all the grains.

*Is the flour affected by this?*

Flour ground from grain heavily infected with bunt is unsuitable for human consumption. Modern seed dressing is used to control not only bunt, but also snow mould and loose smut.

*The fungal diseases attack not only the seed, but also the green plant. Which of these diseases are of worldwide significance?*

Mildew and rust diseases are found in many cropping areas where they attack the stems, leaves and ears, and must be controlled by spraying as soon as the infection becomes apparent. The stem base diseases must be controlled by spraying in springtime. Of the ear diseases, glume blotch and sooty mould fungi also reduce both yield and quality. In intensive wheat cropping, a special sequence of treatment has been developed, which is followed to safeguard the harvest, and includes control of insect pests such as cereal aphids, wheat midges, cereal leaf beetles and saddle gall midges.

*In wheat cultivation, therefore, in addition to choosing the correct choice of cultivar and sowing intensity, the chief measures to be applied are seed treatment and weed control after sowing. Variety-specific crop protection to combat fungeal diseases and insect pests can also be implemented as a means of increasing yields.*

## 3. Maize

*Maize is also prominent among the cereal species. Maize is used for many purposes and has therefore become increasingly important over the last few decades, not least due to the part it plays in the world food supply. What is the current situation?*

Over the last 25 years, world grain maize production has increased by 200 per cent, that of wheat by 120 per cent and rice production by 100 per cent. Maize also has an important future in world cereal production.

*What are the reasons for this?*

Maize gives the highest yield of any crop we know. World production of grain maize in 1970 was 265 million tons and in 1981 more than 450 million tons. For wheat, this figure was 310 million tons in 1970 increasing to more than 450 million tons in 1981, and ten years ago rice production reached a level of almost 310 million tons. The steep increase in maize production throughout the world is due mainly to a rise in yields per unit area and only partially to enlargement of the acreage. As a world average, the grain maize harvest was 3.4 tons per hectare, that of wheat 1.9 tons per hectare and of rice 2.9 tons per hectare. Thus in the European Community from 1960 to 1980 the cultivation area increased from 1.9 to 2.9 million hectares. Over the same period, production rose from 6 to 18 million tons and the yields per hectare have doubled from 3.0 to 6.0 tons. Most of the grain maize production in the EC is taken for fodder grain and only small quantities are processed industrially or used for man's food supply. Much of this crop is additionally grown as silo and forage maize.

*It might be mentioned at this point that the importance of maize as a versatile and high-yielding variety of cereal and forage plant was recognized in Europe long ago. A classical practitioner of European maize growing was Johann Burger (1773—1842), who as professor of agriculture in Klagenfurt published a monograph on the cultivation and use of maize around 1800. In this paper, he summarized the importance of maize in terms of yield level both for food supply and the processing industries. What are the main problems encountered in maize cultivation?*

The limiting factor, particularly for grain maize cultivation, lies in the climatic conditions for cropping. Maize is essentially a warm-weather plant. Successful breeding of hybrids has now produced many different cultivars which guarantee a full yield even in relatively unfavourable conditions.

*And what are the principal crop protection problems associated with maize?*

A review of the previous literature on maize reveals repeated references to seed damage by birds and measures taken for its prevention, more frequently and in greater detail than for the other cereals. This is above all due to the fact that maize, in contrast to the other cereals, needs a large growing space to develop its grain yield.

*What is the crop density?*

The crop density of wheat is 450 to 500 ears per square metre, and for grain maize 8 to 10 plants per square metre. The superior yield of maize compared to the other cereals is attributed to its pronounced Gigas character* and its allometric growth*. Maize is one of those crops in which certain organs, namely the cobs and grains used chiefly by man, are substantially enlarged due to evolution, or in other words, unconscious or deliberate development or selection. The other ear-bearing cereals, by contrast, have developed by spontaneous breeding process so that they provide high yields in only a small growing space, whereas with maize a large growing space for spike formation determines the cultivation method.

*The relatively small number of maize plants per unit area however means that maintaining crop density has always been a problem. Grain yields are after all determined by the number of spike-bearing plants. Moreover, after sowing, sprouting of the germinating maize plants is endangered by bird attack.*

As long ago as 1800, Professor Burger calculated that at least three of every twelve maize grains were eaten by birds. In his profitability calculations for maize cultivation, there is an item under costs for work performed after sowing, dated April 30, 1808: "Covered the exposed seed by raking". This illustrates how important it has always been to prevent damage by birds as a means of maintaining the crop density. Today, maize is protected from birds by incrusting the seed with a bird repellent.

*What other pests threaten maize?*

Severe damage is caused by frit flies and corn borers. The frit fly damages the maize in its early growth stages and is controlled by incrusting the seed with an insecticide which also repels birds, while corn borers must be combated by targeted spraying during their peak flying time. The frit fly attacks the leaves and shoots, and the corn borer causes damage to the cobs and thus to the maize kernels.

*The wide spacing and the slow early development of maize surely raises problems of weed control?*

Maize is one of those crops which need a long time for germination and early development. Because of the wide spacing between individual plants, shadow is

---

* Explanations cf. p. 207

given only at a very late stage, and weed competition is thus very great especially with maize. The hoeing work which was formerly unavoidable has now been replaced by special herbicides which are well tolerated by maize.

*Successful maize cultivation is guaranteed by correct cultivation methods, the use of healthy seed and careful selection of cultivars, paying due heed to the intended use and ripening time. To maintain the desired crop density, seed incrustation against bird attack is necessary and other measures for fertilization and plant treatment must be performed at a sufficiently early stage.*

## 4. Rye

*When we speak of rye cultivation we refer exclusively to winter rye, as spring rye is hardly grown because of its low yield performance. Although winter rye cultivation has been declining for some years, in crop rotations restricted to cereals and in light soils it retains its special importance in commercial farming. What are the chief characteristics of rye?*

Under intensive cropping conditions, the yield performance of rye is considerable. It occupies a special place in cereal-bound crop rotations as a soil regenerating crop. Moreover, rye continues to be unchallenged from the nutritional viewpoint as a bread cereal with a high health value.

*Under intensive cropping conditions in light and marginal soils, the rye varieties now being cultivated give yields comparable to those of wheat and barley. What measures have to be applied in cultivating rye?*

The position of rye within the crop rotation is not subject to any special rules, since rye, in contrast to wheat and barley, is compatible with itself. Particularly in crop rotations of cereals, rye cultivation is specially valuable for maintining the health of the soil. This applies especially to the cultivation of rye in crop rotations with a high proportion of wheat and barley. When preparing the soil for rye sowing, it should be ensured that the soil is firm enough to act as a seed bed. This is best achieved by ploughing to medium depth, followed by stabilization of the soil using suitable implements such as compactors and roller harrows immediately after ploughing. Only in this way can even drilling to the desired small depth be achieved.

*What seed rates are most suitable for winter rye under aspects of technical cultivation and yield analysis and what measures should we take as regards weed control and nitrogen fertilizing?*

The seed rate is around 120 kg per hectare, which is equivalent to a sowing density of 300 to 350 grains per square metre. It is important to perform weed control using soil herbicides during drilling. The stability can be improved by means of technical cultivation measures and staggered nitrogen fertilizing in the spring, making allowances for the previous crop and the nitrogen supply in the soil ($N_{min}$).

*What importance does rye cultivation still have in the Federal Republic of Germany?*

The cropping area in the Federal Republic was almost 1.5 million hectares in 1950 and has now decreased to about 500,000 hectares, or in other words by two thirds. By comparison, 15 million hectares of rye are grown throughout the world, of which Poland accounts for 3 and the USSR for 7.5 million hectares.

*How can this decline in rye cultivation in the Federal Republic be explained?*

Firstly we must establish whether the total cereal cropping area has declined or whether rye has been supplanted by other species of cereal.

In 1950 the cereal cultivation area was about 4.5 million hectares and has now increased to about 5.2 million hectares. The increase over this period was thus almost 20 per cent, while the rye cropping area, as I have mentioned, has decreased by two thirds in the same period. Comparing the cropping areas of the different cereals, we find that rye has been displaced mainly by barley, particularly winter barley, and also by wheat.

*Why has rye been displaced by wheat and barley?*

There are various reasons for this. The most decisive one probably relates to agricultural policy which, by establishing a fixed price system for wheat and barley, promotes the cultivation of these cereals. Another factor is the change in eating habits; a preference has developed for wheat or mixed wheat-rye bread both on the part of producers and consumers.

*What importance does rye continue to have in human nutrition?*

As before, rye continues to be the most important species of bread cereal in Northern and Eastern Europe. These areas also have the largest rye hectarages. Rye in the form of rye wholemeal bread has a special place in our diet, since wholemeal bread is very important both for children and adults because of its health-promoting value. Rye bread is produced in a surprisingly large range of types, offering something for every taste.

## 5. Oats

*Oats occupies a special position among the world's cereal crops. As a bread and porridge crop, it is found in many types of food. It is also valuable as livestock fodder, particularly for horses. What value do oats still have?*

The world oats acreage is currently 27 million hectares. In the Federal Republic of Germany over 700,000 hectares of oats are grown, as well as 150,000 hectares of spring cereal mixtures, which is usually a mixed crop consisting of oats and barley grown as fodder. Generally, oats cultivation is on the decline, since 50 years ago the world cropping area was 58 million hectares and at that time in the Federal Republic of Germany alone 1.4 million hectares of oats were still being grown.

*What are the reasons for this decline in oats cultivation?*

The replacement of draught animals, particularly horses, by motorized vehicles in agriculture and transportation systems has been a major factor in the decline of oats cultivation. Also, the lower yield of oats and its limited processing potential compared to other cereals such as maize, wheat and barley led to maize being replaced by higher-yielding cereals.

Crop cultivation is ultimately governed by market forces. If demand declines, the cultivation area in individual agricultural enterprises decreases accordingly. As a result, a crop valuable for maintaining the health of the soil is being displaced more and more within crop rotations.

*Can oats be grown anywhere?*

Another factor which places limitations on oats cultivation consists in its specific climatic requirements. World cultivation of this crop is concentrated in the "oats zone", a region of moist and moderate climate in Europe, America, Australia and Asia.

It must however be remembered that oats is important not only as a grain producing plant but also as a fodder crop. It is used as a forage and, overseas, also as a pasture crop. Not only the grains but also the straw and chaff have a high fodder value.

*And what is the nutritional value of oats for man?*

Oats have a high biological value and health-promoting properties. Oats contain high grade vegetable fats, protein, vitamins and minerals. Oat flakes and groats are nourishing foods which have always been an important component of man's diet: 100 grams of oat flakes contain 12 grams of protein, 10 grams of fat, 750 milligrams of minerals as well as vitamin E and vitamins of the B group. Oats are particularly rich in vitamin $B_1$, the nerve vitamin, a deficiency of which causes learning difficulties and lack of concentration. The following item is of interest both as economic history and as an illustration of the eating habits of former times:

Adam Smith, the founder of liberal economic theory, applied in 1757 as Professor at the University of Glasgow for duty-free import of oat flakes which the students brought with them each term for their meals. Duty-free import of oat flakes into the city of Glasgow was granted, a very special historical circumstance, being in effect the first free trade law ever passed.

*Oats continue to be very important both for human nutrition and animal fodder. But what does the practical farmer today think of this cereal?*

Oats are distinguished by the very low demands they make as regards fertilization. The oat roots digest the nutrient supplies of the soil more efficiently than the other cereals. Oats are therefore given the final place in the crop rotation. The different ripening rates of the stalk and the panicle however present considerable difficulties for automatic harvesting, since the grains do not ripen at the same time.

*What pests and weeds affect oats cultivation?*

The most well-known pest is the oat nematode which attacks the roots, greatly reduces yield and can also attack other cereals within the crop rotation.

Wild mustard and wild radish were already being controlled by chemical means as oat crop weeds at the turn of the century, since these two types of weeds act as hosts for the turnip nematodes.

A major problem in oats cultivation is also presented by wild oats, a weed related to cultivated oats, which it resembles in its viability requirements and its growth form. It is therefore extremely difficult to control. Special chemical control agents have proven successful in controlling wild oats since cultural methods present no prospect of success for their eradication.

*Oats are a long-established crop, whose importance for human nutrition and particularly for that of children and adolescents is unquestioned. In agriculture generally, however, the farming of oats has decreased sharply compared to wheat, rice, maize and barley, since its special demands and low yields make expansion or intensification of its cultivation an unattractive proposition.*

## *6. Rice*

*More than half the human race lives either entirely or partially on rice. This most important cereal, after wheat and maize, is thus one of the major food plants. What is the acreage?*

Rice is cultivated throughout the world on 145 million hectares compared to wheat which is grown on 240 million hectares. The total rice harvest amounts to over 400 million tons, whereas the harvested wheat quantity is 460 million tons. Rice cropping is thus pursued much more intensively, since the average area yields which are achieved are higher than those for wheat.

The great importance of rice lies in the fact that it is cultivated by peasant farmers on very small areas for their own consumption and that it has a high nutritive value as a basic food in the unprocessed state.

*How high are the yields of rice per hectare?*

The average yields throughout the world are 2.9 tons per hectare for rice and 1.9 tons per hectare for wheat. As a comparison, in intensive rice cropping in Japan an average 5.6 tons per hectare are harvested on a total area of 2.3 million hectares, and in Spain even 6.4 tons per hectare are produced on 70,000 hectares. 90 per cent of all rice production is found in Asia.

*Where did rice growing originate?*

The original home of rice is in the tropical region of Northern and Central India. Rice crops have been grown in South East Asia for 4,000 to 5,000 years. In today's rice cultivation, we make a distinction between paddy rice and upland rice.

*How can this difference be defined?*

Viewed in terms of its development, rice is not an aquatic plant but a hydrophilic mountain plant which has adapted to the monsoon rains. Present-day upland rice cultivation is pursued where there is not enough water to grow paddy rice, but where rain and atmospheric humidity still provide sufficient water for successful rice cultivation. The area yields for upland rice are however only one third of those achieved with paddy rice. The cultivation method for upland rice corresponds to that used for other cereals.

*How is paddy rice cultivated?*

The classical cultivation method for paddy rice consists of two processes: firstly the young plants are raised in the seed bed and are then transplanted by hand or by machine in the paddy fields. Before planting, the rice paddy is levelled off and the subsoil reinforced to prevent losses of water and nutrients.

In fully mechanized rice cultivation in the USA or Australia, paddy rice is sown directly. The most important criterion for a successful paddy rice crop is optimal supply of water for the seed or planting up to the time of harvesting.

*Does the farmer change the crops on the growing areas?*

Paddy rice is a typical monoculture among the cereal varieties. Rice can be continuously cultivated after rice, being compatible with itself. Because of the excessive wetness, it is often impossible to grow any other crop in the rice fields than paddy rice, which has adapted to the excess ground moisture and overflooding. Wherever paddy rice is grown with other plants in crop rotation, however, higher yields are achieved.

*Monocultures are known to be particularly vulnerable to pests. What are the major pests which affect rice plants?*

The commonest rice pests are the rice stemborers which, if present in large numbers, can cause serious harvest losses. Other pests are bugs, locusts, rats and birds. Many fungal diseases occur, such as rice blast, which leaves behind great damage but which can be controlled by timely treatment.

Further substantial yield losses are caused by competition from weeds, so that mechanical and chemical control methods are usual in rice cultivation.

*In addition to modern crop protection methods, plant breeding has also surely contributed greatly to increasing yields in rice cultivation. What more recent developments can be mentioned?*

Plant breeding is of importance in all rice growing countries. The International Rice Research Institute in Manila in the Philippines in particular has over the past few decades bred numerous new cultivars of rice, known as the "high-yielding varieties" (HYV), with short stems, good storage stability, a short vegetation period and steep leaf angles for optimal utilization of the sun's energy. These varieties have led to considerable production increases in the rice growing countries of Asia and Latin America.

*In many countries, rice is the most important food. In view of the continuously increasing world population, this crop will certainly continue to grow in importance in the future due to its high yield capacity?*

At present, rice is the staple food for more than half the world population. In many countries, it is produced by the consumers themselves. Only three per cent of the rice harvest is traded on the world market. The largest crops are to be found in the overpopulated developing countries of the humid tropics such as Indonesia and Thailand, which have 50 per cent of the arable and permanently cultivated areas. As the world population continues to rise, rice production will have to be doubled by the year 2000. Around 2030, the demand for food will be twice as high again, since the population density will continue to increase. This high demand can only be satisfied in rice cultivation if further yield increases are achieved in areas already under cultivation by improving cropping methods, fertilization, water supply, selection of varieties and crop protection methods. In addition, a loss-free harvesting method and storage after the harvest must be provided.

*The United Nations Food and Agriculture Organization (FAO) and the international agricultural research institutes combined in the Consultative Groups for International Agricultural Research (CGIAR), the most important of which are the Rice Research Institute in Manila and that for wheat in Mexico, have made continuous endeavours to improve cultivation methods for rice and other cereals, as an aid to increasing harvests in the overpopulated countries of the tropical and subtropical areas. In the Federal Republic of Germany the Association for Technical Cooperation (GTZ) is responsible for implementing technical development aid programmes in many countries, among which improvement of production conditions for rice and other cereal varieties ranks as an important project. Cooperation between many international and national research institutes as well as governmental and privately funded institutions has created the basis for a further increase in rice harvests.*

## *7. Sugar beet*

*Sugar beet production continues to play a major role in the sugar supply to the world population. 100 years ago the total world production of sugar was 2.5 million tons per year. Of this, 0.9 million tons were beet sugar and 1.7 million tons cane sugar. World sugar production is now running at 85 million tons, of which beet sugar represents more than 40 per cent, the rest being cane sugar. Sugar beet and sugar cane are grown as industrial crops for sugar production. What are the main cropping countries?*

Sugar beet is widely cultivated in the moderate climatic zones. The main growing countries are to be found in Western and Eastern Europe and the USA. Sugar cane cultivation is concentrated in the warm climatic zones, and the main growing countries are in America, particularly in Brazil, Cuba and Mexico. In Asia and Africa, sugar cane is grown in numerous countries such as Thailand, the Philippines, India and Pakistan. Australia also has a sizeable production. In Europe, sugar cane is cultivated in Spain.

*In past centuries sugar was a rarity in Germany, with fruit and honey mainly being used for sweetening purposes, but it is now an essential part of the national diet. How has the price of sugar developed over the centuries?*

In 1437, one kilogram of sugar cost 5 Gold Marks. In 1793, Goethe still paid 2.70 Gold Marks for one kilogram of sugar. During Napoleon's continental blockade at the beginning of last century, the price of sugar rose to 180 Gold Marks. Because of its great value, this precious commodity was kept in locked silver sugar boxes. Due to increased cultivation of sugar beet in Europe and of sugar cane overseas, the price of sugar dropped, and thereafter it became a common commodity. Today one kilogram of beet sugar costs 1,80 DM.

*Who still remembers the beginning of sugar beet cultivation, which after all started 150 years ago?*

Because of Napoleon's continental blockade which prevented the import of cane sugar into Europe, sugar beet cultivation for sugar production was greatly increased. Thus for example Friedrich von Bodelschwingh, the founder of Bethel, became acquainted with sugar beet cultivation as a young farmer around 1850, which he deseribes in his reminiscences as follows:

The beet seed was planted with the aid of the "hopping line" which had 100 knots arranged at equal intervals. When the line was laid out, each of the women seed-planters had to make holes at two of the knots, drop in the seed and then cover up the holes again. Then at both ends of the line the word "hopp" was called out and the line was moved further across the field. In this way, 700 acres of beet had to be sown at the Bodelschwingh school. After sowing, hoeing was done three times followed by "thinning" of the beets, with all but one of the beets, which had sprouted bushily from each cluster of seeds, being removed. The beets which remained in the ground were then cleared of weeds by hoeing. In the autumn, the beets were harvested by hand with the "beet remover", in other words they had to be pulled out singly, freed from earth by tapping and were finally laid out in rows.

*A large workforce was needed for this old-fashioned way of cultivating beets. Just as the cultivation area and the sugar price have changed, cultivation methods must also have been modernized?*

Thanks to technical progress, average yields in sugar beet cultivation have also risen considerably in the last few decades. Major factors in this increase are higher-yielding varieties, improvements in cultivation methods, differentiated fertilization and advances in the fields of disease, pest and weed control. Working methods have become much simpler and cheaper due to fully automated precision drilling with single-germ (monogerm) seeds and deposition of seeds at the desired growing space to a stand. Also of importance are chemical weed control and harvesting methods using modern automatic harvesters.

*How high are sugar beet yields today and how much sugar is produced per hectare in a fully mechanized one-man enterprise?*

In 1981, the sugar beet yield within the Federal territory was 5.48 tons per hectare. Depending on the weather and time of harvest, the sugar content is 15 to 17 per cent. The sugar yield per hectare ist 7 to 10 tons.

*You have mentioned technical progress in sugar beet cultivation and have emphasized crop protection. What measures are particularly important in this respect?*

Because of modern methods of precision drilling and the use of monogerm seed, it is particularly important to protect the seedlings from diseases and pests during germination. In addition to seed dressing and depositing insecticidal granules with the seed, additional surface treatment against emergence pests such as pygmy beetles, thrips, springtails and turnip flies, carrion beetles and weevils is necessary when the beets develop slowly due to weather influences and in dry conditions.

*Beet flies and aphids must surely also be important pests in beet cultivation?*

The control of these pests has for many decades been one of the most vital crop protection activities undertaken in sugar beet cultivation. Long-term trials performed by the Federal Biological Research Centre have demonstrated that the yield losses which can be prevented by means of aphid control are about ten to twenty per cent in terms of the beet yield and one to three per cent in terms of the sugar content.

*Sugar beet cultivation has enormous economic importance not only for agriculture but also because of the industrial processing of the sugar. The sales revenue obtained by West German agriculture from sugar beet reaches about 2.3 thousand million DM per year, the total turnover of the sugar industry in the Federal Republic is more than 5 thousand million DM and the sugar consumption per head of population is 35 kg.*

## 8. Potatoes

*The potato was introduced to Europe from South America more than 400 years ago around 1569. In Germany, the first potatoes are known to have been planted in 1621. At first, the tubers were completely ignored. Because of its attractive blossom, the potato was regarded first and foremost as an ornamental and garden plant. The value of the potato as a food was not recognized in Europe until the second half of the 18th century. No less a personage than Frederick the Great (1712—1786) was responsible for acquainting the German people with the potato. It must surely have been no easy matter to introduce the potato as a new crop for general consumption?*

The shrewd monarch employed an ingenious stratagem to bring this about. He ordered large potato fields to be planted and posted his grenadiers to stand guard over them, but only for appearances. The peasants crept secretly into the field at night to find out what was so precious it had to be guarded. They then stole the potatoes by the basketful and planted them in their own fields. This of course was exactly what the king wanted. Today the potato in its many different forms has become a staple food.

*The importance of potato cultivation throughout the world is evident above all from the cropping area devoted to this basic food. How large is the hectarage of this food plant throughout the world?*

The potato hectarage, which has been established statistically by the Food and Agriculture Organization, at present amounts to about 18 million hectares, on which a total quantity of about 260 million tons is harvested.

*Where does the potato rank on today's menu?*

The potato is served today in the form of salted potato, jacket potato and mashed potato as well as chips, potato fritters and croquettes. Potatoes are also extremely popular in the form of savoury snacks such as crisps. The roast potato, which is a favourite at grill parties, should also not be forgotten. The potato is an important source of vitamin C and contains the minerals potassium, phosphorus, calcium and iron. It also contains vitamin A and vitamins of the B group.

*Why is the potato so important in the world food supply?*

The potato as a starch-containing food commodity can meet man's calorie requirements without the need for elaborate processing. The potato is also an excellent source of protein, or more precisely of albumin. The protein yield from potatoes is 260 kg per hectare on world average, and for peas this value is 235 kg per hectare. An adult who eats enough potatoes to satisfy his daily requirement of 3,250 calories also consumes the necessary daily ration of 70 grams of protein, and the potato also contains a balanced range of amino acids.

*How important is the potato in the physiology of nutrients?*

The potato consists of 78 per cent water, 10 per cent carbohydrates and also contains 2 per cent protein, 0.15 per cent fat and 1 per cent minerals. The percentage composition is subject to variations, depending on the climate and the variety of potatoes.

*We often hear the opinion however that potatoes, as a high-carbohydrate food, tend to be fattening?*

The potato, as food scientists have repeatedly demonstrated, is not a fattening food. However, the unfortunate habit has developed of preparing this essentially low-calorie food, the potato, in fat, thereby increasing its calorie content. 100 g of potato contain only 85 calories whereas ham has 340, noodles 390, butter 770 and lard 950 calories per 100 grams.

*After looking at the history of the potato and its importance in cooking and gastronomy, now perhaps a brief comment on important cultivation problems. What place does the potato occupy in present-day agriculture?*

Although the potato hectarage has decreased compared to the post-war period, potato growing is a permanent feature of many agricultural enterprises.

*To what extent has potato consumption decreased?*

After the Second World War potato consumption was 200 to 250 kilograms per capita and year, and it has since dropped to 50 to 100 kilograms, a decrease by more than half.

*And how has this affected hectarages?*

As recently as 1960, the potato cropping area in the Federal Republic of Germany covered 1 million hectares, but in 1980/81 only about 250,000 hectares, in other words, over the last 20 years the cultivation area has shrunk by 75 per cent.

*What can be said about the development of yields?*

In 1960, potato yields were about 22.5 tons per hectare and have meanwhile increased to about 30.0 tons per hectare. As result of improvements in cultivation methods and varieties, a further rise in yield can be expected, which will compensate for the decline in cropping area.

*What other uses has the potato apart from its consumption as ware potato?*

Contract cultivation for potato processing, which is currently being promoted by the chambers of agriculture, is especially important. In the federal territory alone, 1 million tons of ware potatoes are processed into potato products such as crisps and chips. Not to be forgotton is contract cultivation for production of potato starch and potato spirit which accounts for another million tons, including other processed products for the food industry and intermediate products for many other purposes.

*In addition to ware potato cultivation, therefore, contract cultivation is also important for the processing industry. What are the main technical cropping problems encountered here?*

The first problem is choosing the correct variety for the intended use, which arises from the fact that more than 100 cultivars of potato are grown in the Federal Republic. The overall cultivation technique for potatoes has become simpler; for example, mechanical weed control has been superseded by the use of chemical weed control agents. Finally, disease and pest control has acquired ever greater importance. Thus in today's contract cultivation of potatoes for the table and further processing, precise treatment sequences for the control of potato blight are contractually stipulated; healthy crops are essential for obtaining high yields, satisfactory quality and consistent tuber size.

*What is potato blight?*

The potato plant is attacked by many diseases and pests which can cause more or less severe yield losses. One of the best known diseases is potato blight or Phytophthora. Intensive attack by this fungus can result in complete rotting, as the name suggests, of the foliage and the tubers. Rotting can be prevented by applying timely control measures.

*Which other potato pests are worth mentioning?*

The most notorious pest is the Colorado beetle which has been feared in this country for a hundred years. The voracious larvae of this beetle, when present in large numbers, defoliate the crop and may destroy the entire harvest unless timely control action is taken. Formerly these pests were controlled — also in this country after the Second World War — by laboriously collecting them, with only partial success, but now suitable insecticides do the job reliably and thoroughly the whole world over.

*Are there other pests which damage potatoes?*

We might mention the aphids, and above all the green peach aphids which transmit the destructive, severely yield-reducing virus diseases among potatoes.

The production of healthy, prime quality potato plants thus depends above all else on preventing this virus from being transmitted, by controlling the aphids which act as vectors. This is especially important because the viruses migrate from the leaf into the tuber and the following year cause stunting of the transplanted tubers in various forms, thereby greatly diminishing the yields.

*The production of healthy potato plants with the aid of crop protection measures is therefore just as important as controlling diseases and pests in potato cultivation for human consumption.*

*Moreover, the potato continues to be important in many ways for producers, the processing industry and the consumer. Despite changes in eating habits, the potato is sure to remain a basic food in the future.*

## 9. Indigenous fruit varieties

*In the Federal Republic of Germany the cultivation of apples and pears as well as cherries, plums and soft fruit varieties has always been important. Within the European Community, however, the fruit growing enterprises in the different countries are engaged in fierce competition both because of existing agricultural policies and climatic preconditions. What is the situation in this country?*

The total apple production in the Federal Republic is 1.5 to 2 million tons per year. For pears, the annual harvest amounts to about three to four hundred thousand tons. An interesting fact is that in intensive fruit farming the annual yield fluctuations are lower than in extensive cropping.

*What is the reason for the lower annual yield fluctuation in intensive fruit farming?*

The main reasons for the smaller yield variations are the technical cultivation activities such as fruit tree pruning, soil cultivation, fertilization and crop protection.

*In addition to the marketing organizations such as producer wholesale stores and direct producer-to-consumer businesses, many possibilities of promoting fruit consumption as a source of health have now been opened up. For example, every year Leichlingen fruit market attracts large numbers of consumers into the Bergische Land where they can find out about the health value of the fruit and at the same time purchase many of the different varieties offered in the market. Has fruit growing always been important throughout Germany, or is it a new class of production within the extensive domestic agricultural and horticultural system?*

Fruit growing is one of the oldest forms of cultivation we know in the Rhineland. Even excavations from the Germanic period indicate the presence of fruit growing in this region. The oldest variety of fruit is the cherry, grown in the settlements of the band ceramic potters. In the Middle Ages, the Cistercian monasteries, particularly Altenberg Abbey, from the year 1150 established and encouraged fruit growing in the Rhineland and the Bergische Land. In 200 to 300 monastery estates fruit growing was an important activity alongside agriculture. For example, in the Middle Ages and in the Hanseatic period, fruit was exported in fresh and dried form to the northern countries from Cologne's harbour on the Rhine. In the Middle Ages, before cane sugar came onto our markets, fruit, apart from honey, was the only means of sweetening various dishes.

*Fruit growing had thus already acquired considerable importance in the early Middle Ages and has persisted to the present day as a major branch of trade in our own cultivation area. This development was favoured both by the prevailing climate and soil. As well as the apple, the pear also finds perfect growth conditions in this region, yet surely the southern fruit growing areas of Europe have more favourable conditions for production?*

Compared to the countries of the south, fruit growing in our own region has the advantage of proximity to the market and better sales opportunities in the large conurbations. An additional factor is that certain varieties of apple popular among consumers, such as Cox Orange, russet apple and Berlepsch, cannot be grown in the southern countries, or do not achieve the typical ripeness, aroma and sugar-acid balance specific to the variety under warm climatic conditions. Just as in vine growing, in fruit cultivation too the particular location has a decisive influence on the individual varieties and their popularity, especially for the discriminating consumer.

*The fruit on offer to the consumer should not be restricted only to the harvest period but should also be available in winter and spring, since fruit is a major element of a healthy diet at all times of the year. What must the fruit producer and the marketing organzation do to guarantee this?*

The chief requirement is to harvest healthy fruit and store it correctly under controlled temperature conditions. The farmer can only produce healthy fruit without pathogens if he includes the necessary crop protection in his cultivation programme. All treatments during the growing season and before the harvest must be carried out using antifungal agents, otherwise known as fungicides, which exert a specific action against the fruit rot diseases such as bitter rot, grey mould rot and green mould.

*Fruit tree pruning is also important for production, since only by trimming the tops properly can the fruit size and colouration of the fruits meet the demands of the market. What is the situation as regards soil cultivation for growing quality fruit?*

In soil cultivation, to maintain the fertility of the soil and to prevent erosion, a continuous growth of vegetation in the orchards is necessary. The yield potential of the trees is however maintained by chemical weed control in the rows. By means of "herbicide-strip treatment" along the tree rows, the weed competitors of the apple and pear trees are eliminated and damage by field mice, canker and collar rot is reduced.

*How important is the use of fertilizers in fruit growing?*

Fertilization with phosphoric acid, potash, lime, magnesium and trace elements is necessary in the autumn and spring. Nitrogen fertilizing is best performed in several doses at intervals throughout the entire growth period, in a readily soluble form depending on the fruit species, variety and fruit set, and also the age of the orchard. A method of fertilization which has been introduced with successful results over the past few years is top dressing which, combined with scab and mildew treatment, is performed from blossoming to the end of shooting. To prevent stunting, a physiological disease observed in more sensitive varieties, calcium treatment is given during the fruiting stage.

*What demands does the consumer make on the apple?*

The consumer wishes to have a tasty and healthy apple from domestic production in a wide choice of varieties.

*The other fruit species also have their particular value in supplying the population with vitamins and maintaining good health throughout the year. Which fruit species are available in the different seasons either fresh or from cold storage?*

In summer, at the start of the domestic harvest, strawberries, early apples, red and blackcurrents, raspberries, pears, peaches and gooseberries are on offer. In the autumn we have a choice of plums, damsons, apples and pears and above all grapes.

In the winter and spring, fruit from domestic production is available only from stores in our cellars or from cold storage. In these seasons, importers however tend rather to offer the consumer products from the fruit-growing countries of the south, such as oranges and grapefruit.

*Fruit is not only appetizing, but is also an essential source of nourishment, although it is not one of the staple foods such as bread, meat and fat. Why is fruit so important for our nutrition?*

In addition to protein, fat and carbohydrates, which build up the body tissues and are a source of energy, we also need vitamins and minerals which have protective and regulating functions. Together with vegetables, fruit is one of our main sources of vitamins and minerals. The calorie content of fresh fruit is usually low.

*What specific functions have vitamins and minerals in the human body?*

Vitamins give the body resistance. Particularly in winter, it is important to have as many vitamins as possible. Fruit contains chiefly the vitamins A and C, and also those of the B group. The main minerals found in fruit are potassium, calcium, phosphorus, iron and magnesium. These are mainly responsible for the growth of bone and muscle and play an important role in the metabolism.

*What other special nutritional value does fruit have for man's physiology?*

Fruit acid and other aromatic substances in fruit act together with the water contained in fruit to exert a refreshing and invigorating effect. They stimulate appetite and promote the activity of the gastrointestinal tract. The fructose and glucose in the fruit are absorbed directly into the blood stream, which accounts for the energizing and refreshing properties of fruit. Cellulose, the skeleton substance of fruit, is also an important constituent. Although it is not digestible,

as roughage it stimulates the activity of the digestive organs and safeguards against the diseases endemic in civilized societies.

*The consumption of fruit can therefore be regarded as offering great advantages in terms of physiological nutrition as a contribution to maintaining man's health.*

## *10. Fruit varieties worldwide*

*Fruit growing is a major part of agricultural production in all climatic zones of the world and, together with the staple foods, contributes greatly to human nutrition. Which fruits are at the top of the production list?*

Heading the world production league we find grapes, of which 62 million tons are harvested each year throughout the world, different proportions of which are however processed into wine and grape juice in the different countries and only some of which are consumed in their fresh state. Then come the citrus fruits with 55 million tons, followed by bananas with 40, apples with 32, mango fruit with 13.5 und finally pears with 8.5 million tons.

*Fruit production varies greatly throughout the world, particularly according to the different climatic zones, and so there will doubtless be great differences in production capacities?*

The major fruit production is to be found in the subtropical regions where more than 50 per cent of the harvests are gathered. In the tropics about 30 per cent and in moderate climatic regions 20 per cent of the world fruit harvest is produced. The total world fruit production is more than 250 million tons per year.

*These are very impressive figures, which apart from anything else give us an idea of the importance of our domestic range of fruit within overall world production. Fruit is consumed as a fresh product and consequently often needs to be transported over considerable distances, for which special refrigeration systems are necessary?*

Fruit varieties account for a substantial proportion of total crop exports, and in some countries fruit is even the most important export product. For example, bananas make up more than 50 per cent of the total exports of Panama and Honduras. The fresh fruit varieties which are particularly suitable for export have therefore shown the greatest production increase over the last 20 years.

*The different fruits are extremely important for man's nutrition and health. What are the particular components which give fruit its health-promoting value?*

Most species of fruit provide little energy, since most of them contain only 10 to 12 per cent digestible carbohydrates. Many types are rich in provitamin A, such as apricots and mangoes, or in vitamin C, such as citrus and blackcurrants. Fruit has an important function because of its dietary action in regulating and stimulating digestion; organic acids such as citric, malic or tartaric acid have a mild laxative and diuretic effect and form the basis of fruit cures.

*With the development of modern world trade, the range of fruit available on the market has been greatly enlarged, with other fruits from warmer climatic zones supplementing the domestic varieties.*

Citrus fruit in particular has attained a special position worldwide as a source of vitamins generally available to the population.

*After grapes, citrus has now become the most important type of fruit. How large is the production and what citrus varieties are cultivated?*

The most important citrus species is the orange, of which the annual production is about 38 million tons. More than 1,000 different varieties of orange are grown, with groups of different varieties being distinguished. As well as the commoner types of orange comprising well-known varieties such as Valencia and Shamouti, we also have navel oranges, which are known by the variety names Washington and Thomson, and also blood oranges and sugar oranges.

*So oranges are the major citrus crop. What other types of citrus are important?*

After oranges, mandarins take second place in world citrus production, with an annual quantity of seven million tons. In East Asia, for example, more mandarins than oranges are eaten. There are about 500 types or varieties of mandarin, of which tangerines, clementines and satsumas are good examples.

*How important are lemons in world fruit production?*

Lemons and related types of citrus occupy third place in the world citrus league with about five million tons per year. As well as lemons, which flourish particularly well in Central America, we also have the sour and sweet lime and the citron.

*What role do lemons play in the household and nutrition?*

Lemons are available on the market all year round. Their storage life, juice content and taste depend not only on their origin but also on the time at which they are harvested. Thin-skinned lemons are particularly juicy.

The lemon, like the orange and grapefruit, has a high vitamin C content. However, the vitamin C in lemons is more easily destroyed by heat than that of the orange. Unlike oranges, lemons continue ripening after picking, like apples, pears and other fruits. The most suitable conditions for this after-ripening process are provided by heated rooms.

*Grapefruit and shaddocks have made a very great impression on the market, have you any comments about this?*

The world production of shaddocks and grapefruit is about four million tons per year. Shaddocks are the largest fruits of the citrus family and are found in many different forms, particularly in Southern Asia. The currently most popular varieties of grapefruit are grown in the West Indies and are much in demand in the USA. They have a rather acid and usually somewhat bitter taste. The more bitter substances they contain, the higher their vitamin C content.

*What are the storage characteristics of citrus fruits?*

To prevent premature deterioration, the outer skin of citrus fruits is often given preservative treatment after harvesting. The strict regulations governing the treatment of fruit allow only a small number of non-hazardous substances to be used for this purpose. Furthermore, as a safeguard against spoiling the taste and health of the fruit, these substances may be applied only in precisely specified amounts. Treated fruit must also carry special identifying marks throughout the entire trading system.

*Cultivation of these southern fruit crops must surely also present a few problems?*

Citrus plants generally provide a full yield for 20 to 40 years but there are also hundred-year trees which still produce economic yields. As for our own indigenous fruit species, a permanent crop of this kind requires a special cultivation technique.

*Can you explain this a little further?*

Citrus trees sprout new leaves three times during the course of the year, and the spring shoots, particularly in subtropical climates, are the strongest and richest in blossoms. Generally speaking, citrus trees are not pruned, and only the water shoots and excessively dense growth inside the top are removed. Weed control, however, is very important, and so is crop protection to control insect pests and diseases.

*Why is crop protection so important for this species?*

Hardly any other group of plants makes such great demands on crop protection as citrus fruit. Fungal diseases such as collar rot of the tree, leaf diseases and in particular diseases which attack the fruit during storage, after harvesting and during transport can endanger their economic success. Other major causes of damage are canker and virus diseases and insect pests numbering 100 different species.

*How high is the yield for citrus crops compared to our own domestic fruit cultivation?*

Yields run at about 30 to 40 tons per hectare for oranges or mandarins and 40 to 50 tons per hectare for lemons or grapefruit. Comparable productivity is achieved with apples and pears with 30 to 50 tons per hectare.

For transportation in the freshly picked state, oranges are cut from the branch with knives or shears to prevent the fruit being damaged. When the fruit is to be processed immediately, mechanized harvesting methods can be used. Further marketing of the fruit, particularly for export, is carried out by large organizations which guarantee perfect produce and who distribute the fruit under special tradenames such as "Jaffa", "Sunkist" and "Outspan". In addition to sales of fresh fruit and the manufacture of various tinned preserves, the extraction of juices, concentrates and dried preparations is becoming increasingly important, particularly for the beverage industry.

*Citrus fruits, which enjoy great popularity and have high nutritional value, occupy large sections of the food and beverages industry both in the national and world economy.*

*Because of the large world demand, citrus cultivation and harvest quantities have risen continuously over the last two decades.*

*Over the last 20 years, banana production throughout the world has increased from 25 to 40 million tons. How are bananas cultivated?*

From the rootstocks of bananas, "trunks" develop which, depending on the variety, can reach heights of five to ten metres. The stem is formed from the rolled leaf sheaths. From inside this pseudostem grows the large inflorescence (or "bunch", as it is usually called). The lower parts of this bunch are the female flowers and the upper parts the male flowers. In the varieties which are cultivated, the bananas develop from the ovary of the female flowers without fertilization (parthenocarpy) and as a result remain seedless. From the flowers, the bananas grow in tiers in infructescences known as "hands". Several hands make up a bunch. After the harvest, the bushes are removed, since they can only bear fruit once, and a new trunk develops a sucker from the main rootstock. The growth period from shooting of the bunch to the ripening of the fruit is 12 to 14 months.

*How are bananas harvested and shipped?*

Bananas intended for export are harvested while still green. To do this, the stems are bent over with the aid of a machete, the heavy infructescences are detached and, avoiding mechanical damage as far as possible, are taken to the packaging plant where they are treated against port-harvest diseases. The fruit bunches are separated and packed for shipment in standard boxes containing 18 kg, and recently also 12 kg. In the cold storage compartments of the ships, the bananas are stored at 14 to 15 °C, and after reaching the port of destination are brought to a state of yellow ripeness at slightly higher temperatures and in an atmosphere to which 0.1 per cent ethylene is added.

*Crop protection is very important in banana cultivation for securing both yield and quality. What diseases and pests threaten banana plants as a perennial crop?*

Great damage is caused by banana wilt or Panama disease; wherever this is prevalent, only varieties resistant to this fusarium fungus can be cultivated. The widespread leaf spot or sigatoka disease, which is caused by a Cercospora fungus, is controlled by means of regular treatment with fungicides.

Disinfection of the corms when newly planted and keeping the plantations free of weeds through special control measures is necessary to prevent attack by virus, bacterial and fungal diseases. Also important is control of aphids as vectors of virus diseases, the destructive banana root borer and nematodes. Only by implementing intensive crop protection measures has it been possible to achieve the average yields of 25 to 35 tons per hectare which have been established for the main exporting countries.

*In conclusion, one further question: Where are the main cultivation areas for bananas?*

The main producers and exporters are the Latin American countries, namely Brazil, Ecuador and Honduras, Costa Rica and Mexico and, in the Asiatic region, the Philippines. Production in the rest of Asia, in Australia and Africa serves mainly to cover domestic requirements.

*The banana, which is very popular because of its high nutritional value and its appetizing taste, is acquiring increasing importance throughout the world. Its cultivation and marketing make great demands on farming methods, particularly crop and stored product protection, and also on the refrigeration techniques essential for its shipment over long distances from the producer to the consumer.*

## 11. Soft fruit varieties

*If our ancestors could visit one of our present-day fruit markets, they would be amazed not only by the abundance and huge variety of fruit on offer, but also by the size and colour, aroma and taste of the produce. In contrast to former times, many varieties of fruits are now available to us all year round. Man has learned to keep fruit fresh over prolonged periods and to transport it without damage over long distances. Soft fruit is surely also very important for us?*

Of the soft fruit varieties, only grape vine was cultivated in past centuries. The other soft fruit varieties first grew as wild woodland and hedgerow plants, which in the Middle Ages were used mainly for medicinal purposes. Cultivated soft fruits are mentioned for the first time in the 16th century as produce from monastery gardens. Soft fruit cultivation is thus a much more recent development than that of pome or stone fruit.

*If we now have so many delicious-tasting and high-yielding varieties of soft fruit under cultivation, there must be a special reason for this?*

This is mainly due to the fact that soft fruit is much easier to cultivate than pome and stone fruit: berry bushes bear fruit much more readily and the results of cultivation are visible much sooner.

*What are the most important varieties of soft fruit?*

Of major importance as regards breadth of cultivation and consumption are red and blackcurrants, gooseberries, strawberries, raspberries and blackberries as well as bilberries, cranberries and grapes. Sea buckthorn, common elder, sloe, mountain ash and dogrose also yield edible fruit. These varieties have a highly characteristic taste. Whether they can be classified as genuine fruit is rather controversial.

*Which soft fruit varieties are cultivated here and how large are the cropping areas?*

The largest cultivation area is occupied by red and blackcurrants, followed by gooseberries. Strawberries and raspberries occupy a special place among these crops. Annual harvest yields in the Federal Republic of Germany currently run at 100,000 tons for redcurrants and blackcurrants, 40,000 tons for strawberries, 55,000 tons for gooseberries and 20,000 tons for raspberries. Only a certain proportion of these harvested quantities is officially marketed, and the remainder is for captive consumption or direct sale to the consumer. An analysis of the production figures for the EC reveals that, with the exception of strawberries, soft fruit cultivation in the EC is concentrated in the Federal Republic of Germany.

*Why are soft fruit varieties so popular with consumers?*

This popularity doubtless has much to do with their extreme versatility for household use and their very appetizing taste. The health value of all soft fruit varieties should also be remembered, since they not only taste very pleasant but are also an important food. The carbohydrates like fructose and glucose which they contain are absorbed directly into the bloodstream and are a source of instant energy and refreshment. Other important constituents are minerals, fruit acids and vitamins. The high vitamin C content of blackcurrants and the high vitamin A content of blackberries and gooseberries should be particularly mentioned. With the development of deep-freeze techniques, soft fruits have acquired a new importance, since by this means it is possible to overcome their major weakness, namely their inability to withstand the stresses of transportation and the short storage life of the fresh fruit.

*Does soft fruit have any special characteristics?*

In contrast to pome and stone fruit, soft fruit grows mainly on bushes. Instead of having a core or a stone in the middle of the fruit, the germ seeds, which are usually very numerous, are distributed throughout the flesh of the fruit. Soft fruit is usually picked when ready for eating. It is very juicy and thus has only a limited storage life. Because of its low resistance to transport stresses, soft fruit is imported only in small amounts and usually only from nearby countries. Modern methods of preservation such as deep-freezing have however also opened up not only new transportation possibilities but have also increased the scope for sales and created new market opportunities.

*What can be said about the cultivation, sale, processing and other special characteristics of the various soft fruit varieties?*

In the Federal Republic of Germany, red and blackcurrants are grown in gardens and fields. Most varieties either have red berries and a rather sour taste, and the less frequent white varieties a sweeter taste. Blackcurrants are distinguished by their particularly tart taste. Red and blackcurrants are often processed into unfermented fruit juice and jelly.

*What particular features of gooseberries can be mentioned?*

Gooseberries are cultivated in a similar way to black and redcurrants. The ripe fruits are whitish, yellow, green and red, sometimes hairy and sometimes smooth. Gooseberries are frequently processed into stewed fruit, canned products and, to a lesser extent, into unfermented fruit juice.

*Are strawberries still a special crop among the soft fruit varieties?*

Strawberry cultivation continues to be very widespread. Strawberry varieties often differ greatly both in form and taste. Apart from the single-yield varieties, there are also special varieties which bear fruit twice or three times during the course of a summer, but these are of only minor importance in terms of cultivation area. Ever-flowering wood strawberries are similar to wild strawberries in growth and taste, but do not have the same pronounced aroma.

*How important are raspberries and blackberries?*

Raspberries are cultivated in gardens and fields. As well as the usual single-yield varieties, a few two-yield varieties are known. Following a well-established tradition, the smaller wild raspberries are collected in large woodland areas and offered for sale at market.

Blackberries are the least important variety of soft fruit on the market since they are not grown on a very large scale commercially and are mostly harvested as wild fruit. In contrast to raspberries, when blackberries are picked only the receptacle is detached when the fruit has reached full ripeness.

*Are bilberries and cranberries very popular with the consumer?*

Bilberries (blueberries, blackberries, whortleberries) are typical woodland fruits which ripen in July and August on low bushes about 30 to 40 centimetres in height. Cultivated bilberries, which are larger and firmer but less aromatic than woodland bilberries, are grown in this country only in relatively small quantities.

Cranberries (cowberries) resemble bilberries in their growth form. Their bushes however are even lower, and ripen later. The red berries cannot be consumed when raw; only after it has been cooked does this fruit acquire its characteristic tart flavour.

*The oldest and best known of the soft fruits, namely grapes, must command a large market?*

Grapes are a very special kind of soft fruit. Of all known species of fruit, they are the most widely cultivated in the world. The Federal Republic of Germany grows grapes mainly for making wine and therefore imports considerable extra quantities of dessert grapes.

Grapes are served for dessert all year round; in the first six months of each year, grapes are imported from overseas and from Dutch and Belgian greenhouses, and in the second half of the year from Southern Europe.

*Since man in our present-day society generally tends to do more mental and less physical work, it is important that his diet should have as low a calorie content as possible. Soft fruit is not only of interest because of its pleasant taste, but is also important as an excellent source of nutrition which promotes the health and wellbeing of the consumer.*

## *12. Strawberries*

*In contrast to the various soft fruits grown on bushes, strawberries are produced in large quantities for commercial purposes in all member countries of the European Community. They are also the only species of soft fruit whose production has shown a definite long-term increase. How large is this production?*

While in 1958 almost 200,000 tons were harvested in the entire EC, five to ten years later this figure had risen to between 250,000 and 300,000 tons. Today, 25 years later, the harvest quantity is 450,000 tons grown on an area of 43,000 hectares. The chief contributor to this development was Italy with a far above average growth rate of more than 50 per cent. This country accounts for 40 per cent of the EC production and France for 25 per cent. Belgium and the Netherlands follow with 10 to 15 per cent each and the Federal Republic of Germany with 10 per cent.

*How extensive are the cultivation areas?*

According to the most recent surveys, the cultivation area in Italy is 15,000 hectares. 75 per cent of this is pursued outdoors and 25 per cent is cultivation under glass or plastics.

*What is the situation in the Federal Republic?*

Between 1965 and now, that is in less than two decades, the cultivation area has increased from 2,800 hectares to 4,500 hectares. Over this period, the harvested quantity has risen from 20,000 tons to almost 40,000 tons. The main cultivation areas are in Baden-Württemberg, Bavaria, Lower Saxony, Schleswig-Holstein and North Rhine-Westphalia.

*What is the strawberry production in other countries outside the EC?*

In the USA the production is 330,000 tons, in Poland 160,000, in Spain 50,000, in Yugoslavia 45,000 and in Israel 7,500 tons. Countries like Israel and the USA deliver strawberries outside our own harvest period, whereas Poland mainly supplies the food processing industry.

*What quantity of strawberries is imported into the Federal Republic?*

Imports are currently running at about 85,000 tons, and about 30,000 tons of the domestic harvest are marketed through the producer organizations, while the remainder is accounted for by direct consumption and sale.

*The consumer demand for fresh strawberries and deep-frozen products continues to be large. How do German producers keep up with the competition from imports?*

The advantage of the domestic producer is his proximity to the market. Good quality fruit produce is always in demand and will always bring good prices.

*Apart from commercial production, large quantities of strawberries are probably also cultivated in small gardens for the grower's own consumption?*

Growing strawberries in the domestic garden is an increasing trend and is a major factor in meeting domestic demand, particularly for fresh consumption.

*What are the main types of commercial production?*

Strawberry cultivation in the Federal Republic, apart from a small number of large or specialized enterprises, is concentrated mainly in family horticultural or fruit-growing enterprises, since the main workload occurs during the harvesting period, which may last from four to six weeks. Since strawberries are very popular with the consumer as a fresh product, the family company has scope for expanding the strawberry cropping area and thus of increasing revenue.

*The strawberry is therefore becoming ever more popular and is a firmly established item on today's menu. What means does the strawberry producer employ to adapt to the market demand?*

It is important for the producer to be able to supply the market over a prolonged period with quality goods by selecting the correct varieties. This can only be achieved if cultivation techniques are optimally organized. As well as the choice of suitable varieties and healthy plants, coordinated fertilization, soil cultivation and treatment of the strawberry plants against diseases and pests over the entire cultivation period are also important.

*What specific measures are applied for this purpose?*

Maintaining the fruit quality is achieved primarily by means of targeted control of fungal diseases on the fruit, the major damage being caused by Botrytis or grey mould. Control is effected by treating the strawberry while it is flowering. In this way, Botrytis infection of the strawberry fruits is prevented. Since some of the blossoms are hidden, spraying is performed using a large quantity of water in the region of 2,000 litres per hectare or 20 litres per 100 square metres. Botrytis control in strawberry cultivation is one of the most worthwhile of all crop protection measures, since long-term studies have shown that this treatment brings increased yields of 50 to 60 per cent compared to untreated strawberry plants. If these control measures are not applied, the fruit rots during rainy weather during the growth and harvest periods before the strawberry plant is even picked. Preventive treatment for fruit rot also greatly improves the transportation resistance and storage life of the strawberries.

## *13. Raspberries*

*Raspberries have almost as many different uses in the household and the food industry as apples. The cultivation area in the Federal Republic is about 1500 hectares with an average yield of 15 to 20 tons per hectare and a total harvest of 20,000 tons; raspberries are also imported. Within the EC area, 55,000 tons of raspberries are produced on 6,200 hectares. One of the main growing countries in Europe is Scotland, where intensive raspberry research and growing takes place. What is the reason for the popularity of raspberries and how is such a large harvest quantity absorbed by the market?*

A large proportion of the raspberries which are produced is consumed in the fresh state and is also processed into jam, fruit juice, raspberry ice cream, unfermented fruit juice, syrup, sweets, table wine, liqueur and white raspberry brandy. Since raspberries in the form of preserves tend to deteriorate, deep-freeze techniques offer a great advantage in that raspberries are now available all year round. This has led to an increase in raspberry consumption over the last few years, and they have now become a favourite ingredient in sweet desserts.

*What is the consumer's opinion of the raspberry?*

The raspberry is extremely popular because of its aroma and its fructose content. It contains not only vitamins but also many minerals, particularly calcium and phosphorus.

*Are raspberries cultivated in different ways according to their intended use?*

The garden raspberries grown in this country provide exclusively red fruit and have been developed over the course of centuries from the wild variety, the woodland raspberry. These two types differ above all in the yield they provide and in particular the size of their fruits. The weight of the woodland raspberry is less than 1 gram, and that of the garden raspberry, depending on the variety, 2 to 4 grams. Large fruit varieties are preferred both for fresh consumption and for deep-freezing.

*Cultivation areas for raspberries have varied greatly in extent. What are the reasons for this?*

Of all the species of fruit, the garden raspberry is the most susceptible to insect pests and diseases. Since some of these diseases such as spur blight and virus diseases are either difficult to control or uncontrollable, very intense infection can destroy entire plantations. Furthermore, the raspberry is extremely labour and capital intensive and the fruits are highly perishable, and so they are now grown increasingly either on special farms or for captive consumption. Since the market is severly under-supplied due to the decline in commercial cultivation in the Federal Republic and the Netherlands, and since raspberries as fresh quality produce fetch high prices, their cultivation in establishments which have sufficient manpower at their disposal is of particular interest.

*We have just heard that the raspberry is particularly vulnerable to pests and diseases. Crop protection therefore plays a major role in securing the profitability of this fruit. Which pathogens must receive particular attention from the grower?*

The most potentially damaging of insect pests for raspberries is the larva of the raspberry beetle, popularly known as the raspberry fruitworm. Another urgent priority is the control of aphids and leafhoppers as vectors of virus diseases and of gall midges as vectors of spur blight. In our moist climate, grey mould ranks alongside spur blight as the most destructive disease in raspberries.

*What control measures must the grower apply to prevent grey mould and how successful are they?*

As with strawberries, raspberries should be treated thoroughly three to five times during the flowering period from the beginning to the end of blossom with a fungicide not harmful to bees which is specially approved for this purpose. Spraying should cover not only the blossom itself but also the entire bush, since the botrytis fungus also causes severe damage to stems and buds and infects the blossoms from the wood. In studies with raspberry varieties, timely botrytis control was found to increase the yield by an average 70 per cent for all the tested varieties, while at the same time distinctly improving the market quality and storage characteristics. It is important to remember that not only the high-yielding varieties of cultivated raspberry but also wild woodland raspberries are particularly vulnerable to botrytis, the grey mould of the fruit.

*To summarize, we can say that modern intensive raspberry cultivation, both because of the inadequate supply to the market and the spontaneous increase in demand stimulated by deep-frozen produce, holds a position of special importance in special establishments which have sufficient manpower. Profitability however requires not only the growing of suitable varieties but also intensive cultivation methods.*

## *14. Nuts — the hard shell fruits*

*Everyone is familiar with the different types of fruit and knows that apples are pome fruit and peaches are stone fruit. It is thus easily forgotton that on the market nuts are also regarded as fruit. Statistically, they are grouped together under the heading of "shell fruit" because the edible seeds or fruits which we usually refer to as nuts are enclosed by a dry and partially woody shell. They belong to very different plant families. What are their most important characteristics and where do they grow?*

In contrast to other fruit species, nuts contain little water, and usually also little vitamin C, but do however have substantial quantities of vitamin $B_1$, protein and a particularly large amount of fat, as well as calcium, phosphorus and iron. Some varieties of nuts also contain large amounts of carbohydrates. Unlike other fruits, nuts have a high calorie content. 100 grams of nuts, an amount which can be eaten very quickly, contain 600 to 700 calories. Some varieties of nuts flourish only in very warm countries, whereas others also grow in our moderate latitudes.

*Nuts also play an important role in tradition and custom. How are nuts offered on the market?*

Nuts in the shell are available particularly after the new harvest in late autumn. At this time they are especially fresh and tasty and therefore much in demand. Peeled nuts however are available all year round and are processed in the fruit industry.

*Which nut varieties are specially important traditionally or around the world?*

The only nuts cultivated here are walnuts, hazelnuts and sweet chestnuts. Although these three shell fruits prefer a warmer climate, in Germany they have since very early times been grown in domestic gardens or parks for the grower's own consumption. Commercial cultivation is not profitable in this country, since the yields are too low. These amount to about 3 kg per bush for hazelnuts and about 10 to 20 kg per tree for walnuts.

*What other varieties are also important?*

We must not forget to mention almonds. These are closely related to peaches and prefer a mild Mediterranean climate. A distinction is made between sweet, bitter and shell almonds. Bitter almonds can be dangerous if eaten in large amounts. Sweet almonds are also used in the manufacture of marzipan.

*Are there any other nuts offered on our market?*

Other varieties available here are coconuts, paranuts, pistachios and cashews as well as peanuts.

*Can we briefly characterize the individual varieties?*

Coconuts grow in clumps at the tops of coconut palms, some of which can reach great heights. They flourish in all hot countries, predominantly in coastal areas. One whole year passes between blossoming and ripening. Each single ripe coconut is surrounded by a solid, smooth shell. This in turn is covered by a thick layer of fibre. Coconuts are hollow inside and filled with a sugary coconut water containing carbonic acid.

*Where do the other nuts available here originate?*

Paranuts come from the forests of Brazil where they grow wild as tree fruit. In the ripening period, when the composed fruits weigh two to three kilograms, they drop to the ground where they are collected and then sold. The fruit, which remains closed even after it has fallen, contains 24 to 40 individual nuts which are arranged like the segments of an orange. The shell of the individual nut is hard and difficult to open.

*What about pistachios?*

Pistachios originally come from Persia and also prefer a mild, warm climate. They are eaten as a delicacy raw, roasted and salted and are also used for confectionery and in preparing meat. Because pistachios bear fruit only every two years, their supply is very variable. The best pistachios come from Iran and Sicily.

*Cashew nuts are also found in bags of mixed nuts; what can you tell us about these?*

Cashew nuts are indigenous to South America, but today are imported primarily from India and Africa. On the trees, which can reach heights of up to ten metres, the pear-shaped, fleshy, yellow or red cashew apples grow, which in the tropics are eaten either raw or cooked. Growing from the extreme tip of this apple is a small, kidney-shaped nut, which has a weakly sweetish taste and is enclosed in a hard shell. Cashew nuts are usually sold already peeled and are found for example in assortments of almonds, raisins and nuts.

*What is the biology and the importance of peanuts?*

Peanuts, like peas and beans, belong to the legume family, but grow only in warm climates. The plants resemble bush beans. After fertilization, the stalk bends down until the ovary is buried a few centimetres in the ground. Only then does the somewhat swollen and brittle shell develop.

Peanuts are eaten fresh or roasted, and frequently also in salted form. If they are to remain crunchy, they cannot be kept for long after the pack has been opened. Peanut kernels are used mainly in the manufacture of cooking oil and also as a spread for bread known as peanut butter.

*Hazelnuts and walnuts, and a wide variety of other nuts, provide the consumer with an extremely rich selection, not only in late autumn, but also throughout the year. The range of nuts on offer is constantly growing in size and attractiveness. Who can resist the temptation to crack the occasional nut?*

## *15. Vegetables*

*Vegetables are very important for the world food supply, and vegetable production totals 350 million tons and embraces numerous varieties. The major crops are tomatoes, cabbage varieties, peas, cucumbers, carrots, onions, beans and lettuce. The various types of vegetables each have their own special importance in man's diet, since in addition to nutrients they contain minerals, trace elements, vitamins and roughage and are essential components of a balanced diet?*

Vegetables consist of more than 90 per cent water, are low in calories and the skeleton substance of the vegetables tissue consists of roughage which gives a feeling of repletion. The low calorie content of vegetables is due to the absence of fat. The appetizing quality of vegetables derives from the specific types of aromatic substances, essential oils and gustatory substances which they contain.

*What is the level of vegetable consumption?*

In the Federal Republic of Germany 70 kg vegetables per head of population are consumed every year, whereas in Italy the consumption is more than twice as high at 160 kg. In the European Community, the average vegetable consumption is 100 kg per person, while fruit consumption including citrus runs at 90 kg.

*Another important crop must surely be the tomato, which, with a world cultivation area of 2.5 million hectares, is grown in almost all countries of the world either outdoors, under glass or under plastic?*

The tomato, which originates from South America, has been established as a popular food in Germany for about 100 years because of its valuable health-giving properties and attractive taste. In this country, tomatoes are grown commercially on 400 hectares, half outdoors and half under glass, although for domestic supply they are grown mainly outdoors. Whereas in warmer climates such as Italy, Spain or the USA tomatoes are usually sown directly outdoors, in more moderate climates such as Germany, tomatoes are transplanted exclusively in the form of seedlings either outdoors or under glass.

*Tomatoes are known to be very vulnerable to disease?*

The most destructive disease which affects tomatoes is late blight, Phytophtora infestans, a fungus which also attacks potatoes around the world. Since with heavy infection both the plant and fruits rot completely, regular treatment of the tomato plants with fungicides officially approved for the control of late blight is necessary.

*The intensity of cultivation therefore demands careful and targeted control of diseases, pests and weeds. Which disease mainly attacks lettuce?*

The cultivation of lettuce, which occupies an area of 4,000 hectares in the Federal Republic, is increasing in many places. Apart from aphids, one of the major nuisances in lettuce cultivation is grey mould which is caused by the Botrytis fungus. Long-term studies in salad varieties with multiple application of a special preparation for Botrytis control have demonstrated great efficacy and increased yields in all treated varieties. Moreover, the proportion of marketable produce was increased and the incidence of Botrytis disease in the harvest was reduced, which greatly improved the transportability and storage life.

*In cabbage cultivation, the cabbage fly must still be quite a problem?*

Cabbage growing is extremely diversified in the Federal Republic. 6,000 hectares of white cabbage, more than 2,000 hectares of red cabbage, 3,500 hectares of cauliflower are grown and 5,000 hectares are devoted to the other cabbage varieties. All cabbage varieties are threatened by numerous pests, one of the most troublesome being the cabbage fly. One of the control measures which has met with considerable success over the past few years is band application with granules after planting or sowing. Spray treatment is also performed in small plantations. For cauliflower, the cabbage variety most endangered by the cabbage fly, this control treatment was very effective and prevented a potential yield loss of 25 per cent; a similar yield loss of 15 per cent was also prevented in Savoy cabbage and white cabbage.

*Apart from the many other pests, green flies are responsible for reducing yields and quality in almost all vegetable crops?*

The various aphid species are so destructive because not only do they damage crops by attacking them directly and transmitting virus diseases to them, they also spoil their appearance and make them unsuitable for sale. Control measures must therefore be started as soon as the first aphids begin to appear. This applies particularly to lettuce, broad beans, cabbage and tomatoes. The grey cabbage aphid especially can only be controlled by high-volume spraying. In general, this pest continues to be a major nuisance.

*Finally, a few words about weed control, which must be very important in vegetable crops?*

Weed control is a major factor in vegetable growing, since the different vegetable varieties develop slowly in their early stages and thus have little resistance to competing species of weed which grow much faster. In addition to mechanical methods, which are no longer competitive in vegetable growing because of the large amount of labour they involve, chemical weed control techniques have been applied with increasing success in numerous vegetable plantations over the last few years. These control agents are used in a variable manner, for example before or after sowing or planting, a particularly important criterion being that the plants and crops should safely tolerate the products which are used.

*Partly because of proximity to the market, vegetable cultivation is located around conurbations and each grower chooses his varieties to suit the demand. What is the level of domestic supply of vegetables in the Federal Republic?*

Although for the cabbage varieties which are classifiable as a vegetable commodity the demand can be met almost completely from domestic cultivation, the so-called fine vegetables must be imported in large quantities. For example, there is a supply deficit for cauliflower of 60 per cent, of almost 90 for Brussels sprouts, 60 for lettuce and 90 per cent for tomatoes. A total of 60 per cent of the demand for vegetables has to be supplied by imports, mainly from neighbouring countries.

*Vegetable cultivation is essential in providing us with a healthy diet. Many different vegetable varieties are grown and marketed. Some vegetables have a short growth period. As a result, special demands are placed on the varieties to be cultivated and their relevant pesticides, whose application the legislator will only approve after they have been extensively tested and if the stipulated safety intervals are observed.*

## *16. Asparagus*

*Asparagus is one of the best known fine vegetables and is frequently referred to as the "royal" vegetable. In the "asparagus season" between April and June every year, when harvesting takes place, many consumers indulge themselves with a traditional meal of asparagus. Why is asparagus so popular?*

Because of its special taste and many different uses, white asparagus is rather special among the vegetable varieties. Sulphurous ethereal oils, methylmercaptan and vanillin give asparagus its typical taste. Asparagus is, moreover, low in calories, but rich in vitamins A, $B_1$, $B_2$ and niacin and also in potassium, phosphorus and iron. Also, asparagus stimulates the activity of the kidneys and so increases elimination of water from the body.

*What kinds of asparagus are there?*

We make a distinction between white and green asparagus. White asparagus is what we generally refer to as asparagus, since in this country the underground asparagus shoots are harvested before they break through the cultivation banks and turn green. Green asparagus is cultivated in flatter banks, the shoots grow above the ground and develop a green colouration in the daylight. Green asparagus is grown in Italy and a number of overseas countries.

*Is asparagus cultivation a recent development or has this fine vegetable been known for a long time?*

Asparagus was known to the Greeks and Romans as a delicacy more than 2000 years ago, and subsequently spread throughout Europe. The first large-scale cultivation in Germany began in the mid 16th century near Stuttgart in Southern Germany. The famous book of herbs by the Tübingen Professor Leonhard Fuchs (1502—1566) from the year 1543, makes reference to the specially healthful effects of asparagus on the liver and kidney function. Asparagus has thus been prized since ancient times both as a vegetable and a medicinal plant.

*Asparagus cultivation is therefore still very important. How large is the cultivation area in the Federal Republic?*

Despite increasing consumption, the asparagus cultivation area in the Federal Republic is shrinking and at present is only slightly more than 3,000 hectares, giving a total harvest yield of 10,000 tons. Nevertheless, imports of fresh asparagus and tinned asparagus are steadily increasing and are currently running at about 15,000 tons. The main importers of fresh asparagus, particularly before the start of the German harvest, are France, the Netherlands, Belgium and Tunisia. Tinned asparagus comes mainly from Taiwan, the USA and Spain. It might be mentioned that asparagus cultivation has increased in the Rhineland.

*How high are our own asparagus yields?*

Good asparagus plantations bring a yield of 4000 to 5000 kg per hectare in the main harvest period. The main factor militating against a further increase in the cultivation area is the large requirement for manual labour, particularly during the harvest, since the crop is harvested exclusively by hand. Trained harvesters are in short supply, which is why asparagus is mainly cultivated in family establishments and as a second occupation. Asparagus is harvested in warm weather twice a day, usually in the morning and in the evening, with the aid of a special harvesting implement.

*How is asparagus cultivated?*

Asparagus is a perennial plant which reaches an age of 10 to 12 years. Asparagus seedlings are usually purchased from plant nurseries. Planting is done in mid April, for which 17,000 plants per hectare are needed. With the aid of an asparagus plough, furrows 30 to 40 centimetres deep are ploughed at intervals of 1.5 metres, at the bottom of which the seedlings are planted and then covered over with soil. In the third year of cultivation banks are thrown up for the first time and the asparagus shoots are picked. At the end of each year's harvest, the banks are ploughed up and the field levelled. At the end of November, the asparagus leaves are removed.

*What purpose do the asparagus leaves serve?*

The asparagus harvest is usually finished by June 24 (Midsummers' Day). From the end of June, the asparagus shoots are allowed to continue growing and the asparagus leaves which sprout have the task of supplying the rootstock with new reserve substances for the following year's asparagus harvest through assimilation by the green asparagus plants.

*How important are pests and diseases in asparagus cultivation?*

The asparagus fly is the most dangerous pest encountered in asparagus plantations since it mainly tends to attack the young plants. It can be controlled by means of drench and granule application. Another troublesome pest is the asparagus beetle. Of the fungal diseases, asparagus rust is the most destructive. If control measures are not performed in good time, the asparagus plants wither and their yield is greatly reduced.

Weed control with special products plays a prominent role in asparagus cultivation, for the purpose of keeping the field free from weeds during the harvest period or picking time.

*Asparagus cultivation is both beset by risks and very capital and labour intensive, with the result that the price of asparagus is generally higher than that of other types of vegetable such as cabbage or leek. Have you any tips for the housewife on how to serve tasty asparagus?*

Enjoyment of fresh asparagus depends to a great extent on thorough peeling and preparation. For a proper meal of asparagus, 1 pound of asparagus should be served per person. The peeled asparagus shoots are placed in boiling water and simmered at moderate heat for 25 to 35 minutes and then served with melted butter, raw or cooked ham and parsley potatoes or omelettes. In addition to this classical asparagus dish, asparagus also has many different culinary uses as a soup, sauce, garnish or vegetable. It can also be frozen or preserved in other ways and served throughout the year as desired.

*Asparagus is thus a popular vegetable for which the producer will always find a ready market, and for the consumer is a fine vegetable which is not only appetizing and low in calories but also contains many valuable nutrients.*

## *17. Mushrooms*

*The special delicacies which nature offers us include an impressive number of edible mushrooms. Since very early times these have been served as the basic ingredient of popular dishes and today are increasingly in demand as a garnish for many different foods.*

*We must make a distinction between wild mushrooms and those which can be cultivated. Which are the most important varieties of wild mushroom?*

The varieties particularly deserving of mention are meadow mushrooms, chanterelles, yellow boletus and morels. These sprout from woodland and meadow soil after a warm rain, particularly in late summer and autumn. The higher, cap forming mushrooms usually enter into close symbiosis with the root system of specific types of plants and trees. This high degree of dependency is the reason why mushrooms are so difficult to cultivate under horticultural conditions.

*Which varieties of mushroom can be cultivated on a large scale?*

So far, only the common or field mushroom can be profitably cultivated. At a constant temperature of 17 °C, in shadowy locations and with a well-fertilized subsoil it flourishes so well that after the mycelium has ripened for several months, it can be continuously harvested.

*How is it that only this cultured mushroom can be produced horticulturally?*

In contrast to the cultured mushroom, the conditions under which most of the other mushroom varieties fructify are still a mystery. The simple presence of a host plant is usually far from sufficient for the yellow boletus, russula, chanterelles, morels and truffles to ripen.

*What varieties of mushroom are currently available on the market?*

The range of fresh mushrooms offered in the Federal Republic of Germany leaves something to be desired. Only the champignon is available in shops and markets all year round. Other edible mushrooms are offered only sporadically, usually depending on the prevailing weather conditions. This is why woodland mushrooms are more expensive and usually available only to a select group of purchasers, and also to people who live in woodland areas.

*The question therefore arises as to whether the market can be enriched with new varieties of mushroom in addition to the champignon, by cultivating oyster mushrooms and those of the genus Stropharia?*

The oyster mushroom and cultured Stropharia fungi, in addition to other mushroom varieties, have already been under cultivation for a considerable time in special enterprises and have also been offered to the consumer. These mushroom varieties are relatively undemanding as regards cultivation methods and, when prepared correctly, are both appetizing and have a high nutritive value.

*What can be said about the nutritive value of mushrooms?*

Mushrooms contain valuable protein, carbohydrates, salts essential to life and vitamins. Their nutritional value is superior to that of most vegetables. For example, champignons contain 10 per cent dry substance, half of which is protein and one third carbohydrates. By comparison, potatoes contain 35 per cent dry substance of which less than one tenth is protein and eight tenths carbohydrates.

*How extensive is mushroom production in the Federal Republic at the present time?*

About 100 specialized establishments in the Federal Republic currently produce 30,000 tons of champignons which satisfy a major part of the demand for fresh mushrooms. About three to four times this amount is imported from abroad in preserved form. The annual consumption of champignons is about 3 kg per head of population.

*Can German mushroom production be increased further?*

Successful cultivation requires that a number of hygiene measures be performed, in particular thorough cleaning and disinfection of the rooms after each culture, sterilization of the covering soil, preventive pest control and the elimination of possible routes of contamination and infection. The cultured champignon is threatened by numerous diseases and pests. This is because they are continuously cultivated in the same room, the room climate favours the development of many pathogens and pests, and the nutrient substrate of the cultured mushroom greatly encourages their propagation.

*Is crop protection necessary for mushrooms?*

Although most fungicides are toxic both to champignons and the other varieties of cultivated mushroom, which naturally makes it harder to control fungal diseases, the use of approved insect control agents presents no problems and is usually necessary to control the high intensity of infestation with mushroom fly grubs.

*To promote sales of domestic mushrooms it is necessary to improve production methods for a number of cultured mushroom varieties and to develop new and improved methods of cultivation for practical application.*

## *18. Beverage plants*

*Many cultivated plants growing throughout the world are used for producing beverages. Which are the most important ones?*

The principal plants in this category are coffee as well as tea, cocoa and cola. Also important in this respect are the citrus and all other fruit varieties used for manufacturing fruit juice, as well as barley or other cereal varieties and hops for beer production. In addition, cereals, sugar, potatoes, grapes and also wine and fruit are used for distilling brandy. Last but not least we have the grape vine, which from the earliest times has played a major role in the production of beverages.

*Viniculture has always been particular important in Europe. How large is the world cultivation area?*

The total world cultivation area is more than 10 million hectares and is limited to the "wine climate" countries. The biggest wine producers are Spain and France, each with an annual wine harvest of 70 million hectolitres, and Italy with more than 80 million hectolitres. In the Federal Republic, depending on the seasonal weather, five to fifteen million hectolitres are harvested. World wine production is currently about 300 million hectolitres per year. Wine as a beverage occupies a different status in each consumer country. While in the Mediterranean region it is an integral part of each daily meal, in other countries it is regarded as a luxury. Much can be said about wine, which is such a widely enjoyed beverage all round the world.

*Having talked about wine as an alcoholic beverage, perhaps we should also mention brandy and beer?*

Whereas brandy and other spirits distilled from wine, grain, potatoes and fruit are classed as semi-luxury items, beer to some extent is also regarded as a "food" wherever it is consumed. To brew beer, barley or other cereal varieties, as well as hops are needed. The hop, with world hectarages exceeding 85,000 hectares, gives the beer its special flavour and prolongs its storage life.

*Where is coffee grown?*

Coffee cultivation is concentrated in the tropical countries in the latitudes between 15° north and south of the equator. The cultivation area totals nine to ten million hectares and the production is five million tons. The major exporting countries are Brazil, Columbia, El Salvador, Guatemala, Mexico and Costa Rica in South and Central America as well as the Ivory Coast, Uganda, Kenya and Angola in Africa. Indonesia should also be mentioned. These countries export half of the world's coffee production.

*Who imports coffee?*

The main importing countries are the USA, the Federal Republic of Germany and France. These are followed by Italy, the Netherlands, Great Britain, Switzerland, Belgium, Canada and Japan. These countries consume two thirds of the world's coffee production.

*How many litres of coffee are drunk in the Federal Republic compared to other beverages?*

The coffee consumption per head of population is more than 150 litres per year, running level with beer consumption at just under 150 litres. By comparison, wine consumption is 25 litres and that of milk 85 litres per person each year.

*As well as coffee, tea should also be mentioned as a stimulating beverage?*

The tea cultivation area is 2.5 million hectares, and annual tea production 1.8 million tons. World production has increased more than threefold over the last 50 years. The main tea-growing countries are India, Ceylon, China, Japan, Indonesia and Pakistan. The major part, roughly two thirds, of the tea traded on the world market is imported by the English speaking countries.

*Where does cocoa rank among the beverages?*

The world cultivation area is 4.7 million hectares. Cocoa is a tree-like tropical crop. The major cultivation areas are now found in tropical West Africa and Brazil, the former cocoa-producing countries of America having declined in importance because of a high level of disease. The main importing countries are the USA, the Federal Republic of Germany, the Netherlands and the Soviet Union. The use of cocoa in the manufacture of stimulating mixed milk drinks is only one of its many possible uses as a constituent of foods and confectionery.

*What special role is played by the cola tree?*

The cola tree, which is closely related to cocoa, is grown in the West of India, East Asia and South America. Only the cola nut is harvested. This is used both in pharmaceuticals and in particular for the manufacture of stimulating soft drinks.

*This was a short survey of the many useful plants cultivated around the world which provide the basis for producing stimulating and refreshing beverages for private consumption, the catering trade and the beverage industry. We should not conclude this review without mentioning the great importance of citrus and the various other fruit varieties for beverage manufacture. Citrus and fruit production is on the increase worldwide with 80 to 100 million tons, a large proportion of which has always been used for the industrial and private preparation of beverages.*

## *19. Spices and medicinal plants*

*Spices are substances which, without themselves having any special nutritive value, are added to food to give it a special appetizing taste and aroma, in other words they serve to give zest to many different foods. What significance do spices have for us today?*

Spices are used to enliven our food in many ways. Food which has no aroma and no particular taste and which therefore no one wants to eat is nutritionally worthless, even though it may be rich in all the life-sustaining constituents such as protein, vitamins and trace elements.

*Can you give us some more details?*

The different spices have traditionally been used to make food more appetizing and to vary its taste. Modern research into spices is also pursued mainly to characterize the action of spices on bodily functions and particularly the digestive organs.

*Among the spices, we distinguish between exotic varieties and the domestic aromatic herbs. Which are the most prominent exotic spices?*

Pepper comes to mind immediately since it is cultivated throughout the tropical regions and is a perennial climbing plant. It is usually harvested twice a year. The harvesting time depends on whether black or white pepper is desired. Black pepper is a product of the whole unripe fruit, and the white pepper is obtained from the ripe kernels. Generally speaking, pepper is the most important spice on the world market.

*Where does cinnamon stand among the spices?*

Cinnamon bark is one of the oldest spices known to man. The most prized variety is the bark of the Ceylon cinnamon tree. This high tree flourishes in the wild in the South of India and in Ceylon, is grown in plantations to a height of two to three metres and is cultivated in most tropical countries. Cinnamon is used among other things as a fine spice for the meal table, cakes and pastries. The Greeks and Romans also seasoned their food with cinnamon, which was brought to Europe by the Arabs.

*What other spices should also be mentioned?*

Ginger, another long-familiar spice, also has many uses. Ginger is a reed-like perennial which is cultivated in South East Asia and other tropical countries. The subterranean runners, known as rhizomes, are harvested.

Nutmeg is another interesting spice. The nutmeg tree is today cultivated mainly in South East Asia, Indonesia, the West of India and Brazil. The clove tree is cultivated especially in Zanzibar and Madagascar. The flower buds, and recently also the leaves, are used.

*Among the other exotic spices, perhaps a word about vanilla?*

Vanilla is a popular spice with a range of uses not only in the household but also and especially in the confectionery industry where it is added as flavouring to puddings, cakes and pastries and ice cream. Vanilla is a climbing orchard plant indigenous to the tropics where it is cultivated. Genuine vanilla has now largely been replaced by the synthetic compound vanillin.

*Curry powder must be rather special even among the exotic spices?*

Curry is a mixture of spices with an ancient pedigree in the culinary arts of India, which was formerly reserved for rice dishes but is now used also for many other foods. It is a mixture of curcuma or turmeric which gives it the intense yellow colouring, and of cloves, ginger, cardamom, coriander, caraway, nutmeg, paprika, pepper, pimento (Jamaica pepper) and cinnamon.

*In addition to the tropical spices, which indigenous aromatic herbs enjoy continued popularity and are grown in the kitchen garden?*

There are a number of spice plants which are still cultivated in the kitchen garden as seasoning for cooked food; as well as dill, tarragon, fennel, savory, borage, pimpernel and basil we also find parsley, watercress, chives, celery leaves and onions, although these latter include varieties which are used as vegetables.

*Many spices and nutritious plants, but also other plant varieties have important curative properties and have traditionally found many applications in medicine. Cultivation of medicinal herbs must therefore have a special place in worldwide crop growing?*

While many herbs are gathered in the wild state, numerous medicinal herbs are cultivated commercially, each type in the most suitable climate. It should however be remarked that many substances such as ethereal oils are used in the perfume industry to produce cosmetics, so that the borderline between curative substances and cosmetics is rather a fluid one. Cultivated medicinal herbs are classified according to their main uses. For instance, root, herbal, leaf, blossom and grain drugs are harvested. Special establishments have been developed for the cultivation of valerian, dandelion, chamomile, peppermint and lavender, to give but a few examples.

*The cultivation of spice and medicinal herbs is therefore dispersed widely throughout the world. Only some of the many effects which these different varieties of plants have on the human organism have as yet been precisely identified. In addition to the major varieties which we have mentioned, there are many other spice and medicinal plants throughout the world which are either gathered in the wild state or cultivated.*

## *20. Illustrations of the different nutritious plants*

The food plants discussed in the radio talks are illustrated on the following pages 71—90.

Barley, the oldest cereal variety, is widely cultivated. Winter barley (above) is cultivated mainly as fodder grain, while spring barley is used mostly for brewing.

More than 4000 varieties of grass grow on the earth's surface, but only a few are directly useful as food for man. Wheat (below) is grown in many countries as the major bread cereal and has been traded throughout the world for more than 2000 years.

Maize, a very high-yielding cereal, is indigenous to America and was introduced as a new crop in Europe in the 16th century.

The male maize flowers form as panicles at the top of the stem.

From the female maize flowers, the cobs grow in the lower leaf axils.

Winter rye, an important bread cereal which grows in light soils in Nothern and Eastern Europe, is an undemanding crop and is cultivated as far as the Arctic Circle.

Oats is one of the most nutritious foods and is cultivated in moist climates.

The spikelets with 2—3 flowers hang from the lateral shoots of the 30 cm high oat panicle.

Rice ist the major cereal crop in many tropical and subtropical countries. Rice can be grown in continuous rotation. The rice paddy is the most widespread form of cultivation in South East Asia.

Control of rice pests safeguards the harvest.

Rice ready for harvesting. It was first cultivated 5000 years ago.

Sugar beet has been an important crop since the beginnig of the 19th century. An equal crop stand is only achieved by careful soil cultivation, drilling and crop protection. The beets on the left of the picture received no treatment against insect pests.

The sugar containing root of the beet plant bears a rosette of long-stemmed leaves above ground.

The reed-like sugar cane has stems 4 to 6 cm thick, from whose pith the sugar is extracted.

The potato is an important crop which is cultivated in many countries.

The potatoes are gathered with the aid of automatic harvesters, which can only operate in weed-free fields.

The apple blossom is vulnerable to late frost. The blossoms are fertilized by bees.

Apples are grown in many countries. Harvesting them requires intensive manual labour.

The pear is a popular fruit which gives high yields.

In commercial plum growing, control of insect pests (plum fruit moth) is very important.

The cherry blossom needs special protection from fungal infection.

Sour cherries are widely used for canning and beverages and also as a dessert fruit.

The citrus varieties grapefruit, oranges, mandarins and lemons are extensively cultivated in warm climates and are extremely popular as exotic fruit rich in vitamins.

After the large, white blossoms of the orange tree are fertilized, the large spherical orange-coloured fruits grow.

Oranges (Citrus sinensis) as a permanent crop are attacked by many pests.

Each banana tree forms a large inflorescence and dies after the fruits have ripened. The heavy bunch consists of smaller clumps or "hands".

Bananas shoot again from the rootstock and after one year form another inflorescence.

After harvesting, the bananas are packed immediately for shipment.

Redcurrants are grown for fresh consumption and are also used for making jams, jellies and fruit juices. They have good transport and storage properties.

Blackcurrants contain much vitamin C. They have been cultivated since 1750.

Blackberries take many forms, are widely grown in Europe and have existed as a cultivated crop since the 19th century.

Gooseberries are cultivated in many European countries. They are heavily attacked by American gooseberry mildew.

Strawberries are very popular with consumers. During the flowering period, they are infected by the grey mould rot pathogen which attacks the strawberry fruits.

Only good quality strawberries are marketable.

Raspberries are also among the most popular soft fruit varieties.

Hard shell fruit embraces the varieties of nuts belonging to different plant families, and have many important traditional uses: coconuts, walnuts, hazelnuts, paranuts, sweet chestnuts, almonds, peanuts and pistachios.

The fruit of the walnut tree has a green, non-edible flesh, inside which a wrinkled shell encloses the seed.

The peanut is one of the papilionaceous plants. The seeds are eaten raw or roasted, or processed to extract the oil.

The coconut palm, which can reach a height of 25 metres, flowers and fructifies from its 7th to 70th year. The coconut can weigh up to 1 kg. The coconut tree has an extremely wide range of uses.

The tomato originates from South America, where it has long been cultivated. It is now a popular fruit vegetable grown in many countries with a warm and moderate climate.

Head lettuce is a widely cultivated and popular leaf vegetable. Crop protection is necessary to control green aphids and grey mould.

The head cabbage forms heads whose outer leaves are green and inner leaves pale to white due to exclusion of light.

The cauliflower is an only recently cultivated plant from the Mediterranean area and is grown in many countries.

Red cabbage has been cultivated in Germany since the 12th century and is important as a winter vegetable.

The Savoy cabbage, first mentioned in the 16th century, is a popular cooking vegetable in summer and winter.

The Brussels sprout was introduced from Flanders in 1785. Sprouts are much in demand as a winter vegetable.

Weed-free bush bean crop cultivated under contract.

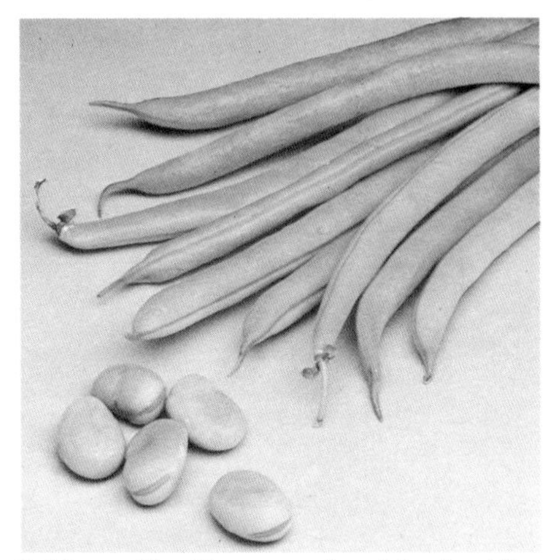

Bush beans and broad beans are popular varieties of vegetable.

Harvesting onions in Africa. The onion, familiar to ancient Egypt, is now cultivated in all continents.

Seed onion crop. As a bi-annual plant, the onion only forms seeds in its second year of cultivation.

Celeriac was known to the ancient Egyptians and was also an important food in Roman times.

Picking asparagus shoots which are formed by the perennial asparagus plant from its underground sprouting system.

After the asparagus harvest, the asparagus plant is left in the field to assimilate and incorporate nutrients into its underground sprouting system.

Spice plants are also cultivated and harvested on a large scale: dill crop in Canada (Winnipeg 1983).

As well as the cultivated champignon, the giant or cultivated mushroom Stropharia rugosa annulata is grown in America, Asia and Europe.

The cultivated champignon, known since 1600, is grown as an intensive culture in specially air-conditioned cultivation rooms. More than one million tons of champignons are harvested every year around the world.

The coffee plant has white blossoms; after fertilization, green, then yellow and finally red cherry-like stone fruits develop in which the coffee seeds (coffee beans) grow. Development from the flowering stage to the bean harvest lasts eight months.

Tea, cultivated in China for 5000 years, flourishes in the tropics up to an elevation of 2400 m and in the subtropics in areas with mild winters. The tea leaves are pruned every seven to ten days all year round. The buds with the two to three topmost leaves provide the best quality.

Cocoa blossoms grow from the thicker branches and trunks (cauliflory).

The 10 to 20 cm long, cucumber-like cocoa fruits contain 30 to 50 seeds in their pulp (cocoa beans).

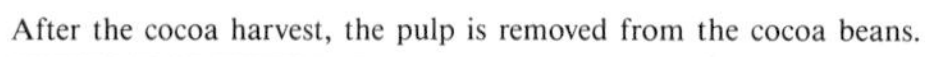

After the cocoa harvest, the pulp is removed from the cocoa beans.

Viniculture is important in many countries with warm climate throughout the world. Varieties for dessert or wine production are grown as required.

Hop growing is concentrated in certain areas on the borders of the wine climate. The ripe hop catkins are used for brewing beer, and the substances they contain giving the beer its special taste and long storage life.

Cress, paprika, parsley, dill, chives, ginger, nutmeg, pepper and cloves are important culinary herbs and spices.

## III. Changes in agriculture and crop cultivation

With the coming of the industrial era in the 19th century, agriculture began to undergo important changes. Before this time, agriculture had played a dominant role in economic life. With the arrival of industrialization, it lost its central and regulating function for wages and prices. Trade and industry acquired economic power and gained ascendancy within the national economy. Another factor contributing to this development was the migration of workforce from agriculture to industry, at a time when more than 65 per cent of the population were rurally based. In the course of this upheaval in the economic structure, wages were freed from their previous close dependence on agricultural determinants such as the ground rent system and the law of declining growth in crop yield from increasing input of effort, and were now linked to industrial development. Whereas in the earlier, pre-industrial period, productivity increases depended on the area of land cultivated and amount of labour invested, the technical means of production provided by industry and trade increasingly became the decisive factor in agricultural development. As well as land and labour, capital had now become a key element in production in the agricultural sphere.

While this shift in the economic structure was taking place, the scientific era began to make its mark and, through the invention of mineral fertilization, ushered in a change in agriculture by removing a natural obstacle to the intensification of farming which had been imposed by the laws of inertia. At the same time, agricultural engineering appeared on the scene. Only with these new techniques could yields be raised on land already under cultivation and new areas of arable land be made cultivable. The increasing demand for food from the growing population could only be satisfied through bigger harvests.

The problems which still resisted solution in the last century were those of crop protection. Potato blight, which made its appearance in all the countries of Europe in 1845, still caused major harvest losses, since it could not yet be controlled. Only 40 years later did scientific research into the causes and control of this disease and other major, yield-reducing pests provide the means of countering this threat with specific control techniques.

As a result, crop protection has over the last 100 years become a major production factor in agriculture and horticulture, whose major service worldwide has been to secure yields by means of control measures.

Given the present state of technical development, and in view of the advances in agricultural science to be anticipated for the future, further production increases will be possible by stabilizing yields and intensive farming.

In addition to boosting yields to a local maximum, efforts should above all be directed towards compensating for yield fluctuations by applying the latest technical know-how in crop cultivation, fertilization, agricultural engineering and crop protection, although this is sometimes prevented by climatic conditions. Nevertheless, this approach could bring about a further stabilizing of agrarian production, as well as a general increase in average yields and yield levels. There is, after all, a difference between achieving a cereal yield of 8 to 10 tons per hectare on the individual farm and as a national average.

Yields can therefore be secured and increased over the long term by reducing yield fluctuations. Climatically, the decisive factors for intensive cultivation of the major food plants such as cereals are temperature and water supply. By using all the technical resources at his disposal, each farmer must create the right conditions for achieving a large harvest by applying suitable cultivation techniques, paying particular attention to choice of varieties, fertilization and crop protection. If all the appropriate measures are taken, yield increases of about 25 per cent can be achieved now and in the future.

## *1. Agriculture in the industrial age*

*Whereas in former times agriculture and forestry were the main occupation of the population which they pursued to meet their own demands, agriculture in the industrial age is one element within the national economy based on division of labour. Can we illustrate this change in our national economy with figures?*

At the start of the 19th century, 80 per cent of the economically active population in Germany worked in agriculture, 8 per cent in trades and 12 per cent in the service sectors. Today, 5 per cent of those economically active are engaged in agriculture and forestry, about 50 per cent in industry and more than 40 per cent in the trades and service sector.

*What fundamental changes have led to the great decrease in the number of persons engaged in agriculture and forestry?*

Meeting the demand for agricultural and forestry products continues to be the most important task. Due to improvements in cultivation methods, yields have increased many times compared to previous levels. The appearance of the countryside has also been changed by urbanization and industrialization. Agriculture and forestry therefore have another important function to perform, in that they help to protect the environment by preserving the countryside, which should retain its traditional identity with a balanced pattern of arable land, gardens, orchards and woodlands.

*We can therefore conclude that agriculture and forestry have undergone a kind of metamorphosis which has gone unnoticed by many people. In what manner has this process of change taken place?*

In times past, the farming family produced the food and drink they needed themselves; moreover, most of their clothing, domestic utensils and equipment were manufactured on their own farms. Compared to today, the degree of self sufficiency of urban households was also great. Agriculture produced only the raw products for food and clothing; the processing, preparation and preservation was the task of the urban households.

*Has the increasing integration of agriculture into the national economy led to far-reaching changes?*

Between the farm and the urban household, there has grown up a constantly increasing sphere of preparation, processing and distribution of agricultural raw products by the food processing industry, food crafts and trades. As in agriculture, so too in the urban household this surrender of functions was accompanied by a release of workforce for other areas of the national economy.

*Despite this development, what areas are still used in the Federal Republic of Germany for arable farming and forestry?*

In the Federal Republic, 12.5 million hectares of land are used for farming. Of this, 7.3 million hectares are arable land, 0.5 million hectares are used for horticulture, viniculture and fruit growing and 4.7 million hectares are permanent grassland. The forest area comprises 7.2 million hectares. The area used for agriculture (without forests) in the Federal Republic is 0.2 hectares per inhabitant. Compared to this, the Netherlands have 0.14 hectares and France 0.59 hectares per inhabitant, while for the total EC area this figure is 0.38 hectares.

*Is the population density in the Federal Republic particularly high?*

Together with the Netherlands and Belgium, the Federal Republic of Germany, particularly the heavily industrialized areas of the Rhine-Ruhr and Rhine-Main, is one of the most densely populated regions within the EC area. Particularly in these areas, agriculture and forestry, in addition to supplying the demand of the population for food, wood and game, also have a number of other tasks.

*What are these tasks?*

As well as being a supplier of raw materials, income and work, in other words the economic function, agriculture and forestry also exercise a protective function in respect of plants, water, land and protection from climate. In view of the increasing population density, it is also more and more acquiring a recreational function.

## 2. Crop rotation and crop protection

*In arable farming, vegetable and fruit cultivation, crops are grown according to certain rules. In addition to the cultivation methods, in other words how sowing, planting or fertilizing are carried out, it has always been and still continues to be highly important to follow a certain crop rotation, in other words, wheat should not always be grown after wheat, or beets after beets, to give a simple example. What are the basic reasons for this?*

The cultivation of certain types of crop in immediate succession on the same area of land frequently leads to reduced yields which may have various causes and which with certain plants results in soil exhaustion.

*What does the specialist understand by soil exhaustion?*

This may have a number of causes, for example unbalanced nutrient extraction, certain diseases, pests or weeds achieving dominance or mutual incompatibility of the crops which are grown, which may be due to an accumulation of toxic agents in the soil.

*How do farmers, horticulturists or gardeners counter these problems?*

The long-established remedy is crop rotation, which means planting mutually promoting or tolerating species of plants in a given sequence. The intercalation of a fallow or resting period has also made a special contribution in this respect.

*What form does modern land use take?*

The intensification of land use in arable farming and horticulture over the last few decades has led to increasing specialization. As a result, the overemphasis on certain crops has greatly increased. The consequences of this unbalanced land use, in some cases disregarding well proven rules of crop rotation, has resulted in certain diseases, pest or weeds gaining ascendancy.

*What problems does this create for crop protection?*

Cost and price trends on the labour and sales market are forcing the farmer to simplify his operation by adopting unbalanced crop rotations with a high proportion of cereals and to abandon the entire animal husbandry side of his farming enterprise. In some cases, however, specialized livestock production is retained. The problems arising in arable farming due to these one-sided crop rotations are manifested above all in the spread of certain weeds such as blackgrass or as an increase in the incidence of powdery mildew on cereals. The increase in soil pests in beet or cereal cultivation is also due to these developments. Nematodes can inflict severe damage. In all cases, timely control measures are vital for securing yields and profitability.

*What are the effects in fruit growing and in the cultivation of ornamentals?*

Soil exhaustion caused by growing certain types of crop in immediate succession, which leads to yield deficits and stunting, is a grave problem particularly in fruit growing and ornamental plant cultivation. This is caused by a number of nematode species which mainly attack the roots, and also by soil fungi. Control takes the form of chemical soil decontamination by means of fumigation, water soluble nematicides or fungicides. Soil exhaustion, just to mention this once again, is more important in fruit growing and tree nurseries than in other areas of agriculture, since in many cases it is not possible to remove cultivation to another area or to adopt a varied crop rotation.

## *3. Modern cropping methods in cereal cultivation*

*Because of changes in agricultural policy and working methods, cereal cultivation has expanded increasingly in the EC countries over recent years, with the result that the proportion of cereals in crop rotations has now reached 70 to 80 per cent. High yields per unit area are important for achieving economic profitability and therefore optimal organization of cropping methods is the prime consideration in individual farms. What principles must particularly be followed in sowing winter cereal?*

In addition to proper soil tilling and fertilization, the choice of cultivars is important for all species of winter cereal. Furthermore, the sowing time, seed rate, row spacing, seed depth and above all careful seed dressing is decisive for achieving an optimal crop density, since the crop density, in other words the number of ear-bearing stems, is the major determinant of the yield per unit area.

*What rules apply for crop rotation and sowing methods?*

The crop rotation arrangement for cereals, the use of green manuring, ploughing down of straw and soil cultivation are subjects of continuing topicality. These aspects are very significant for yield formation. Particularly important however is the sowing method, in other words achieving an optimal depth and distribution of the seed on the surface. Modern sowing methods with a narrow row spacing in drilling, band sowing or broadcast sowing, especially for wheat with high seed rates, create the preconditions in which the individual cereal plants flourish.

*You mentioned the row spacing; is there any special reason for this?*

Wheat used to be grown in rows drilled 20 centimetres apart to make it easier to control weeds with the hoeing machine. With the introduction of chemical weed control, however, other aspects, including optimal spacing of individual plants, are decisive in selecting the row spacing.

*How does this work out in practice?*

Today we drill with a row spacing of 10 to 12 cm; band or broadcast sowing equipment and special sowing ploughshares are also used on an experimental basis. This improved distribution of the cereal plants over the field has so far been found to give increased yields, since it greatly reduces the competition between the cereal plants themselves. A further advance is the single grain sowing method for cereals, in which the grains can be deposited singly in the drilling row at the desired spacing.

*An essential element in farming techniques is weed control. Experience over the last few years has shown that, for winter cereals, particularly winter barley, and when weed infestation is high, chemical weed control should be carried out as early as autumn. What are the chief practical considerations for the farmer?*

Weed control in winter cereal growing, particularly for winter barley and winter wheat, is performed with soil herbicides applied in the autumn, which reliably control both waste grasses such as blackgrass and bentgrass and all weeds including stubborn species such as chamomile. Most of the soil herbicides which are applied are not only effective against weeds but are well tolerated by all crop varieties, as proven by extensive testing. Long-term trials have shown that autumn treatment gives an average 10 to 15 per cent yield increase in all species and varieties of winter cereals.

*We should also mention that for effective weed control, the herbicides should be carefully applied to a highly friable seed bed. Finally, the question should be asked whether, despite the great expansion of cereal growing, yield levels are continuing to rise?*

Even though the great expansion in cereal growing has been accompanied by an increase in diseases, pests and weeds, improvements in control techniques and other cultivation methods have produced a continuous pattern of yield growth. However, under intensive cropping conditions, it has not been possible to fully utilize the theoretically or genetically existing yield potential in spite of all these advances in chemical crop protection.

## 4. Advances in sugar beet farming due to improved working and cropping practices

*Over the last twenty years, the yield situation in sugar beet cultivation has undergone several thorough changes compared to cereal, maize, rape and potato crops. As a result, discussion as to where and on what scale sugar beet growing is most economic, is still continuing. What factors have exerted a decisive influence on the profitability of sugar beet growing over the last few decades?*

Over the last few decades, standard wages in West German agriculture have doubled, and effective wages have risen even more sharply. Consequently, the workforce in this sector has shrunk by about 40 per cent. This marked decline in employed workforce has been achieved only through substantial investment and by drastically reorganizing the production programme.

*Can this trend be illustrated with figures?*

The active capital expenditure has meanwhile increased from 36,000 to over 100,000 DM per worker, and the pulling capacity of tractors and number of automatic harvesters have more than doubled. The proportion of the farmed area covered by cereals has grown from 60 to more than 70 per cent; and the root crop component has decreased from 24 to slightly less than 12 per cent; the rapid rise in wage levels has mainly affected the labour intensive areas of agriculture such as root crop cultivation. Nevertheless, the sugar beet growing area, at more than 400,000 hectares, has remained relatively constant over the last ten years due to savings in manual labour, whereas potato and fodder beet cultivation is showing a marked decline.

*What cultivation and processing measures have resulted in an improvement of profitability in sugar beet cultivation at the current high wage levels?*

The first contributory factor after the war was the use of automatic harvesters and the introduction of monogerm seed, which greatly reduced labour levels. As a result, work input was reduced from 375 to 215 working hours per hectare. The labour bottleneck which still existed in beet growing was overcome by the use of chemical weed control agents and by drilling single germ seed to a stand, bringing a further saving from 215 to 60 working hours per hectare of sugar beet. These advances in work saving in the cultivation of sugar beet have led to a decrease in work input of 85 per cent.

*Sugar beet is thus no longer "hoed free" by hand, and weeds can be removed from the beet crops by means of special herbicides requiring little manual labour, as is usually practised with other crops. This must have major economic consequences?*

As result of the decline in work input from 375 to 60 working hours per hectare, sugar beet, as the industrial management expert would say, has become wage tolerant. Labour costs in sugar beet cultivation today therefore account for only 8.6 per cent of the raw yield and thus correspond to labour costs in cereal cultivation.

*Sugar beet yields increased from a prewar level of 33 tons per hectare to 39 tons per hectare at the end of the fifties, and now reach almost 55 tons per hectare in good years. This has meant an improvement in the profitability of sugar beet cultivation, not only as a result of labour saving, but also through the increase in beet and sugar yields. What are the main factors which have brought about this enormous increase in yield?*

These large yield increases have resulted chiefly from the breeding of new and better varieties as well as planned fertilization and crop protection measures. Key factors in this development have been weed control and thus the guarantee of undisturbed growth of the young beet plants and also the control of diseases and insect pests.

*Which are the most important insect pests in sugar beet?*

With drilling of monogerm seed to a stand, particular attention should be paid to the control of early pests, in other words pests which damage or destroy the young beets during their emergence. These pests include the pigmy mangold beetle, flea beetle, springtails ans millipedes. Control of the beet fly during the horse chestnut flowering period, and of greenfly, is also important. The green peach aphid and blackfly not only cause damage by sucking but are also vectors of yield-reducing virus diseases, known as yellowing, and consequently aphids must be given special attention.

*If modern methods of arable farming are judiciously applied, production of sugar beet is therefore a rewarding branch of German agriculture. What are the future prospects for sugar demand?*

World sugar consumption is increasing more rapidly than the world population. Sugar production in the Federal Republic and the European Community however exceeds the level of consumption. These circumstances effectively determine future production levels in this country. Since the labour productivity of our sugar beet cultivation equals even that of the highly mechanized sugar cane farming in the USA, and since national economic trends demand that greater emphasis be placed on labour productivity even in the tropics, sugar beet will continue to compete successfully with sugar cane as a source of sugar.

## *5. Changes in fruit growing due to new farming systems*

*Apple cultivation as it used to be practised with the standard tree system, using grass as undergrowth for animal feed has, for reasons of labour and industrial economy, been replaced by modern plantation fruit growing and, on a distinct and separate basis, by rationalized green fodder production for animal feeds and livestock premises.*

*Plantation fruit growing has however undergone certain changes over the last few decades. In our own time, the dense cropping system with low trees has been introduced in practice. What features of this cultivation technique deserve particular mention?*

The pillar dense cropping system was developed by a Britisher, Gordon McLean, in Kingston (Berkshire) and has been introduced to an increasing extent over the last twenty years in Belgium, the Netherlands as well as the Federal Republic of Germany and in Italy (South Tyrol). The pillar, a familiar feature in architecture, is in this context a "tree pillar", a trunk with a maximum height of 2.25 metres, from which the fruit-bearing boughs are developed directly without main or lateral branches. Grafts of the different apple varieties are planted on the weakly growing rootstock Malus 9 and need no further pruning after planting. These grafts are given their optimal form by binding, according to whether the fruiting laterals are long or short. Not only annual, but also bi-annual grafts are planted, particularly for varieties which have a poor branching capacity. In the first two years of the crop no pruning, as it were, is performed. As result, a considerable fructification with a yield of 5 to 10 tons per hectare develops on the lateral branches as early as the second cropping year. Due to this early fruiting phase, the rootstock develops only to a slight extent, as result of which the trees remain low.

*What particular features of cropping technique should be mentioned?*

Under our own conditions, the optimal plant spacing is 3.50 metres between rows and 1—1.5 metres within the row. To guarantee sufficient light for the lower branches and fruit, the row spacing should be one and a half times the tree height, in other words, about 3.5 metres for a height of 2.25 metres. Only in this way can the tree be completely exposed to the sun, thereby preventing the growth of inferior shadow fruit.

*What economic advantages does this cultivation system offer?*

The pillar system, although involving higher laying-out costs per hectare, provides an earlier harvest and therefore more rapid amortization of the laying-out costs. In this way, the running production costs are reduced due to the low input for pruning and harvesting operations, while at the same time achieving higher yields. As early as the second year of cultivation, yields of 5 to 10 tons per hectare, and in the third year of 10 to 20 tons per hectare are achieved. The maximum yields can reach 60 tons per hectare. In comprehensive Dutch trials, 60 tons per hectare more were harvested over the first eight cropping years than in the widely spaced plantations which formerly predominated.

*What effects does this dense planting of trees have on crop protection?*

Completely new aspects arise for crop protection. Of particular importance is regular weed control and also the systematic control of field mice and voles. In the control of tree pests and fungal diseases, it has been possible to achieve a reduction in the amount of water used from 2,500 to 2,000 litres per hectare in widely spaced plantations to 1,500 to 1,000 litres per hectare in densely planted orchards. Furthermore, because of the small crowns, more careful and effective control of pathogens is guaranteed, since the crowns of the trees are wetted more effectively during crop protection treatment.

One of the first combine harvesters drawn by horses, used at the turn of the century in the big wheat growing regions of North America. The combine harvester inaugurated the mechanization of agriculture.

Compared to its beginnings eight decades ago, modern mowing and threshing is performed by a technically sophisticated combine harvester operated by one man and having an hourly performance under our conditions of 1 to 2 hectares. Combine harvesting is only profitable in standing, dry and weed-free crops.

# IV. Agrochemistry as a production factor

Agriculture differs from the industrial economy in that it is linked to a given location and depends on natural factors, and therefore has a biological-technical orientation. Arable and horticultural production is a process bound to animals and plants which, although conceived, introduced and controlled by man, is essentially a biological growth process contingent on the natural conditions of location and climate. In contrast to commercial or industrial production, this dependence on the rhythm of the seasons, and thus on the growth and ripening process of cultivated plants, does not generally permit short-term changes in cultivation planning.

The seasonal rhythm has certain consequences for the labour economy, since the crops cultivated throughout the year make different demands on the labour market.

Location factors such as soil quality and climate as well as economic factors such as farm size and organization are fundamental in determining the economic success of the farmer.

The organization and success of agricultural enterprises are influenced to a major degree by technical advances, which frequently derive from considerations of national economy and agricultural policy. Over the last century, new technical developments have continuously taken place in agriculture. Innovations are adopted in individual enterprises if they offer advantages in terms of working or production methods. Major changes have resulted from industrialization, migration to the cities and the increased cost of labour. The change in the labour market due to mechanization and the decrease in labour resources have altered the relationship between work and capital in individual enterprises.

Generally it can be stated that technical developments in arable farming relate mainly to cultivation methods, mechanization and farm organization. Whereas advances in cultivation methods in crop growing can be rapidly applied in the form of selection of varieties, fertilization and crop protection, bringing advantages to all types of enterprise irrespective of their size, in economic terms the mechanization of cultivation and harvesting methods is essentially governed by the size of the enterprise. In certain cases, developments in the field of mechanization greatly affect the farm organization, as for example when new units of large equipment have to be used on several farms to ensure profitability.

These considerations illustrate the extent to which agrochemistry has within a very short time achieved an important position worldwide as a production factor in arable farming and horticulture, independent of the size of farming enterprises, for improving profitability by increasing and securing harvests. Agrochemistry embraces fertilization, seed dressing, soil cultivation and weed control, as well as all other methods of crop protection in arable farming and horticulture, which are now presented in detail in the following sections.

## *1. Mineral fertilization and crop protection for securing yields*

*Mineral fertilization and crop protection are extremely important for increasing yields in agriculture and horticulture. At today's advanced level of development it would be interesting to briefly outline how this came about. How did plant nutrition and fertilization develop?*

Plant nutrition was originally thought to correspond to the nutritional processes in man and animals. Since man ingests mainly organic substances for his nutrition, it was erroneously assumed that this was also the case with plants. Aristotle (384—322 B.C.) taught that the roots of plants take their nutrition from the soil in the form in which it is present in the plants. This view was still given credence in the Middle Ages. Only in the 17th century were the teachings of Aristotle placed in doubt by Malpighi and Mariotte, when the importance of green leaves as nutritional organs was recognized and the significance of the inorganic substances in the soil for plant nutrition was realized. In the 18th century, the gas exchange of plants and the nature of photosynthesis first began to be understood. The beginning of the 19th century witnessed another change with the "humus theory" postulated by Albrecht Thaer. According to this theory, apart from water only humus constitutes the nutrient substance of plants, whereas inorganic materials at most served only as stimulants.

*What were the consequences of this theory?*

The humus content of the soil was equated with its fertility. The principal aim of fertilization was to enrich the soil with humus-forming vegetable and animal substances.

The Englishman Humphrey Davy, who coined the term "agricultural chemistry", and the German Carl Sprengel, the originator of modern plant nutrition science, attempted in vain at this time to demonstrate the importance of minerals for plant nutrition. Not until Justus von Liebig did the minerals theory gain acceptance. This scientist proved that plants build their organic substance by means of photosynthesis from the carbon dioxide in the atmosphere and the inorganic nutrients taken up in ground water, whereas humus is not used but rather enriched by plants.

*Opinions on nitrogen fertilization at this time were at first divided. What was the nature of these speculations?*

The agricultural chemist Boussingault proved by means of experiments that plants cannot use directly the atmospheric nitrogen which makes up 79 per cent of the air and must therefore absorb nitrogen in the form of ammonia salts and nitrate from the soil. While Liebig had first assumed that the nitrogen compounds formed as a result of electrical discharges in the atmosphere and, introduced into the soil by means of rainfall, would be sufficient to supply the plants with nitrogen, Lawes and Gilbert, the founders of Rothamsted, the famous experimental station in England, demonstrated in experiments that nitrogen fertilization is a basic necessity for plant nutrition.

*How was fertilization performed at this time?*

Potassium fertilization was formerly carried out by spreading wood ash, and from 1860, the saline deposits from the rock salt mines of Central Germany. Phosphoric acid fertilizer was applied in the form of bone meal. From 1820, according to contemporary reports, even the battlefields of Europe helped supply the increasing demand for bone meal, a not very edifying memory. The invention and manufacture of superphosphate at the beginning of the last century initiated modern phosphoric acid fertilization. Thomas slag, a by-product of steelmaking which contains large quantities of phosphate and was marketed as "Thomas phosphate", was widely introduced as a successor to bone meal fertilizer.

Nitrogen fertilizer was applied at this time in the form of Chile saltpetre and Peru guano, and as sulphuric ammonia produced by gas works and coking plants. The production of larger and lower priced quantities of nitrogen fertilizers only became possible with the introduction of the Haber Bosch process. In this process, the elementary nitrogen in the air is converted to soluble nitrogen compounds and is then made available as fertilizer for plant nutrition.

*How was lime fertilization carried out?*

Lime fertilization was performed by marling the soil, in other words by fertilizing it with lime-containing earths to improve the soil quality, and by applying powdered limestone. Today, lime fertilizers are applied in a variety of different preparations.

*How important is soil for plant nutrition?*

Although plants can grow in water without soil with the aid of nutrient salt solutions, a method known as hydroculture, in agriculture and horticulture only the natural soil has practical importance as a growing base for plants. Mineral fertilization however is only successful if the soil is in a state which promotes the effectiveness of the nutrient substances which are added. The precondition for this is good tilth or the consistency of the friable structure of the soil. This is achieved by careful soil cultivation, optimal water and temperature conditions, regulated lime supply which counteracts soil acidification, and an adequate supply of organic substance for the soil supplied by green manuring, harvest trash and commercial fertilizer.

*Soil biology is also very important in this interaction?*

The activity of the microorganisms in the soil is particularly significant for achieving the optimal soil conditions just described. Not only do the bacteria, fungi and mircoorganisms improve the quality of the soil, they also convert organic and inorganic materials into water soluble substances which can be taken up by the plant roots, in which form they first become available for plant nutrition.

*Together with fertilization, crop protection is a major production factor which is also claimed to contribute greatly to the optimal growth of cultivated plants as a means of achieving a large and healthy crop. Crop protection however must also extend to the soil as a nutrient medium and the crops which grow there?*

The useful soil organisms we have mentioned are unfortunately accompanied by numerous harmful organisms which live in the soil and which do not promote plant growth. These include the nematodes, cutworms, voles, root pests and also fungal and bacterial pathogens of crop diseases, as well as the root-propagated weeds and seed weeds as competitors for space and nutrients. The control of all these harmful organisms which injure the roots or the young plants is the task of soil treatment and seed dressing. This aspect of chemical crop protection is highly important in all cultivation areas for securing yields by maintaining the health of the crops.

*Maintaining the health of the aerial parts of plants by means of crop protectants is the second, equally important aspect of chemical crop protection. What are the principles which govern this activity?*

Insect pests or fungal diseases are suppressed for two reasons: firstly to maintain the health of the leaves as organs of assimiliation to create the preconditions for yield formation, and secondly to secure the yield and quality of harvest products for example in fruit, vegetable or cereal crops.

*What do fertilization and crop protection have in common?*

The more intensive the cultivation method, the more important it is to harmonize fertilization and crop protection. Only the application of yield-securing crop protection measures makes the use of fertilizer economically worthwhile. High yields can only be achieved if the production factors within the chosen cultivation system are optimally matched to each other.

## 2. Seed treatment

*"As the seed, so the harvest", runs an old proverb, which is as true as ever both in agriculture and horticulture. What factors must be considered in relation to sowing and the seed itself to create the basis for a good harvest?*

Since ancient times, seedbed preparation, sowing time, sowing method and the seed rate as well as the choice of seed and its treatment on sowing have been paid special attention. All too often, the seed which is sown is damaged, limiting the harvest expectation from the very outset. In particular, the sowing time in relation to the moisture and warmth of the soil determines the time which elapses from swelling of the seed, through germination to emergence. The germination phase is an essential stage in the development of cereals and other crops.

*Seed germination after sowing depends to a great extent on weather conditions?*

Germination of the seed is determined primarily by the amount of water and oxygen in the soil and the soil temperature. Swelling of the seed due to uptake of water is the basis for germination. Apart from the water, the temperature is important for initiating germination. Optimal soil temperatures for germination of cereal species are 20 to 25 °C and the required minimum is 3 to 5 °C. The lowest demands as regards temperature are made by rye, and the highest demands by maize.

*Can any empirical rules be stated for the period between sowing and emergence?*

The time between sowing and emergence is shorter the warmer the soil and the air and the more intense the insolation. These relationships are essentially governed by the sowing time. Winter barley sown in September emerges most quickly, that is after eight to ten days, and wheat sown late in October to the end of November by contrast emerges only after five to six weeks, and the spring barley cultivars emerge after two to three weeks. The emergence of beets and vegetables is also determined mainly by the time of sowing and the warmth of the air and soil.

*Is it possible to influence germination of the seeds by treatment before or during sowing?*

More than 2000 years ago, Vergil wrote in his Georgica: I have seen that many people dress their seed before it is sown. They place it in saltpetre and in pressing lees of olives in order to produce a full grain. In other words, even in antiquity seed was fertilized with saltpetre to promote the development of the seedlings and the plants and also to stimulate them and induce germination. It should however be remembered that the germination capacity of seeds in olden days was less than that of today's specially bred varieties.

*Today, the main aim of seed dressing is to control the germs of crop diseases present in or on the seed and to keep down seed and seedling pests which live in the soil. What experience has been gathered?*

Although extensive trials have shown that seed dressing for the purpose of fertilization and stimulation no longer has any importance, dressing of seed as a means of controlling bunt of wheat or bean anthracnose is a highly beneficial crop protection measure. Powdering of cereal seeds or pelleting the seed of beets and vegetables with insecticides serves to protect the seedling and the young plant against insect pests. Seed dressing or treatment is one of the most rewarding crop protection measures and is also ecologically safe.

*What contribution have technical advances and the synthesis of new chemical substances made to the current state of development of this versatile and essential area of agrochemistry?*

In the 18th and 19th centuries, the major discoveries in the fields of chemistry, physiology and biology laid the foundations for present-day seed dressing practice. Bunt of wheat was first successfully controlled with copper in 1807, but not until 1914 did seed dressing to prevent many crop diseases become possible with the introduction of organic mercury compounds, which were applied to cereals, beets and other seed crops. A major advance was achieved 60 years later with new systemic seed dressings, which not only disinfect the seed grain on the surface, but also penetrate into the seed grain and the seedling, thereby controlling diseases such as loose smut of wheat and barley which formerly could not be controlled by means of dressing methods. Some of these new dressing agents also protect the young plant from attack by mildew and rust diseases.

The efficacy of seed dressing however always depends on the technical condition of the dressing equipment used and the quality control of the dressing process.

*The seed quality is also decisively important for successful crop growing. What factors influence the seed quality?*

The seed quality is essentially determined by the weather during harvest and the subsequent preparation of the seed. The size of seed in particular exerts a major influence. The later development of the plants and their resistance and yield are better with large grain than with small grain seed. Seed dressing as a protection against fungal and insect pests is performed above all to assure the optimal development of crops from the outset.

## *3. Care of soil and weed control*

*Care and cultivation of the soil is essential if crops are to grow successfully. Many soil conditioning activities are also effective means of weed control. What possibilities of weed control are offered by soil cultivation?*

Soil cultivation is practised to create the preconditions for crops to give high yields. The most important equipment in soil cultivation consists of ploughs, rotary cultivators, grubbers and harrows. These, when used in an appropriate manner, help to create a satisfactory seed and root bed for the different crops. Cleaning and loosening the soil is performed by ploughing, rotary cultivator tillage or grubbing, levelling and preparing for sowing or planting by using floats, harrows and crumblers. The implements used for firming the seed bed are packers, rollers or rotary harrows. With the aid of modern interacting equipment, the major soil cultivation processes can be performed in one or two operations.

*How does soil cultivation help to eliminate weeds?*

The soil is turned by ploughing, during which the skim coulter and the mouldboard bury the harvest and root trash of the previous crops and the weeds to the desired depth, ensuring that the surface of the soil is cleared. Harrowing or brushing after sowing, before "spiking" or after emergence of the cereal was frequently the only way of controlling weeds. Weeds however are sensitive only from the cotyledon to the rosette stage, during which the harrow only buries the weeds, without pulling them out or injuring them to any great extent. It must however be remembered that any form of soil cultivation has the effect of promoting the germination of weed seeds, and thus of spreading the weed growth. Moreover, harrowing or brushing is only effective against weeds in dry weather. This gives the cereal plants only a slight advantage, since usually more than half the weeds continue to grow after harrowing.

*Surely hoeing is a very effective means of weed control?*

Hoeing of weeds has long been practised to make weeding by hand easier. In addition to the hand hoe, the mechanical hoe has been extensively adopted in large-scale agricultural and horticultural cultivation. With this method, however, weed control is only possible between the rows and not within the rows themselves. For this purpose, the rotary hoe with automatic swivelling device was developed for use in fruit tree plantations. A disadvantage of hand and mechanical hoeing is the damage which is done to the roots of the crop.

*Hand pulling must surely be a wearisome task?*

Hand pulling, in many countries still the main method of weed control, is certainly a fatiguing and time-consuming business. In our own country, hand pulling was particularly important not only in garden crops but also in flax crops which had to be completely free of weeds to guarantee the fibre quality. To weed a "quarter sheath" of flax, in other words 355 square metres, the farmer's wife needed six days.

*What other means of weed control does soil cultivation offer?*

The oldest and least laborious method is burning. Also possible is mowing, a method formerly practised in cereal growing for pruning the wild radish to prevent its flowers and seeds from forming. This is still occasionally done in beet growing by mowing down the white goosefoot with the club mower. A method often employed is mulching with grass or straw, as for example in fruit growing and horticulture, causing the weeds to choke in darkness. Covering the plants with black plastic sheeting, commonly practised in vegetable growing, follows the same principle and is being tried out in maize crops. Flooding is a long established method of weed control in paddy rice, although it is only effective against those species of weed which die underwater.

*The problem of soil cultivation as it relates to weed control is faced every day by the farmer and gardener. A famous artist of our own century, Oskar Kokoschka, once said: Weeds are nature's permanent opposition against government by the gardener. What other new methods of weed control are known?*

Scientists are currently engaged in trials involving the use of electromagnetic radiation, which embraces thermal, gamma, microwave and laser radiation. The use of thermal radiation for hot sterilization, evaporation and burn-off has long been practised in horticulture and tree nurseries. The principle of the burn-off method, in which weeds are burned away, is to increase the temperature in the plant cells, causing the cells to increase in volume, the cell walls to burst and the cell protein to coagulate, both of which processes result in cell death. The burn-off method has been re-introduced as a subject for discussion by alternative agriculture. The use of gamma radiation, however, is still in the experimental stage because of safety reasons. Similarly, experimental weed control using VHF radiation in the ultra high frequency range has not yet produced any practical results.

It might however be noted that physical weed control requires a much higher input of energy than the chemical methods which need at least one power of ten less energy.

*Chemical weed control must be the most important method both for reasons of labour economy and profitability. How did this situation come about?*

Weed control has undergone fundamental changes over the last few decades. Whereas 30 years ago mechanical control methods such as shallow ploughing, harrowing, brushing and hoeing predominated, they have been increasingly superseded over the years, due to the changing labour structure, by the various chemical control methods. A number of reasons account for these changes in weed control. Firstly it has been technical progress generally, with improvements in production conditions making higher yields possible, and secondly technical factors relating to workforce such as the migration of labour, higher wages or for example the introduction of automatic harvesters in cereal growing, which can only be used in weed-free crops.

*Has the expansion of cereal growing in recent years raised additional problems?*

After the Second World War, the so-called plant-growth substances were extensively used as chemical weed control products. In this way it proved possible to control widespread yield-reducing weeds such as field thistle, corn marigold, chamomile, wild mustard, wild radish, cornflower and corn poppy. The suppression of the broad-leaved weeds however made way for the proliferation of grass species which were more difficult to control. These include above all blackgrass, bentgrass and meadow grasses. These species have spread further in certain areas due to the increasing trend towards crop rotations with over-emphasis on winter cereals.

*What means does the farmer have at his disposal to cope with these more stubborn types of weed? After all, the farmer can only grow those crops which are commercially marketable and he will not allow his economic objectives to be governed by theoretically optimal crop rotations.*

This is probably the most important question facing the farmer, who must come to terms with the effects of this change in his own enterprise. The answer to your question is that chemical crop protection research has meanwhile developed suitable ways and means.

*Can you explain these ways and means in more detail?*

Over the last few decades, new weed control agents have been developed, known as soil herbicides, which reliably control weeds. Soil herbicides are weed control agents which kill the weed seeds in the soil during germination or emergence. This means that a much wider range of weeds can be controlled. These agents are applied while the cereals are being sown.

*These new active substances have provided a new approach, and represent a change in control strategy. What are the advantages for the farmer and horticulturist?*

In contrast to former methods, control of weeds when sowing the cereals, potatoes, beets, peas and beans immediately eliminates the competition from the weeds for water, nutrients and light, and allows the crops to develop undisturbed. Numerous scientific studies have shown that the competition from weeds is most intense in the early growth stages of crops. When treatment is given directly after sowing, depending on the intensity of weed infestation, yield increases of five to twenty-five per cent can be achieved by using these new soil herbicides. These figures have been determined in trials conducted over many years.

*When controlling weeds with soil herbicides at the time of sowing, is it only necessary for the farmer to observe the correct application time, or must he also consider other aspects?*

With new methods it is essential for the application instructions to be strictly followed. Clearly, when using soil herbicides which are applied over a wide area, the following points should be noted: firstly, the seedbed must be prepared in such a way as to produce as friable a soil structure as possible, secondly, the herbicide must be dosed as precisely as possible and thirdly the treatment method must be exact, in other words the equipment must be correctly adjusted and the application must be performed carefully.

*This new method has been widely adopted in agriculture and horticulture. The profitability of this procedure, which is ultimately the central problem of farm economics, derives from the following factors: firstly, the advantage in terms of labour economy due to the simple application on sowing. Secondly, elimination of competition from weeds at an early stage positively influences and at the same time secures the yield, thus also guaranteeing the profitability of the crop.*

## *4. Crop protection in arable farming*

*Together with cereal cultivation, sugar beet growing is also a major activity in many farms, since sugar beet is an important cash crop for further industrial processing. What is its position in the overall economy of the individual farm?*

Sugar beet is an intensive crop which can only be successfully integrated into the farming system if the farmer familiarizes himself in detail with the cultivation method. Due to the high cost of manpower, sugar beet cultivation is now fully mechanized, from sowing right up to the harvest. The most significant thing about mechanization is the way in which it has changed sowing techniques. To eliminate the costly manual labour involved in hoeing and separating the beets, monogerm beet varieties have been bred which can be sown with the aid of special equipment to the desired beet spacing of 18 to 20 centimetres in the row. This single beet, which is in the beet field from the seedling stage, must be tended very carefully if it is to grow successfully. The necessary crop protection activities should be adapted to these conditions.

*What methods of crop protection are most suitable for this purpose?*

Firstly, the seed grain must be protected by treating it against soil insects and soilborne fungi. However, since the beet seed takes too many different forms for it to be sown with precision drilling equipment, the seed is pelleted to ensure that the single grain seed is equally placed. Into this coating material, an insecticide and fungicide have been incorporated to protect both the seed and the seedling. On heavy infestation with soil pests, an insecticide in granular form is deposited with the seed in the furrow as a means of providing more prolonged and effective protection for the young plant.

*So this is a new development which, borne of scarcity of labour, has led to a technical innovation, which itself resulted from the breeding of monogerm varieties. Seed and crop protection have finally set the seal on this technical advance. Should weed control be regarded as a parallel activity?*

Due to scarcity of labour and excessive wage levels for manual workers, hoeing and pulling of weeds by hand has increasingly been replaced by chemical methods of weed control. Before or after sowing, chemical weed control agents are applied, with the aim of eliminating from the outset the competition from weeds for light, water and nutrients, to the advantage of the beets.

*What other crop protection measures are needed to secure yields in beet growing?*

Beet flies and aphids are the main problems. Timely control measures against aphids are particularly important, the necessity for which is notified by the crop protection authorities and sugar refineries. These treatments with special insecticides are given to prevent sucking damage by the aphids and also to prevent the spread of virus diseases by these pests.

*Has potato cultivation also undergone similar fundamental changes?*

Chemical weed control has been particularly important for potatoes, as it has substantially reduced the effort involved in developing the crop. Regular control of late blight is needed to secure yields. Seed potatoes require special treatment for this purpose, and extensive targeted control measures are applied to prevent attack by aphids and the consequent spread of virus diseases, which take effect only in the following year, causing serious yield losses of up to fifty per cent when the potatoes are planted.

*Crop protection is an important production factor for the different crops in arable farming, since it not only helps save the harvest from losses but increases yields by initiating new production methods or, as has been illustrated with an example, by making them possible in the first place.*

## 5. Crop protection in horticulture

*Alongside agriculture, horticulture is an important activity which embraces the growing of fruit, vegetables and ornamental plants and supplies the consumer not only with food but also with flowers and plants for the household and environment. Can you illustrate this with some figures?*

North Rhine-Westphalia, for example, is the most important horticultural region in the Federal Republic of Germany. It accounts for one third of our horticultural production. Here we find some 6,000 vegetable farms, more than 5,000 establishments growing ornamental plants, about 1,000 fruit growing enterprises and 750 tree nurseries. These enterprises farm more than 30,000 hectares with a workforce of 50,000 and supply horticultural produce to the value of 1,000 million DM. North Rhine Westphalia, with its population of 17 million concentrated in a relatively small area, is a major market for agricultural produce, and also absorbs a considerable proportion of domestic horticulture produce.

*These are impressive figures, particularly considering the heavily industrialized nature of North Rhine-Westphalia. More than half of these enterprises grow vegetables and fruit to supply the consumer directly with fresh produce. Which crops are chiefly produced?*

At present there are 4,000 hectares of fruit, 12,000 hectares of outdoor vegetables and about 300 hectares of vegetables under glass in North Rhine-Westphalia. The main vegetable products are kohlrabi, leek, Brussels sprouts, Savoy cabbage, lettuce and white cabbage. In response to consumer demand, radishes are grown under glass, as also are aubergines, celery, Chinese cabbage and chicory. Champignons grown on special farms are also an important crop. In fruit growing, not only Cox Orange, the main apple variety, and Golden Delicious, but also Red Boskoop und Berlepsch and new cultivars such as Elstar, Gloster, Jonagold and Melrose have been grown in increasing quantities over the past few years and are much in demand.

*What is the situation with ornamental plants?*

Flowers and ornamental plants are produced to a value of 500 million DM, representing half the horticultural production between the Rhine and Weser. This output is made up by more than 100 different species of plants. Of these, 50 per cent are cut flowers, 25 per cent flowering pot plants and 25 per cent garden, balcony and indoor plants. The annual expenditure on flowers and ornamental plants per head of population in North Rhine-Westphalia is seventy DM, although the national average for the Federal Republic is only about fifty DM.

*Such intensive production, generally found in horticulture, is only possible with careful production planning which takes account not only of sales but also and especially of the specific cultivation techniques. Crop protection must therefore be a highly significant production factor?*

Crop protection is a primary production factor in horticulture because it not only helps to increase yields and improve the quality of the produce, but above all because it safeguards the harvest and minimizes the risks involved in growing these capital-intensive crops, and also provides a security for other expenditures. Chemical crop protection, which on average prevents yield and quality losses of potentially thirty per cent of operating turnover, is one of the most beneficial practices in horticulture.

In recent years, chemical crop protection has been of great service, espencially in horticulture, in raising yields and improving quality. Economically important diseases and pests such as fruit scab, mildew, the codling moth, as well as aphids and red spider mites, are reliably controlled by applying the recommended treatments. Indeed, we have now reached a stage where special forecasting methods for individual pests can even eliminate the need to apply one or the other forms of control, if the critical level of infestation is not reached. The first priority remains to supply the consumer with healthy fruit.

*With vegetables too, it is important that the consumer should be offered fresh quality produce all year round. Achieving the required quality demands skilled cultivation and appropriate crop protection. What are the main problems in this sector?*

Special conditions obtain in vegetable cultivation due to the intensity of farming and the short growing season of the crops. The plants which are grown must be healthy if the crop is to be profitable. Measures taken to ensure this include seed dressing to control emergence diseases and eradication of insect pests after plant emergence. Control of vegetable flies such as the turnip root fly is also of great consequence. The products used for this purpose must be safe for the plants and must also be non-hazardous to the health of the consumer, as required by the legislator.

*Great efforts to improve production methods have been made in horticulture in recent years, mainly with a view to cutting down investment of capital and labour. Crop protection has a key role to play in this respect as a means of assuring profitability and minimizing risks.*

## 6. Crop protection research

*The advances accomplished in chemical crop protection research over the past few decades have led to crop protection becoming a major production factor in modern agriculture. It plays an essential part in increasing yields and improving the quality of harvested products. Another decisive influence exerted by chemical crop protection, particularly in economic terms, is the elimination of the pronounced annual variations in yield formerly also found in intensive cropping. The increasing scarcity and cost of labour in agriculture and horticulture, and the general introduction of mechanization, have greatly accelerated the development of new weedkilling chemicals and methods. How is a new crop protectant developed?*

A large number of new chemical compounds are synthesized every year by chemists throughout the world. These substances are then tested by biologists for their efficacy against diseases, pests and weeds in the laboratory and greenhouse. The development of a new crop protection product starts in the laboratory and greenhouse and is continued in outdoor trials, where screening for tolerance and efficacy, decisive factors for their eventual acceptance, is carried out under practical conditions.

*The vast field of chemical research covers many different aspects. Is it possible to state the number of chemical compounds tested each year?*

The number of compounds tested each year for suitability as crop protectants is very great. Each year, about 100,000 newly synthesized compounds are subjected to a wide variety of tests in crop protection research around the world.

*Certainly a large number. What are the chances of success?*

Only a few of these substances successfully complete all the tests and finally take their place as commercial products on the market, since their viability is decided by other aspects as well as efficacy and plant tolerance.

*What other aspects are decisive for a crop protectant gaining final acceptance?*

The safety of the product in terms of human and industrial toxicology is the main aspect. However, the price of the chemical compound, the fabrication method and the registration of the product by the Federal Biological Research Centre for Agriculture and Forestry and the Federal Health Office are also important.

*How long does it take to develop a new crop protectant and how important is testing under practical conditions during this process?*

The development of a new crop protectant from synthesis to marketable product generally takes from eight to ten years. Decisive factors during this period are the outdoor trials under practical conditions, toxicological studies and official registration trials, which are conducted either in parallel or successively.

*How much does it cost to perfect a new crop protectant?*

According to American and German cost estimates, the outlay required to develop a new product runs to 70 to 100 million DM. A large proportion of these costs is allocated to testing for health hazards to detect any side effects when the product is applied and on consumption of the harvested crops. The principal task of crop cultivation and protection is to secure food supplies for the peoples of the world in this time of population explosion in the second half of the 20th century.

*What are the central problems currently existing in crop protection research?*

Since this is a very important question, it should be emphasized that crop protection, as applied in modern farming, has developed into an extremely diversified complex of problems, especially with the present trend to specialization in agricultural and horticultural enterprises and the simplification of fruit and crop rotations. With reference to intensive cropping, we should mention the problems presented by pests developing resistance to certain chemical agents, the control of fruit rot in fruit growing and the necessity for chemical weed control in all crops and of all weeds, mildew control in cereal cultivation, the development of growth inhibitors for grassland areas and of stem strengthening agents in cereal cultivation, as well as the continued search for less toxic products, which has already been in progress for many years.

*The last point you have mentioned is particularly interesting for the consumer of fruit, vegetables and other field and garden produce. What progress has been made in this respect and what safety factors have been incorporated to protect the consumer?*

A good example of these endeavours is the development of fast-acting insecticides which are used in arable farming, fruit and vegetable cultivation and in small gardens to control insect pests, and which are degraded within the plants within a few days. The fungicides which are being used at present in agriculture and horticulture and the majority of weed killers are metabolized into non-toxic compounds in the plant.

*As well as chemical pest control, the biological approach is also of interest. What are the principles underlying this method?*

Biological pest control is based on the principle that each pest has its own parasite which destroys it, thereby preventing the unlimited propagation of a given pest species, a circumstance which is known as the balance of nature. Predators of this kind include the parasitic ichneumon flies. All these problems of biological pest control are being studied at international level to evaluate their viability in practice.

*And what place does integrated pest control occupy in this scheme?*

The aim of integrated crop protection is to harmonize all the physical and biological control methods to allow chemical crop protection activities to be locally targeted with a high degree of precision according to the type of pest infestation. In other words, the nature of the attack must be accurately defined before each control measure is applied. This method of crop protection however requires that scientific research should first investigate in detail the relation between the intensity of attack by the pest and the possible extent of the ensuing damage. Control programmes are only recommended if the damage which would be prevented would be more costly than outlay for the chemical, physical or biological control activities. It must however be remembered that a pest does not occur in isolation, so that the damage thresholds or critical infestation levels must be weighed in relation to each other. This method also requires that the farmer or gardener should have extensive specialized knowledge, since the general advisory service cannot be organized in such a way that each enterprise can be advised on an individual basis.

## *7. Farm profitability of agrochemistry*

*Present-day cultivation methods in arable farming and vegetable and fruit growing could not be applied unless backed up by a wide range of crop protection measures. Crop protection has become a major production factor, not only because it increases yields by suppressing diseases, pests and weeds, but also because of its vital role in securing yields and maintaining harvest quality and, thereby, the economic profitability of farms. In addition, crop protection, for example in the form of weed control in beet growing, has had the effect of reducing labour input and rationalizing working methods or, as for example in cereal cultivation, has created the preconditions for automatic harvesting. How is such new knowledge gained through research?*

As in other areas of farming research, the development and testing of new fertilizers, crop protectants and application methods is carried out in experimental stations, since only under such controlled conditions can mistaken conclusions from experimental results be avoided.

*What criteria are applied when deciding the economic profitability of specific crop protection measures to be recommended for practical application?*

An important area of activity for research and the technical service is assessing the profitability of crop protection activities, in other words, determining the yield losses which can be expected to result from attack by various diseases and pests, or by infestation of crops with weeds. This information also allows conclusions to be drawn regarding the critical infestation levels and the damage thresholds of the individual pathogens.

*Can you quote an example from trials carried out in potato crops?*

In a trial lasting several years in 30 different varieties of potato, chemical weed control as compared to mechanized weed control was found to increase the yield by 20 per cent, and by no less than 180 per cent compared to untreated potatoes. Chemical as against mechanical weed control has not only had a labour-saving effect but also a definite yield-promoting influence, which is also evident in the tuber size and the quality of the harvested produce. In contrast to mechanical methods, chemical weed control also prevents late weed infestation, thus making it much easier to harvest the potatoes using fully mechanized techniques.

*Cereals are the main crop in this country. Does weed control also bring this high profitability for cereals?*

Pre-emergence treatment with a weed control agent is important for winter cereal varieties, as it prevents weeds competing against the cereal plants from the seedling stage. As early as autumn, major weed grasses and broad-leaved weeds such as blackgrass, bentgrass, meadowgrass and chickweed make their appearance as competitors for the cereals and, unless control is implemented in the autumn, continue to grow throughout the winter if the weather is mild. In long-term trials, a yield increase of 15 to 30 per cent was achieved for winter barley, winter rye and winter wheat. Not only does the good efficacy against weeds improve the yield balance, but the weed-free condition of the crop is also essential for automatic harvesting.

*In addition to weed control in cereal crops, over the last few years the suppression of fungal diseases has acquired economic importance for securing yields. What is the cost-benefit relation of this activity?*

Due to the expansion of winter and spring barley cultivation and the wheat hectarage, attack by mildew, promoted by mild weather, has become a serious problem with cereals. Moreover, the problems presented by this disease are also aggravated by the many different forms which this fungus takes and its great adaptability. To cultivate high quality cereals, control measures are thus indispensable. Whereas particularly for brewing barley, control must be performed during the shooting stage when the disease first appears, wheat also needs to be sprayed during ear emergence to preserve the flag leaf and the ear from contamination. Average yield increases achieved through mildew control are 25 per cent both for spring and for winter barley, winter barley being attacked and treated both in autumn and in spring. Freedom from disease is also vital in winter wheat if peak yields are to be achieved.

*While we are on the subject, perhaps another question about complete leaf fertilization which has been introduced in arable farming, vegetable and fruit growing in conjunction with many different types of crop protection activities, as a means of promoting and securing yields. What effects does it have on yield?*

Leaf fertilization has long played an important role in special crops as a means of protecting sensitive growth stages and generally promoting plant growth. However, leaf fertilization is in no way intended to replace, but rather to complement, plant nutrition through the soil and roots. Numerous trials have shown that leaf fertilization appreciably promotes plant growth and yield formation in all crops.

*We are currently hearing a great deal about integrated crop protection. How significant are these endeavours in terms of operating economy?*

The primary aim of integrated crop protection is to optimize the control methods while paying due heed to the principles of environmental protection. Reduced to a simple formula: as much crop protection as necessary and as little as possible. Crop protection is moreover an integral feature of cultivation technique. Encompassing aspects from choice of location through soil cultivation and sowing techniques, plant nutrition, crop rotation and selection of varieties to crop care and harvesting methods, targeted crop protection is an important element within the general scheme of integrated crop management. The economic profitability of crop growing is the result of optimally utilizing all the production measures which can be devised by human ingenuity.

## *8. Illustrations of weeds, pests and diseases*

The following pages 117 to 124 present the major weeds, pests and diseases discussed in Sections IV and V.

Blackgrass (Alopecurus myosuroides); heavy infestation causes great losses in cereal harvests.

Bentgrass (Apera spica-venti), a prevalent weed in barley crops.

Wild oats (Avena fatua), a widespread weed since ancient times, in a field of wheat.

Heavy infestation with barnyard grass in a maize crop.

Flowering common chickweed (Stellaria media) among cereal plants.

Cleavers (Galium aparine) in a winter barley crop.

Field sow thistle (Cirsium arvense) growing among cereal plants.

Corn marigold (Chrysanthemum segetum) in a barley crop.

Late blight of potato (Phytophthora infestans) causes severe damage to foliage and tubers in moist weather. Above: leaf infestation. Below: heavy infestation with perishing of the potato plants and crop.

Heavy infestation with powdery mildew of cereals in winter wheat.

Leaf infestation with yellow rust on barley (spores).

Leaves infested with brown rust of cereals (spores).

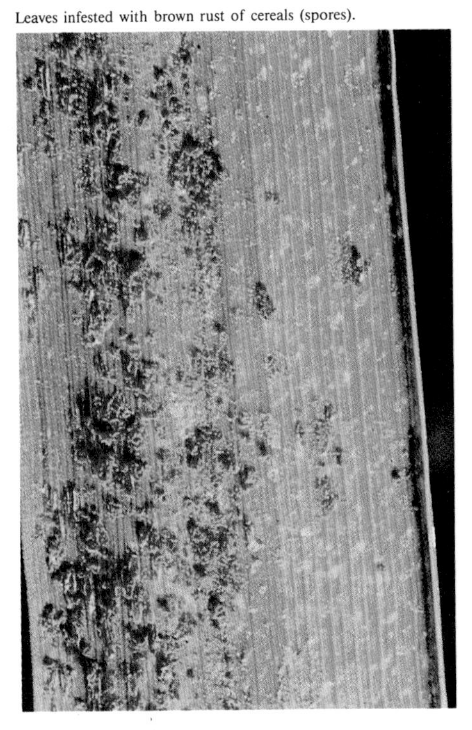

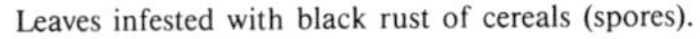

Leaves infested with black rust of cereals (spores).

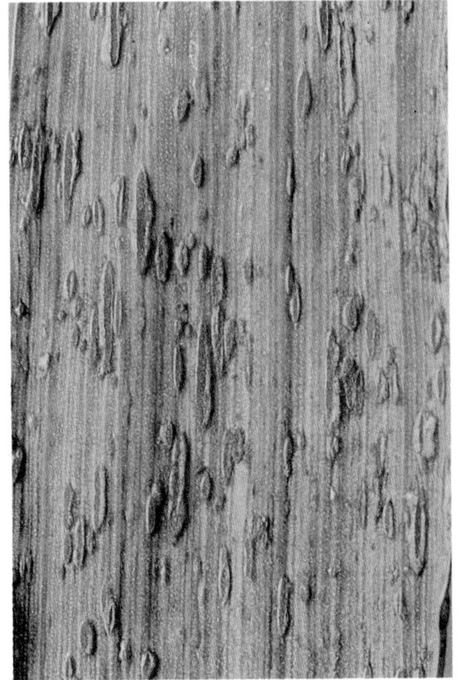

Ears of barley infested with loose smut (Ustilago nuda).

Ears of wheat infested with loose smut (Ustilago tritici).

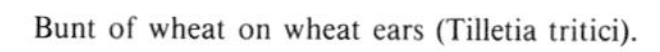

Bunt of wheat on wheat ears (Tilletia tritici).

Winter barley attacked by snow mould (Fusarium nivale) and Typhula rot.

Grain aphids (Macrosiphum avenae) attacking an ear of wheat.

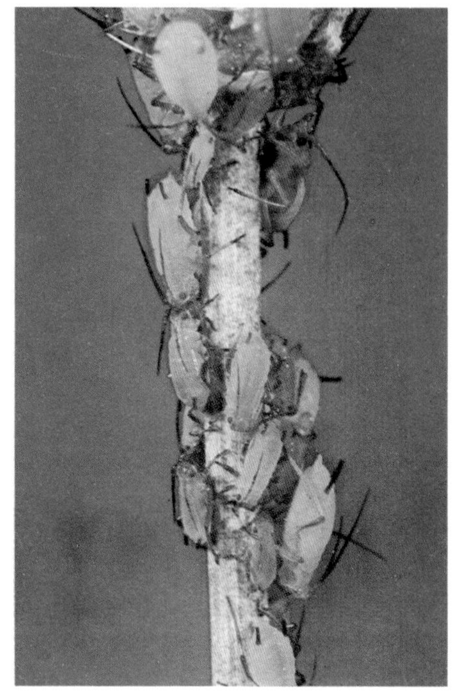

Grain aphids (Macrosiphum avenae) sucking an ear spindle.

Grain or apple bud aphids (Rhopalosiphum padi) attacking an oat panicle.

Maize under attack by the corn aphid (Rhopalosiphum maidis).

Strawberry fruits infested with grey mould (Botrytis cinerea) and leathery rot (Phytophthora cactorum).

Raspberries infested with grey mould (Botrytis cinerea).

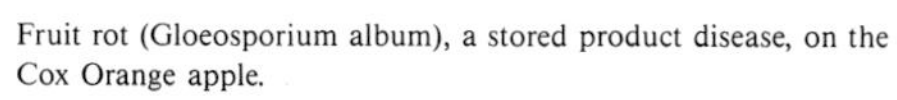

Fruit rot (Gloeosporium album), a stored product disease, on the Cox Orange apple.

Fruit rot (Gloeosporium perennans), a stored product disease, on the Golden Delicious apple.

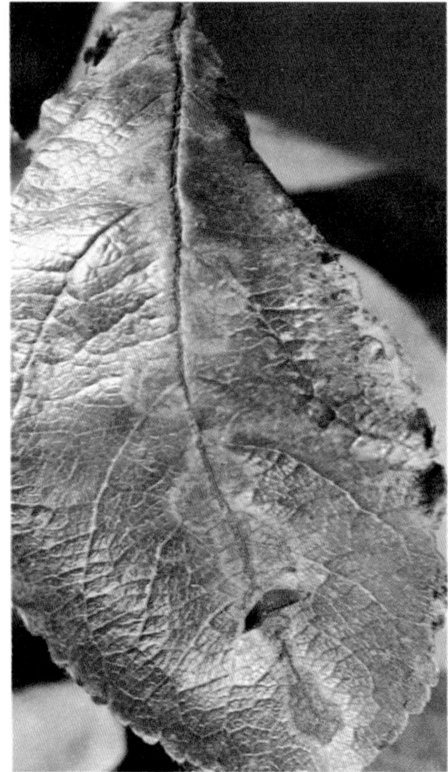

Apple scab infection on a leaf.

Apple scab infection on a fruit.

Heavy attack by apple mildew on an apple shoot.

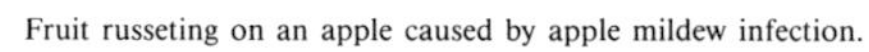

Fruit russeting on an apple caused by apple mildew infection.

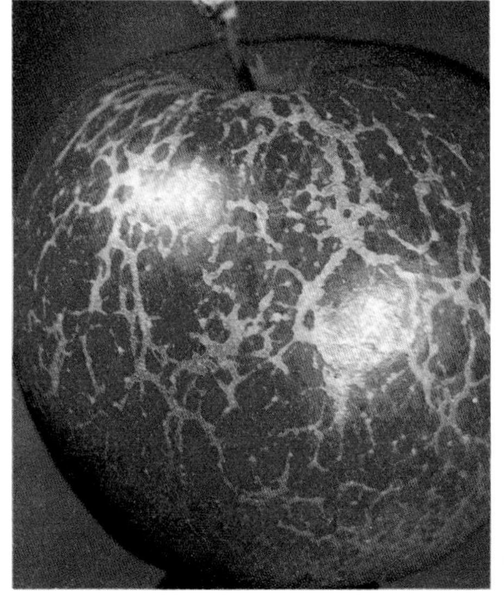

## V. Pests as food competitors

The existence of man and animals on the earth is impossible without the presence of green plants. Only plants, with the aid of chlorophyll, the green substance in their cells, can directly utilize the sun's energy and produce carbohydrates and oxygen from the carbon dioxide in the air and from water. In this process they metabolize inorganic materials which they extract from the soil through their roots, and synthesize organic substances. Animals are unable to perform this physiological process. The cells of plants, most of which are only 0.01 millimetres in size, produce more different chemical substances than the chemists working in all the laboratories throughout the world. This is due to the vast number of plant species and climates. The 1.2 million species of animal which have so far been described, more than two thirds of which are insects, utilize the myriad forms of the vegetable kingdom as food plants. Cultivated plants, which serve as man's source of nutrition in the many different regions of the world, are also preferred by some animals as a source of food.

The task of the gardener and farmer is therefore to protect his crops from animals as food competitors for man. Valuable crops such as fruit and vegetables are protected from large animals by fencing or by fitting sleeves to tree trunks to save them from the depredations of game animals. Methods of repelling attack by birds include the use of protective netting or acoustic scaring devices. Things become more difficult where insects are involved, since not every development stage of insects can be collected, as is the case with Colorado beetles or vegetable caterpillars in small gardens. Man therefore soon began to use chemical substances to control the insects which appear as pests in cultivated crops. Insects and also nematodes, slugs, snails and mites are important crop pests, as are some birds and rodents.

Among all these pests, the most destructive are those which regularly, or with great frequency, persistently cause damage in extensive cropping areas. They are therefore referred to as major pests, but only if the pest attacks in large numbers and if the plant reacts by showing a definite decline in yield and quality. The economic importance of a pest thus depends on its spread and ability to propagate.

Disasters caused by pests are familiar to us even from ancient times. In the Bible, for example, in the Book of Joel, these calamities are bemoaned in the following words: "What the caterpillars do not eat, is devoured by the locusts, and what the locusts leave is eaten by the beetles, and what the beetles leave is destroyed by the vermin."

Many descriptions have been handed down to us of plagues of vast numbers of plant-devouring insects. The best known example is the migratory locust, which descends upon crops in huge swarms and "totally destroys man's laboriously planted crops in the winking of an eye". Also known to migrate are butterflies and the rape beetle, which appear for example in certain areas along the Baltic coast. The caterpillars of the cabbage butterfly and nun moth caterpillars have also been observed in mass migrations.

Many pests change their host plant during their life cycle, or, as so-called polyphageous insects, colonize a large number of host plants.

Crop damage inflicted by insects and certain species of animal is caused by biting beetles or caterpillars and by juice-sucking insects like aphids, chief among the sucking pests. Animals are also responsible for causing severe infectious diseases in plants, to which they transmit viruses, bacteria or fungi. The first crop disease which caused and continues to cause worldwide damage, and which was found to have been transmitted by insects, was identified in 1891 as fire blight in apples and pears, a disease caused by a genus of bacteria.

Disasters caused by pests occur wherever crops are cultivated over large areas and are attacked by a pest with a high rate of propagation. Given man's large demand for food, however, it is only rarely possible to cultivate crops in plant societies, with the aim of minimizing the yield losses caused by major pests which specialize in a particular species of plant. It should after all be remembered that even in the primeval forests, with their protean communities of flora and fauna, about one quarter of the leaf substance is destroyed by insects alone. Even in virgin forests, under the conditions prevailing in biotopes uninfluenced by man, vast tracts of certain species of tree such as the Murray pine (Pinus murrayana) have been totally destroyed by bark beetles.

Exchange of goods between the continents must bear much responsibility for the occurrence and spread of new major pests. The importation of new pests such as the Colorado potato beetle resulted in sudden and devastating disasters. The best known example is the grape phylloxera, a root pest on grapevine which was imported from America to Europe more than 100 years ago and which almost wiped out European vine cultivation. This danger was finally eliminated through the use of phylloxera-resistant rootstocks of the American vine. This is the best-known example of the use of resistant crops.

Attempts are now being made on a global scale to prevent the importation of pests and diseases by enacting appropriate national legislation. International agreements, promoted for example by the FAO (Food and Agriculture Organization of the United Nations, Branch Plant Protection, Locust Control), emphasize the "importance and benefits of international cooperation in the fight against the importation and spread of diseases and pests in plants and plant products".

Not only insect pests, but also plant diseases caused by fungi, bacteria or viruses can inflict total destruction on crops, as for example late blight of potato, which is given particular attention among the "major pests" described in the following reports.

## *1. Slugs and snails*

*Snails and slugs occupy a special place among the pests encountered in agriculture and horticulture, since they are not very discriminating in their choice of food. Snails are "omnivores" and can become a plague upon the land. What species of snail are there?*

Within the animal kingdom, the snail species belong to the molluscs or soft-bodied invertebrates, which are found in all regions of the world. The majority of snails live in the sea or in fresh water, and only one order of snails, the pulmonate molluscs, lives on land. To the extent that they feed on the green parts of plants, they are plant pests. Among the pulmonate molluscs, we distinguish between the species which live in fresh water and those which live on land.

*Which are the major pests among the land slugs?*

The most serious pest is the field slug, which is classified as one of the land molluscs, a distinction being made between the netted and the somewhat smaller grey field slug. These creatures prefer moist loamy soils and avoid dry sand. They seek out their food with the aid of their well developed sense of smell. Although they are not selective in their choice of food and devour all species of plant, it should be emphasized that they prefer to feed on young plant tissue.

*What form does the damage take?*

With their rasp-like tongue, slugs damage the leaves or stalks of the plants by grating them away. Because of this abrasion, parts of the leaves or the stalks are often so severely gnawed that they subsequently decay. Large, irregular holes are often eaten into the leaves.

*What are the typical signs of damage by slugs?*

A telltale sign that slugs have been at work is the presence of silvery or chalky white glistening trails on the plants and the surrounding soil, since the snail protects itself from desiccation by continuously secreting mucus. Another typical sign of attack by slugs is the presence of moist, greyish-green droppings which they leave behind around their feeding sites.

*What can be said about the biology or behaviour of slugs?*

Slugs feed mainly in the evening and at night. Within the space of 24 hours, one slug will eat about one gram of leaf tissue. They procreate through eggs which are deposited in the earth in capsules of four to ten. To deposit their eggs, which are the size of millet seeds, the slugs excavate a hole in the soil or deposit them in spaces between stones and the ground. Three to four weeks later, the young slugs hatch out. During the warm season, the eggs need only two to three weeks to develop. Slugs become capable of breeding after three months, and their maxium lifespan is one year. They tend to overwinter most frequently in the egg stage.

*What control methods are applied?*

The use of corrosive substances to control slugs, once commonly practised, raises problems due to the risk of damage to plants; also, this method requires two treatments at short intervals of 15 to 30 minutes, since older slugs are able to discard the corrosive substances with their slimy coating. Therefore, bait formulations, known as "snail pellets", are now generally used. Two forms of control technique are used, namely broadcast and trap strip treatment. Broadcast treatment is applied in the afternoon or evening, spreading the pellets evenly over a wide area to kill the pests which are already present. The aim of the trap strip method is to protect valuable crops from slugs which appear later; for this purpose, pellets are spread in a line about three to five centimetres wide around the seed beds liable to attack. Because of the attractive effect of the snail pellets, it is also effective to deposit them in the garden in the form of small heaps.

*Snails as well as slugs are of economic importance?*

The best known snail is the grapevine or edible snail, highly valued as a delicacy among gourmets, but which appears as a pest in viniculture, and caused a great deal of destruction during the last century. This creature eats the buds, shoots and leaves of vines but also damages other vegetable and horticultural crops. It also has a considerable lifespan. While slugs reach an age of at most one year, the lifespan of the grapevine snail can be two to three years, and in captivity even as long as five to ten years.

*What is the extent of the damage caused by snails?*

Particularly in moist, warm weather, snails in large numbers can completely defoliate both cereal and vegetable crops. In fruit crops such as strawberries, in which the fruits are eaten, the damage can also be serious since the snails even crawl up the trees.

The damage inflicted by snails on garden plants is particularly marked and is an age-old problem. For instance, on 30th May 1798, Christiane Vulpius wrote to Johann Wolfgang von Goethe: "You are fortunate in your own work, since what you have once created remains forever; but things are quite different for us poor creatures. I had the kitchen garden in excellent order, planted and everything. In a single night, the snails have eaten almost everything away, my best cucumbers are almost all gone and now I have to start all over again."

## 2. Aphids

*In cereal, beet and potato crops and also in fruit and vegetables, in tree nurseries, greenhouses and even in ornamental and kitchen gardens and allotments, large numbers of aphids attack the different plant species all year round. The damage caused by these sucking pests leads to major harvest losses both in arable farming and horticulture. But even the small gardener is not exactly pleased to see the roses or lettuce in his garden heavily infested by aphids, causing the roses to wither away and making the heads of lettuce uneatable. How can the farmer or gardener protect himself against them?*

There are about 800 species of aphid in Central Europe which attack many different useful, ornamental and wild plants. Some of these species of aphid are very host-specific, in other words, like the hop aphid, they colonize only one or perhaps a small number of plant species, whereas some, like the green peach aphid, attack a large number of host plants, both outdoors and in greenhouses. This biological multiplicity has caused serious problems for chemical control. However, since the introduction of the organophosphates into crop protection, new approaches have been realized. The so-called systemic insecticides in particular have radically improved the efficacy of control, whereas aphids were formerly controlled mainly by means of nicotine-containing products.

*What are systemic insecticides and why have these products so decisively improved the prospects for control?*

A systemic insecticide is an insect control agent which, when poured on the roots in aqueous solution or sprayed onto the leaves, penetrates into the roots or the leaves and is then translocated through the veins of the plant. The aphids then die when they pierce the plant cells to suck up nutrients. With this method, it is not necessary for the aphids to be wetted directly by the spray. However, the effect persists in the plant only for a limited period after spraying. The active ingredients are degraded in the plant after a certain time and become ineffective.

The application of systemic pesticides is one of the most important elements within the scheme of integrated crop protection.

The Crop Protection Law enacted by the German Bundestag (Parliament) specifies precise safety intervals for the different pesticides, which state the number of days which must elapse between treatment and harvesting, and which guarantee that any hazard is excluded on consumption of the harvested produce.

*If the control of aphids now presents relatively few problems thanks to the use of modern pesticides and techniques, why is the danger presented by these pests still such a cause for concern?*

Aphids are a problem not only because they attack plants and impair their development, but also and much more seriously because aphids are vectors of numerous virus diseases in different crops. Particularly harmful in this respect are the virus diseases transmitted by the green peach aphid to sugar beet and potatoes, and the viroses in many fruit and vegetables crops, all of which substantially reduce yields and quality. Timely control of aphids as vectors prevents yield losses due to viroses, which in some cases can be transmitted through the seed and planting material itself.

*You have mentioned 800 different species of aphid which are found in this country. Are there any more recent examples of aphid species formerly found only on wild plants or which occur only sporadically becoming serious pests in cultivated plants?*

Changes of this kind within the spectrum of pests are actually occurring all the time, either unobtrusively or in a more obvious manner. Pests such as the Colorado potato beetle, which twenty years ago was still "public enemy number one", have now become relatively unimportant in this country, although in other countries they continue to cause severe damage. This shift in the importance of pests has come about because of changes in cultivation methods and other environmental conditions of the crops and the pests, or as a result of intensive and successful control programmes.

In recent years, both in Germany and neighbouring countries, a new situation has arisen with aphids in cereal cultivation. Formerly, when less cereals were grown, aphids appeared only sporadically among the various cereal crops. Now, however, species of aphid which attack cereals all year round or which colonize them as intermediate hosts in the summer have become cereal pests to be reckoned with, especially since they also transmit virus diseases such as the yellow stunting virus which causes considerable yield losses.

*How can targeted and successful control of aphids in different crops best be ensured?*

Sucking damage caused by the different aphid species is prevented by crop monitoring, paying careful attention to the warnings issued by the crop protection offices and advisory services, and also by correctly applying the control agents and using properly functioning spraying equipment when treating crops. Also very important is to comply with the instructions for the use of pesticides and to follow the recommended rules and precautions.

*How does this severe damage caused by aphids come about?*

Aphids are plant juice sucking pests one to four millimetres in length. By combining the bristles of their beaks, when piercing the plant tissue they can form two tubules, one to suck the nutrient flow from the plant and one for secreting sputum into the plant. The sputum contains a pectin-dissolving ferment which makes it easier to penetrate into the plant tissue, but also causes tissue proliferations and growth disturbances in the plant. The sputum and beaks of the aphids also serve to transmit the viroses. The wide distribution of aphids is due to the development of migratory aphids which travel great distances by riding up-currents of air and, on landing, commence their predatory activity in new locations. The high reproduction rate of aphids is due to the parthenogenesis of the summer generations which occurs in most aphid species.

*How quickly do aphids breed?*

The biology and reproduction of aphids has long been a subject of research for naturalists. The Remscheid physician, Dr. Wilhelm Ludwig Döring, wrote in 1835 in his celebrated book on roses that one aphid can produce offspring numbering 24 million in a single summer. This author observed the aphids very carefully and describes their plant-destroying sucking activity as follows: "Ugly aphids, deformed by their fat stomachs swollen with stolen plant juices, surround the nutrient-conducting leaf stem of the rose bud, moving slowly forwards on their skinny limbs and constantly producing countless progeny through amazonian birth".

## *3. Nematodes*

*The intensity of land use in arable farming and horticulture has progressively led to specialization. Accordingly, the emphasis on certain crops has greatly increased. This specialized approach, in some cases disregarding certain rules of crop rotation, has allowed certain diseases, pests or weeds to gain ascendancy. How important are nematodes in this respect and what are nematodes?*

Nematodes are microscopically small threadworms which suck at the aerial or underground parts of plants and which, when present in large numbers, impair the development of the plants and thus lead to yield losses. The much-discussed subject of soil exhaustion following repeated cultivation of the same species of plant is often due to nematode damage.

*What are the main nematode species which damage plants?*

In horticulture we distinguish two major groups, firstly the root nematodes and secondly the stem, leaf and seed nematodes. At regards soil exhaustion, only the root nematodes are of interest. Within this group, a distinction is made between the cyst-forming species such as potato, beet and oat nematodes and the so-called free-living migratory nematodes which live either on or in the roots. Only some of the free-living root nematodes specialize in their choice of host plant and these pests therefore damage many different types of crop.

*What nematode problems are encountered in arable farming?*

In recent years the beet nematode has reappeared on the scene in farms where, despite observance of the four-year beet crop rotation, rape and cabbage varieties have been incorporated in the cultivation scheme as the main or intermediate crop. Where this is the case, cruciferous plants should not be included in the crop rotation.

*Nematodes are also a particular problem in potato crops?*

The potato root eelworm has appeared wherever potatoes have succeeded each other too closely in the crop rotation. In such cases, these pests can be halted or at least prevented from spreading further by employing a four-year crop rotation and by cultivating resistant varieties of potato. Also very damaging to potato crops are the free-living root nematodes of the genus Trichodorus, which are vectors of the rattle virus. The rattle virus causes tuber malformation and necrotic patches which greatly impair the quality of ware potatoes.

*Do nematodes which act as pests also cause yield losses in cereal crops?*

Due to the expansion of cereal growing, the oat or cereal nematode has greatly proliferated and causes severe yield losses particularly in oats, spring barley and spring wheat, but also causes damage to winter wheat and winter barley. The most effective countermeasure is to restore a balanced crop rotation and to grow resistant varieties, which so far exist only in oats and spring barley.

*What nematode problems are encountered in special crops?*

Complaints are frequently expressed about soil exhaustion due to nematode infestation, particularly in fruit crops and tree nurseries, and since these crops cannot be moved to different areas or grown in multiple crop rotation, chemical soil disinfection with soil fumigants or water-soluble nematicides is necessary.

*Apart from the plant-damaging nematodes, do other species of nematodes also exist?*

The nematodes are one of the most widespread groups in the animal kingdom. There are 5,000 different species, of which only 200 species are known to damage plants. New species are discovered every year. Scientists anticipate that many hitherto unknown forms which have not yet been described will be identified. These pests live in soils, plants, on animals and in water and only develop into pests when, for example in arable farming and horticulture, over-specialized cultivation offers ideal conditions for their propagation.

*What can be said about the biology and behaviour of the nematodes?*

The plant-damaging nematode species which live in the soil or on and in plants, often do not grow beyond one millimetre. Because of their eel-like appearance, they are also known as eelworms. Moist conditions are essential for their growth. Humid years are therefore “nematode years”. Nematodes pierce the plant cells with their stylets and suck out nutrients from the plant. In doing this, they tear the cell tissue and destroy its function, leading to the formation of giant cells or galls, which are a defence reaction of the plant.

*What forms of control are possible for the major nematode species?*

Preventive measures are an optimal crop rotation in which the nematodes can only attack their host plant at intervals of several years, which deprives them of the conditions for their survival and propagation in the intermediate years when no nutrient supply is available. Direct control measures are possible in intensive crops and take the form of soil disinfection with special preparations.

## 4. Colorado beetle and potato blight

*Whereas the potato cultivation area in Germany before the First World War was more than three million hectares and the potato ranked alongside cereals as a staple food, only 250,000 hectares are now cultivated in the Federal Republic of Germany. The world area on which this important food plant is currently grown in more than 100 countries is 18 million hectares. In many countries, the potato continues to be a basic food, while in other countries it can be found on the menu as a vegetable or delicacy. However, not only is the potato a cultivated plant used for man's food, it also acts as a host plant for numerous parasites. The most notorious of these pests is the Colorado beetle. What accounts for this reputation?*

The Colorado or potato beetle was first described as a pest on the potato plant around 1850 in the American state of Colorado, although previously it had colonized only other night shadow plants as hosts. The important aspect of this change of host plant was that this pest multiplied at such a tremendous rate that, for want of food, it moved on to attack potatoes. Within the space of fifteen years it crossed the USA from the west to the east, reaching the Atlantic coast of America in 1874.

*Because of continuous shipping movements and world trade between Europe and America, it was not long before the Colorado beetle turned up in Europe?*

As early as 1877 the first concentrated area of damage caused by the beetle appeared, extending over four to five hectares in Mülheim on the Rhine, present-day Cologne-Mülheim. As in other places, the spread of the beetle was successfully halted. As a means of educating the population to this threat, the Stollwerck chocolate factory in Cologne manufactured Colorado beetles of confectionery, selling them together with explanations of their life cycle. To prevent further importation of the Colorado beetle, quarantine laws were introduced by many countries.

*What are the biological characteristics of the Colorado potato beetle?*

This pest was spread throughout the world mainly in a passive manner through man's means of communication. The beetle, which measures one to two centimetres in length, owes its name, Leptinotarsa decemlineata, to the ten black lengthwise stripes on its wings. It overwinters in the soil as a beetle. In the spring, when the dandelion flowers, it leaves the soil and feeds on the potato shoots which have emerged. Two weeks later, the females lay 400 to 1800 orange-yellow eggs from which, several days later, the voracious larvae emerge which, after three weeks of feeding on the plants, pupate in the soil. Depending on the climate, one to three generations develop. Since the beetles can reach an age of two years, the progeny of a single female is calculated as potentially 8,000 million, which would need 650 hectares of potatoes to sustain them.

*This potato insect is thus a major pest offering serious competition for man's food. How was it controlled in former times?*

The pest was controlled by collecting the beetles and larvae. Infestation had to be officially reported. A special governmental "Colorado Beetle Defence Service" was commissioned with the task of eradicating the main concentrations of attack. In America, control by chemical methods, in the form of arsenic preparations, was introduced in 1867. In Germany in 1943, however, soil treatment for newly notified epidemics was still being performed with the aid of 5 litres of benzene or crude petroleum per square metre. Synthetic insecticides for the control of Colorado beetle which presented no hazards to man and cattle were first recommended forty years ago, which attacked only the pest and left the crop intact.

*How is the Colorado beetle controlled today?*

Control is now practised using modern low-toxicity products. The timing of control is set by the crop protection offices. In retrospect we can see that the spread of the Colorado beetle in Europe could not be halted, and it is now indigenous everywhere. With timely control measures, however, the economic damage can now be kept within limits. Nevertheless, because of the boundless fertility of this pest, systematic control performed in many countries in compliance with legal regulations has not resulted in its eradication.

*Together with the Colorado beetle, potato blight continues to be a serious problem which has long afflicted agriculture?*

The appearance of potato blight, in the form of a devastating epidemic sweeping through all growing areas, also coincided with the expansion of potato cultivation in North America and Europe around the middle of last century. The pathogen responsible for this disease is the fungus Phytophtora infestans, which flourishes most readily in a humid climate. With heavy infection, the potato foliage rots within a few days, resulting in reduced tuber formation. The fungus also infects the potato tuber, injuring it severely.

*What effect did this have on the food supply of the population at that time?*

The heavy attack by potato blight completely obliterated the potato crop in 1845 and 1846. A state of panic set in especially during the autumn harvest, when it was realized that all the potatoes had rotted in the soil. Since by this time the potato had joined cereals as a staple food in Europe, famine inevitably followed. Hunger and rising prices lead to an increased wave of emigration to America. Hunger in Europe was thus caused by a fungus which made its unheralded appearance as the destroyer of one of man's most important food plants. After all, the potato had been regarded in Europe for a hundred years as a reliably yielding cultivated plant, whereas cereal harvest failures had often been suffered as result of adverse weather conditions, diseases and pests.

*How is potato blight controlled?*

From 1845 to 1885, a fruitless search was conducted for a control agent. Successful control only became possible in 1886 through the use of Bordeaux mixture (copper vitriol) which was sprayed prophylactically as soon as the potato plants had given full coverage to the field. Repeated treatment at regular intervals provided protection against potato blight. Today, not only copper compounds but also organic fungicides are used. These leaf treatments also prevent the fungus progressing to the tubers. Potato blight control is one of the most effective crop protection methods in existence. Long-term trials have shown that potato blight treatment secures a yield increase of 20 to 25 per cent and ensures that the harvested potato tubers are of prime quality.

## 5. Locusts

*Since ancient times, plagues of locusts have been a synonym for devastation and disaster. Locusts were the eighth plague visited upon the Egyptians. Wherever their swarms descend, the entire harvest is destroyed. Why are locusts so well known as major pests throughout the world?*

Locusts have at all times been serious competitors for man's food. The locust years which have occurred over 1800 years of our time scale have been identified by research into historical sources. Severe crop damage caused by these pests has been described for a total of 220 years during this period.

*Did locusts also appear in Germany?*

In Germany, serious damage has been reported for 1475 and between the years 1527 to 1544. We also have descriptions dating from 1684. Particular mention is given to Silesia, Saxony and Schleswig. From the reign of Frederick the Great, severe damage is reported for seven years over the period from 1746 to 1763. On 25 June 1749, Maria Theresia issued a decree for the control of the locust epidemic.

*What areas are mainly affected today?*

Plagues of locusts are today concentrated typically in the warm climatic zones of Southern and Eastern Europe and in Asia, Africa, America and Australia. The last heavy epidemics in Germany occurred in 1873 and 1874.

*Why has the plague of locusts always been such a popular subject?*

This is best explained by an eyewitness report of the arrival of a plague of locusts in recent years in North Africa. The observer gives the following description: "Suddenly the sun disappears. Clouds of shimmering dots blot out the sky. As far as the eye can see: locusts! In their thousands of millions, they descend upon the land in vast swarms. Our vehicles advance only with difficulty. Like huge hailstones, the eight to ten centimetre insects rattle against the car. For the thousands crushed under the tyres, millions follow in their wake."

*For inhabitants of the temperate climatic zones such as ourselves, such descriptions are scarcely imaginable and alarming. What effects does invasion by these pests have on agriculture?*

In giant swarms which can reach a size of up to 150 square kilometres, they fall upon the fields and crops ready for harvesting and devour them at an almost unbelievable rate. A single locust can eat five times its own weight within a single day.

*The Arabs refer to locusts as the "scourge of Allah". What is the life cycle of this pest and how does it breed in such vast numbers?*

The different species of migratory locust appear in large swarms every six to seven years. The females lay their eggs eight to ten centimetres deep in the soil with the aid of their ovipositor tubes in the hot, treeless steppes and desert regions. Only in favourable growth conditions of heat combined with humidity, do the larvae hatch from the eggs. In periods of drought, the eggs can lie unhatched for several years, accumulating for several generations, and then suddenly develop after heavy rainfall. This is why such vast numbers of locusts suddenly appear in conditions favourable for an outbreak. One female can lay up to 120 eggs at once and in some species, this process can occur up to about ten times. The hatching larvae, known as hoppers, shed their skin eight to ten times until the wings are formed. The locusts come together in large swarms, and in the flying phase can travel two to three thousand kilometres at a speed of eighteen kilometres per hour.

*What control measures are applied to prevent damage due to an outbreak?*

The most effective method is to eradicate the "hoppers", as the young larvae are called. In former times, the soil was ploughed over to damage the deposited eggs, and rollers were used to crush them. They were beaten with wet sacks, or domestic animals were released to eat the locusts.

Very soon, farmers began to use spray formulations, consisting for example of arsenic with molasses as bait component, which they applied over large areas. Today, control is carried out in the breeding areas using modern insecticides, and it is also possible to treat the swarms of insects in the affected areas by aerial application of insecticides with a short safety interval, ensuring that crops are free of residues when harvested.

*A worldwide organization has now been established dedicated to the prevention of locust damage?*

International and national research institutes have investigated the biology and behaviour of the major species of migratory locusts and monitor the breeding areas and the mass development of these pests. The establishment of an international warning service and coordination of the control programmes represent attempts to prevent recurrences of the catastrophic damage seen in the past.

## 6. Fruit flies and fruit rot

*Every year, fruit pests cause renewed concern among producers of domestic fruit, exotic fruit and vegetables. Some of these fruit pests are also known to the consumer, since fruit infested with maggots is repulsive. The most feared of the fruit flies is the Mediterranean fruit fly. Which types of crop does it attack and what damage does it cause?*

The Mediterranean fruit fly (Ceratitis capitata) attacks many different species of fruit. As the name indicates, it prefers warm climates and warm locations. It attacks oranges, pears and apples and also some species of vegetable. Overall, the fruits of 180 species of cultivated plant are affected. Damage first manifests itself as an area of soft, brown discolouration on the outside of the fruit. When the fruit is cut open, depending on the type of fruit, large numbers of maggots can be seen seething among the rotten or eaten-away flesh of the fruit.

*How does this damage come about?*

The Mediterranean fruit fly, which is about the size of a small housefly, but whose wings and eyes shimmer with variegated colours, lays its eggs through its ovipositor tube under the surface skin of semi-ripe fruits. The maggots which hatch from the eggs after two and three days eat away and destroy the flesh of the fruit. A highly typical sign of Ceratitis attack is the rapid softening and decay of the fruit flesh. In the tropics and subtropics, Ceratitis is followed by other species of fruit fly such as Lampeolonchaea aurea, invading each fruit with up to 1000 maggots which hasten its destruction.

The development of this pest from the egg, through the maggot and pupa stage into the fly is temperature dependent and at 24 °C takes 30 days. The number of generations therefore increases according to the climate; in Hawaii, for example, there are fifteen, in Italy six and in our country there are two, the second generation causing the most damage.

The Mediterranean fruit fly is particularly damaging because of its long lifespan and high fertility. Each fly lives for up to six months and, in the absence of control measures, lays from 300 to 400, and even as many as 1000 eggs.

*How then is this pest controlled?*

The large number of host plants it colonizes makes control difficult and the cultivation of mixed crops of many different fruit species whose fruits ripen at different times encourages the development of the pest population and should therefore be avoided.

Fruit fly control is performed not only to prevent yield losses caused by the maggots, but also to maintain the fruit quality which already begins to suffer when the fruit is pierced.

A long-established practice is therefore to suspend trap bottles containing a toxic bait solution in the trees to catch the flies before they deposit their eggs. Tree spraying is now performed using special insecticides containing a bait additive before the flies start to emerge, both to prevent the eggs being deposited and the maggots from hatching.

Moreover, international agreements have been concluded which prohibit the import and export of affected fruit. The great hazard presented by this pest is also reflected in the fact that international Mediterranean fruit fly conferences are held, at which the different problems raised by this destructive creature are discussed.

*Another species of fly which has been known to damage fruit since ancient times is the olive fruit fly. Although it is also a major pest, in contrast to the Mediterranean fruit fly it concentrates on a single plant, the olive tree. What can we say about this pest?*

Since time immemorial, the olive tree has been one of the most important crops of the Mediterranean region. Olives and olive oil are still important foods in all Mediterranean countries. The largest cultivation areas are in Spain, Italy, Greece and Portugal, where olive oil and olive fruits are major export products. Olive growing has meanwhile spread beyond the Mediterranean to Australia, India, South Africa and North and South America. World production of olive oil amounts to 1.7 million tons.

The main pest affecting olive cultivation is the olive fruit fly, which every year destroys an estimated 25 per cent of the harvest. The olive fruit fly has always been a plague upon the land in the Mediterranean area, and was mentioned in the writings of the Greek naturalist Theophrastus (372—287 B.C.).

*If the olive fruit fly has for so long been known as a pest, attempts must already have been made to control it?*

As a means of reducing the damage, the affected olives were formerly harvested and pressed in the unripe state. To eliminate the pupae overwintering in the soil, the soil was interspersed with ash and charcoal and with cloths saturated in petroleum. In the past, the most effective form of control was a heatwave which, with temperatures of 35 to 40° C, completely wiped out the olive fruit fly population.

A more modern form of control, practised on a larger scale, was introduced at the start of this century. This was the Berlese method, in which a liquid bait consisting of molasses and sodium arsenate was sprayed onto the south-facing side of the tree. The use of arsenic bait exploits the fact that the flies leave their puparium with immature ovaries and only start to lay eggs eight days after hatching. This technique was used on a large scale in Italy and Greece after the First World War. In 1922, it was made mandatory in Italy and in 1923 an olive fruit fly congress was held in Madrid. The governments represented at this meeting decided that laws should be enacted requiring that control of the olive fruit fly by the Berlese method should be made compulsory and implemented by all growers at the same time.

The Berlese method was later improved to include monitoring of infestation levels by means of trap bottles containing attractive substances which were suspended in the trees, as a means of detecting the presence of the pest and thereby determining the most favourable times for its control.

*How is this pest controlled today?*

Different control measures are applied depending on whether the crop is grown for picking or oil production. With olives for picking, control is practised to prevent the fruit being pierced, whereas with olives grown for oil the priority is to prevent the grubs developing.

Instead of the formerly practised partial bait spraying, which was successful only if carried out over large areas and by all growers simultaneously, after the Second World War trees were treated in their entirety with organophosphorus compounds. The advantage of overall treatment with bait additives is that only one to two treatments of this kind per year are needed to exert a simultaneous action against flies, maggots and eggs, compared to at least six treatments with arsenic bait formulations.

*In our cropping areas, the Mediterranean fruit fly is accompanied chiefly by another species, the cherry fruit fly, which exclusively attacks cherries. How important is this pest?*

The cherry fruit fly concentrates mainly on sweet cherries, but also attacks wild and sour cherries. Only morellos are immune to the cherry fruit fly.

The life cycle of this pest is similar to that of the fruit flies just discussed. Control is aimed at preventing attack, since cherries with maggots are unsaleable and are suitable only for distilling purposes.

Treatment against cherry fruit flies is performed with special insecticides when the pests start to lay their eggs.

*What other forms of control are available?*

In Switzerland, control trials involving the use of a yellow cherry fruit fly trap have been in progress for some time. This trap consists of glue-coated yellow-coloured panels, which are suspended on the south-facing side of the trees as a means of determining both the time and intensity of the attack. This method is an important aid in performing biological and ecological studies. However, the cherry fruit fly cannot be reliably controlled by trapping, a fact which has already been established in olive and citrus cultivation.

*As we have heard, fruit flies are a worldwide pest with a formidable capacity for destruction, and which can threaten entire harvests, particularly in warm cropping areas such as California. Yet the risk of fruit being attacked by fungus and putrefying is equally great. What are the main types of fruit?*

A very well known example is the botrytis fungus which attacks many crops plants. Grey mould fungus on strawberries and raspberries, grapevine and lettuce, and also blossom drop in grapevine, redcurrants and other plant species are caused by the botrytis fungus.

Various fungi attack apples as fruit rot pathogens, which can be controlled by spraying during the growing period. This is especially important since the fruit rot pathogens usually first start to cause damage when the apples have been stored for the winter. Very great losses can result. Since modern refrigeration systems, sometimes including controlled atmosphere, incur high storage costs, it is vital that only healthy fruit not infected by fruit rot should be put into storage to preserve the keeping quality of the fruit and the profitability of storage.

*Crop protection thus has the task not only of ensuring that crop plants can germinate and grow unharmed, but also and primarily of saving the fruit, the harvested products, from attack by insect pests and fungal infection before the harvest and also after harvesting by providing suitable protection for stored products.*

## *7. Edict of Frederick the Great, King of Prussia, on locust control*

The following pages 140 to 143 present a facsimile of the edict on eradication of locusts issued by Frederick the Great on 24th November 1752, following a previous Prussian edict in 1731. Securing of the harvests was essential for the food supply of the population.

## *8. Illustrations of pests*

The pests discussed in Section V as important competitors for food are illustrated on pages 144 to 147.

Renovirtes und

erneuertes

wegen

Vertilgung

der

Heuschrecken

oder

Sprengsel.

De Dato Berlin, den 24ten Nov. 1752.

---

BERLIN,

Gedruckt bey dem Königl. Preuß. Hof-Buchdrucker, Christian Albrecht Gäbert.

Wir Friderich, von Gottes Gnaden König in Preussen, Marggraf zu Brandenburg, des heiligen Römischen Reichs Ertz Cämmerer und Churfürst, souverainer und Oberster Hertzog von Schlesien, souverainer Printz von Oranien, Neufchatel und Vallengin, wie auch der Grafschaft Glatz, in Geldern, zu Magdeburg, Cleve, Jülich, Berge, Stettin, Pommern, der Cassuben und Wenden, zu Mecklenburg und Crossen Hertzog, Burggraf zu Nürnberg, Fürst zu Halberstadt, Minden, Camin, Wenden, Schwerin, Ratzeburg, Ostfrießland, und Meurs, Graf zu Hohenzollern, Ruppin, der Marck, Ravensberg, Hohenstein, Tecklenburg, Schwerin, Lingen, Bühren und Lehrdam, Herr zu Ravenstein, der Lande Rostock, Stargard, Lauenburg, Bütow, Arlay und Breda rc. rc. rc. Thun kund und fügen hiermit zu wissen, daß, nachdem sich in Unseren Chur- und Neumärckischen Landen das verderbliche Ungeziefer die Sprengsel oder Heuschrecken letzt vergangenen Sommer in grosser Menge eingefunden, und an verschiedenen Orten grossen Schaden verursachet, auch nunmehro ihre Bruth in die Erde geleget, woraus zu befürchten, daß künftiges Früh-Jahr eine noch grössere Menge junger Heuschrecken zum Vorschein kommen, und das Unglück des Sprengsel-Frasses allgemein werden dürfte; So haben Wir solchem Uebel vorzubeugen aus Landes-väterlicher Vorsorge nöthig gefunden, nicht allein alle dasjenige, so wegen Vertilgung dieser Land-verderblichen Bruth albereits durch die Edicte vom 13. April und 24. Octobr. 1731. verordnet worden, hiemit zu wiederholen, sondern es wird auch hierdurch noch ferner zu künftiger Beobachtung fest gesetzet:.

1) Daß an den Orten, wo Heuschrecken gelegen und liegen geblieben, wovon die Hirten die beste Nachricht geben können, die Gerichts-Obrigkeiten die Unterthanen so fort bey harter Leibes-Strafe anzuweisen haben, die Sprengsel-Bruth sowohl im Herbst als in dem darauf folgenden Früh-Jahr fleißig aufzusuchen und auszurotten, ausser dem auch die Oerter, wo sie lieget, mit den Schweinen, welche davon Witterung haben, fleißig zu betreiben.

2) Müssen vor Winters diejenigen Oerter, wo die Sprengsel liegen geblieben und Bruth geleget, flach umgepflüget und wenn solches geschehen, dergleichen Oerter mit den Schweinen abermals öfters betrieben, und die Bruth so wohl dadurch, als durch fleißiges Aufsuchen ruiniret werden.

3) Solte hierdurch dem Uebel nicht gäntzlich vorgebeuget werden können; So müssen die Gemeinden-Hirten und Schäfer, wie Wir auch Krafft dieses ihnen ernstlich befehlen, fleißig vigiliren, und wenn sich etwa junge Bruth im Früh-Jahre sehen lässet, solches so fort nicht nur ihrer Gerichts-Obrigkeit, sondern auch den benachbarten Gemeinen anzeigen,

anzeigen, und in Zeiten ihre Felder, wo die Bruth sich findet, mit Graben beziehen, es müssen aber diese Graben wenigstens 1½ Elle breit und eben so tief seyn, damit diejenigen Sprengsel, welche schon etwas zu fliegen beginnen, nicht darüber weg fliegen können, auch ist die Erde aus diesen Graben jederzeit auswärts zu werfen, die Graben selbst aber sind nicht schief, sondern gleich unter zu stechen, damit auf der andern Seite die Heuschrecken nicht hinauf kriechen können. Ferner, müssen in dem Graben 15. bis 16. Fuß von einander Fang-Löcher einer halben Elle tief gemachet, und auf solche Art der Graben und das Stück Landes, wo die Heuschrecken liegen, herum gezogen werden.

4) Müssen die Unterthanen die Heuschrecken zu treiben anfangen, dabey aber wohl beobachten, wohin dieselben selbst Lust hinzulaufen haben, massen man observiret, daß sie aus dem Morgen nach dem Abend zugehen, mithin muß das Treiben auch darnach eingerichtet werden, weil man anderergestalt mit dem Treiben nicht fort kömmt, und die Heuschrecken sich lieber zertreten als zwingen lassen, einen contrairen Gang vorzunehmen.

5) Wenn solchergestalt die Sprengsel in dem Graben getrieben sind, laufen sie von selbst in die darin gemachten Löcher, oder können mit Besem dahin eingekehret werden, da sie sodann zu Tode zu stampfen und zu zerquetschen sind, worauf diese Löcher wieder verscharret und neue Löcher in dem Graben angefertiget, auch alle Morgen renoviret werden müssen.

6) Die Sprengsel pflegen auch selbst in die Graben zu laufen und die Löcher anzufüllen, mithin muß die erste Arbeit des Morgens seyn, daß die Löcher visitiret, und die darin befindlichen Heuschrecken todt gestossen werden.

7) Das Treiben auf dem Stück Landes, worauf die Heuschrecken liegen, muß so lange wiederholet werden, bis die Heuschrecken vertilget sind, wobey das Getreyde nicht zu schonen ist, sondern wo viele im Getreyde liegen, müssen die gewöhnlichen Graben und Abschnitte durch die bestellten Stücke gezogen, und die Heuschrecken hiernechst aus dem Getreyde in die Graben getrieben werden.

8) Solten aber die Heuschrecken weiter auf der Feldmarck überhand nehmen, und in die Sommerung kommen; So müssen auch daselbst die Graben gezogen, und so wohl damit, als mit dem Treiben so lange noch die Heuschrecken auf der Feldmarck vorhanden, überall continuiret werden.

9) Sobald eine Stadt, Dorf, oder Gemeine erfähret, daß in ihrer Nachbarschafft Heuschrecken sich eingefunden, müssen sie auf dergleichen Oerter ein wachsames Auge haben, und daselbst fleißig acht geben lassen, ob auch die Stadt oder das Dorf allen vorgeschriebenen Fleiß anwendet, die Heuschrecken auszurotten, zu welchem Ende sie alle Morgen jemanden dahin schicken müssen, damit sie allenfals bey fernerm Fortzuge der Sprengsel ihre Feldmarcken mit Graben einziehen und dadurch die Heuschrecken von sich abhalten können.

10) Wie denn auch der Burgermeister der Stadt, oder Schultze des Dorfes, wo sich Heuschrecken sehen lassen, sie seyn jung oder alt, denen benachbarten Gemeinden und Dörfern, sonderlich wenn sie im Zuge liegen, sogleich bey harter Strafe davon Nachricht geben muß.

11) Sollen

11) Sollen alle und jede nahe belegene oder angränzende Städte, Dorfschafften und Gemeinden, welche etwa von diesem Unglück noch zur Zeit ihrer Situation halber befreyet, schuldig und gehalten seyn, ihren Grentz-Nachbaren auf geschehene Anzeige und des Lands-Raths Ordre zu Hülfe zu eilen und mit Ziehung der nöthigen Graben ohne alle Weigerung und bey harter Strafe hülfliche Hand zu leisten, damit sodann dem Uebel unter göttlichem Beystand vorgekehret werde, und sie durch alle Mensch-mögliche Præcaution davon befreyet bleiben mögen.

12) Und weil bey den grossen Heuschrecken, welche schon fliegen können, gleichfals sehr gut gefunden, die Schweine an denen Orten, wo nicht gesäet, zu jagen, welche die Heuschrecken auffressen, imgleichen daß die Puthen die Heuschrecken consumiren; So kan bey Vorfallenheiten auch dieses Mittel mit Nutzen gebrauchet, und wo es sich thun läßt, die Schweine und Puthen unter die Heuschrecken getrieben werden.

13) Damit man auch versichert seyn möge, daß Schultzen und Gemeinen alles gethan, was in ihren Kräfften gewesen, so werden die Schultzen in den Dörfern, wo die Sprengsel liegen geblieben, hierdurch ernstlich befehliget, von Zeit dieses ihnen publicirten Edicts längstens alle 14. Tage an den Land-Rath des Creyses zu berichten, ob Sprengsel bey ihnen liegen geblieben? ob die Sprengsel-Bruth auf ihren Feldern geleget? ob und wie viel Tage die Unterthanen die Bruth aufgesuchet? wie viel Bruth sie gefunden? und an wem sie solche abgeliefert? desgleichen wie viel Land sie wegen der Sprengsel-Bruth umgepflüget? wie viel Brache sie aufgerissen, und was sie noch vor Winters an Land oder Brache zu Vertilgung der Bruth umpflügen werden, welches so dann von dem Land-Rath bey der Bereisung des Creyses untersuchet werden soll, und wenn sich finden möchte, daß demjenigen, was verordnet, nicht überall nachgelebet worden, so hat derselbe solches so fort der Krieges- und Domainen-Cammer anzuzeigen, damit die Contravenienten zur gehörigen Strafe gezogen werden können.

Wir befehlen demnach allen Unseren Land- und Steuer-Räthen, Magistraten, Beamten und Gerichts-Obrigkeiten bey Vermeidung Unserer höchsten Ungnade, nach dem Inhalt dieses und der vorhin wegen Vertilgung der Heuschrecken unterm 13. April, und 24. Octobr. 1731. ergangenen Edicte aufs genaueste zu verfahren und darüber nachdrücklich zu halten. Uhrkundlich haben Wir dieses Edict höchst eigenhändig unterschrieben und mit Unserm Königl. Insiegel bedrucken lassen; So geschehen und gegeben zu Berlin den 24. Novembr. 1752.

Friderich.

A.O. v. Viereck. F.W. v. Happe. A.F. v. Boden. A.L. v. Blumenthal. H.C. v. Katt. J.D. v. Arnim.

Swarms of migratory locucts attacking citrus plantations being driven off by beaters.

Complete defoliation by locusts.

Aerial control of locusts with insecticides.

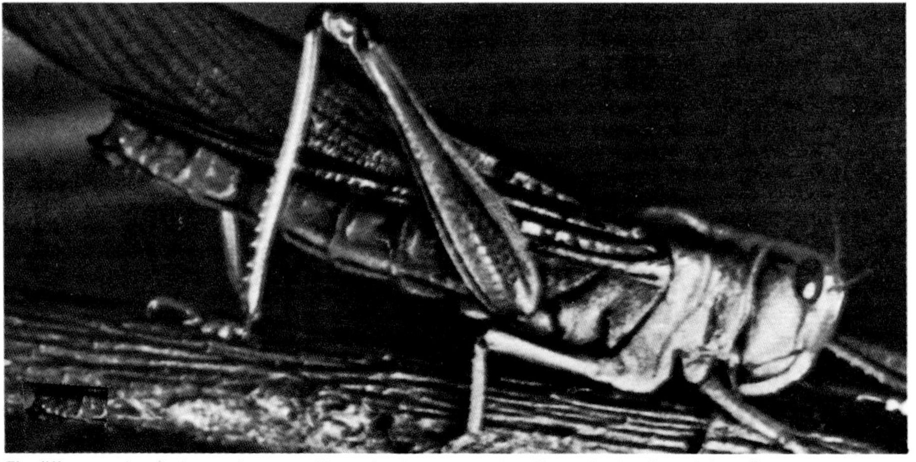

The different species of migratory locust are still a major threat to crops in Africa, Asia, America and Australia.

Eggs laid by snails.

The grapevine snail was formerly a serious pest in the vineyard.

Field slugs attack many species of crop plant and, when present in great numbers, can cause major damage by feeding on leaves.

The black bean aphid damages plants by its feeding activity.

Severe damage to broad beans caused by the black bean aphid.

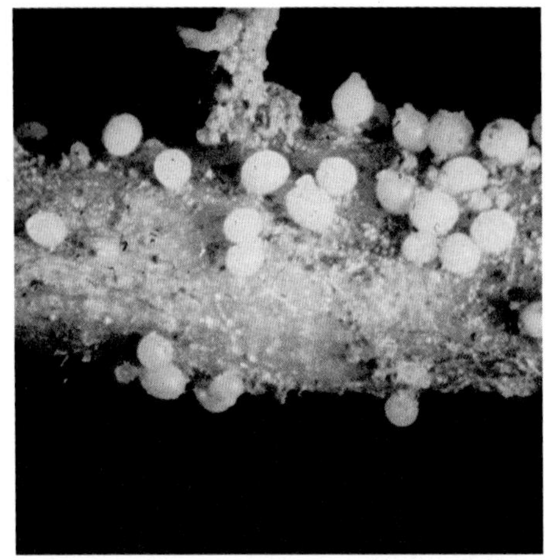

Potato root eelworms (Heterodera rostochiensis) attacking a potato root.

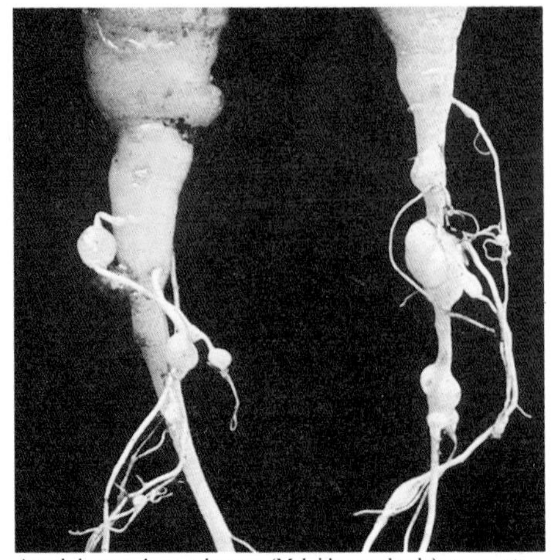

Attack by root-knot eelworms (Meloidogyne hapla) on carrots.

A pest with a wide range of host plants is the green peach aphid (Myzus persicae). It transmits many virus diseases such as yellows and potato viroses.

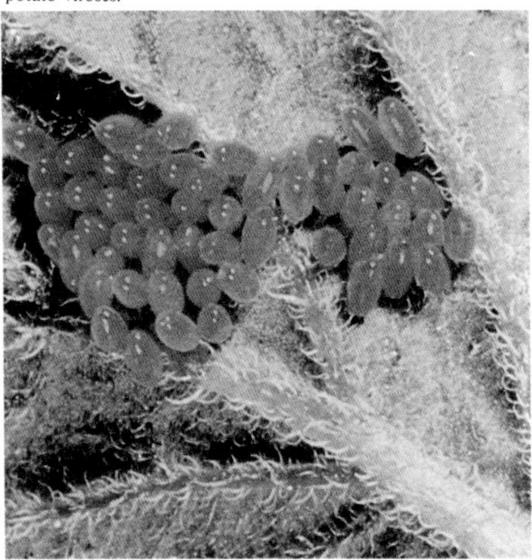

Eggs of the Colorado potato beetle.

Beetle and larva of the Colorado potato beetle (Leptinotarsa decemlineata).

The fruit fly (Ceratitis capitata) laying eggs on an orange. This fruit fly attacks many species of fruit and vegetables.

The olive fruit fly (Dacus oleae) laying eggs on an olive fruit.

The larvae of the olive fruit fly feed on and destroy the flesh of the fruit.

The cherry fruit fly (Rhagoletis cerasi) laying its eggs.

The larvae of the cherry fruit fly devour and destroy the fruit.

## VI. Storage and protection of food supplies

The need to secure food supplies has led many peoples, both in ancient and modern times, to engage in stockpiling. Stores are accumulated in summer and autumn so that food and drink will be available in winter and spring when no crops are gathered. Similarly, it has always been important to lay up stocks of food in years of good harvests as a precaution against poor years resulting from drought or flood. Whatever the reason, stores must always be protected from inclement weather and pests. No less than 15 per cent of stored food throughout the world is still lost due to inadequate protection. Yet this problem is by no means exclusive to the modern age.

Stored product protection has been practised throughout the ages. Examples which spring to mind are the smoking and salting of fish and meat and the drying of fruit. The best-known historical example is the storage of grain in Egypt in biblical times. Even at this early period, the grain weevil or corn worm, as it is referred to in ancient chronicles, was the deadly enemy of stored grain.

We know from history that surplus grain from the seven fat years was stored against the seven lean years. Thus even before the Christian era, special measures were being applied to protect stored grain.

The oldest source known to us, the Sefer Hagaschar (Book of the Honest Man), describes something which is of great interest to those concerned with modern pest control for the protection of stored products. In the Egyptian granaries, unthreshed ears were stored and mixed with dust from the fields where the crop had been grown. This kept the grain healthy, since grain weevils prefer to feed on the threshed bread grain. The admixture of dust also has a lethal effect on the encroaching grain weevils, which become dried up and die owing to the hygroscopic action of the dust. The Babylonian Talmud mentions that powdered potash was mixed with the stored grain to protect it from the grain weevil.

Today, harvested grain is protected from despoliation by grain weevils by storing it in silos, using the most advanced methods. By employing both indirect measures such as circulation, ventilation and climate control, and also direct control in the silo, losses caused by this destructive pest are prevented.

In modern times, with the vast quantities of grain produced in the highly developed agriculture of the industrialized countries, safe storage continues to be indispensable for cereals, since cereal grains with a water content of less of 14 per cent have a virtually unlimited storage life.

In grain storage, we must distinguish between the private and the state sector. To guarantee a continuous supply of high quality produce to the consumer, the trades and the food industry must pursue a far-sighted storage policy to compensate for fluctuations on the market. Governmental storage policy, on the other hand, aims to ensure that a sufficient supply of cereal products is also available for the population in times of crisis. In Berlin, for example, the law requires that supplies sufficient for one year should always be available. In the EC countries including the Federal Republic, however, there is some question as to whether existing cereal stocks are in fact sufficient for times of shortage. Every year, crop failures in Russia, India and the interior of Africa, the result of winter starting too soon or lasting too long, or caused by droughts or floods in summer, repeatedly remind us of the limitations imposed by climate on the agricultural production of wheat and other crops. Stored product protection prevents disasters of this kind.

## 1. Stored product protection as a contribution to world famine relief

*Since time immemorial, man's food supplies have been threatened by all manner of pests, making it necessary to apply suitable measures to protect the stored harvest products from losses, in other words, to practise stored product protection. Throughout history, prudent storage policy has been an important expedient for achieving a balance between successful and poor harvest years and also for stabilizing prices, particularly for cereals, in unproductive years. What are the major problems in this respect?*

All crop protection activities carried out in the field can only bring temporary benefits unless the harvested products are subsequently protected from losses caused by pests.

*Which stored product pests are known?*

As an example, let us start with cereals as the most important staple food. Apart from rats and mice, cereals are attacked primarily by the grain weevil, other species of beetle and various species of cockroaches, moths and mites, which can cause great storage losses by devouring or fouling the grain.

*The most notorious stored product pest must surely be the grain weevil?*

The grain weevil is without doubt the most damaging stored product pest for stored cereal. This is because even a small number of these insects are capable of mounting a devastating attack within a short time. In our climatic conditions, the grain weevil breeds three generations in a single year. One female can lay 200 eggs, and can thus produce 250,000 offspring in a single year. The female pierces a hole in the cereal grain with its snout, lays an egg in the grain through its ovipositor tube and then seals the hole. The entire development from the hatching of the egg through the larval stages to pupation occurs inside the cereal grain and is invisible from outside. When the weevil has hatched, it then eats its way out of the cereal grain and the development cycle starts again from the beginning. The weevil can also live on flour, semolina and bran and can reach an age of two years. The damage it causes can be calculated since the total food requirement of one grain weevil is about 1 g. Since the female grain weevils lay their eggs beside the seedling through their ovipositors, the ability of the seed grain to germinate is also destroyed. Furthermore, for reasons of hygiene, grain which has been attacked by grain weevils must be separated from grain intended for further processing in the food industry, which may also involve great losses.

*Stored product pests thus cause not only direct, but also indirect damage?*

Stored product pests cause damage not only by feeding on the produce. The value of the harvested crops is also diminished by contamination of food and feedstuffs with excrement, webs, insect fragements and discarded skins as well as mould fungi and putrefactive bacteria, which all degrade the quality of the stored products.

*How are these pests controlled?*

Cereals are now stored mostly in silos. Before the silo compartments are filled, they are thoroughly cleaned and the cereal pests are eradicated by spray or fog treatment with products officially approved for this purpose. In filled silos, flour mills and grain transporter ships, grain pests are exterminated by fumigation carried out by specialist contractors.

*What other stored product pests are found in cereals?*

Together with the grain weevil, we also find other major pests such as the wheat beetle, khapra beetle, maize weevil and mealworm. Damage is also caused by various species of moth such as the corn, rye, grain and flour moths. All of these cereal pests must be eliminated by careful, well-timed control measures. In addition to the direct damage caused by these pests, substantial losses occur because the affected cereals become unsuitable for human consumption.

*Stored product protection is thus an essential factor in securing food supplies?*

Stored product protection is generally essential in all spheres of food production for achieving a regulated supply for the population. When practised correctly, these protective measures minimize the great losses which may be caused by pests during storage. Stored product protection therefore contributes greatly to securing man's food supply and banishing hunger throughout the world.

*Pest control thus plays a role not only in the fields but also, and to a much greater extent, in storage, since every year about 30 to 50 million tons of grain are lost around the world because of pests. Stored product protection is thus an active way of relieving world famine. Since stored product pests are also vectors of epidemics and diseases, their control also benefits man's health.*

## 2. Pest control in man's environment — a worldwide problem

*Throughout human history, pests have always exerted great influence on man's environment. Down the ages, insect pests — also referred to as vermin — have threatened man's health and food. Could you give us a few examples?*

Man's food supplies are decimated by many different pests unless they are effectively controlled. Besides rats and mice, we can include all the pests which attack harvest products, such as the different species of cockroach and moths and mites and grain weevils, to name but a few examples. The damage caused by ants and wasps should also be mentioned. After rats and mice, however, cockroaches are of special importance.

*How important are cockroaches?*

Cockroaches are known already to have existed 250 million years ago. This has been proved by the discovery of fossilized remains. Viewed on this time scale, man's mere one million years of existence seem modest indeed. 3500 species of cockroach are known. They inhabit mainly tropical and subtropical regions. The ubiquitous presence of this pest has been confirmed by an investigation carried out in the USA: Its findings indicated that cockroach infestation must be regarded as a far more serious problem even than ants or rats. Investigations by health authorities have also revealed heavy cockroach infestation in kitchens and hospitals.

*Which species of cockroach are found in this country?*

In Central Europe, three species of cockroach are most often encountered: The yellow-brown "German cockroach", the dark brown "Oriental cockroach" and the medium brown "American cockroach".

*Which foods does the cockroach damage?*

Cockroaches eat everything they can find. The damage they do through eating is, however, insignificant compared to the way food becomes contaminated with their droppings, cockroach cadavers or chitinous remains. They are also a nuisance to man because of their penetrating smell and repulsive appearance. Cockroaches were formerly encountered chiefly in restaurant and canteen kitchen, bakeries, food-processing and other plants, but today they occur much more widely. In the food sector they can be found anywhere drinks are dispensed, including vending machines. Cockroaches wander from rubbish bins to and over food intended for consumption, into restaurants, hospitals, boarding-houses, hostels, laundries, even housing blocks and barracks, aeroplanes and ships become infested with them.

*How can we explain the extraordinarily wide distribution of cockroaches?*

Very few places now remain which are free from cockroaches. This is due to the fact that they are spread far and wide by service companies such as food and drinks processors and laundries. The species of cockroach found in our temperate climates rely on buildings for shelter and live in close proximity to man. During the day, cockroaches remain concealed in their haunts. They prefer warmer places, for instance near heating installations, stores, fireplaces or ovens. Here they go to ground in cracks in walls or under wallpaper or panelling. At dusk, they come out in search of food.

*What form does control take?*

This is performed by high and low volume spraying or dusting with officially approved public health insecticides in the rooms or houses infested with cockroaches; above all, it is important to flush out their hiding places.

*Are cockroaches, like rats, not only stored product pests but also vectors of disease?*

Cockroaches indeed not only attack stored products; they are much more dangerous as vectors and propagators of disease. For instance, they are responsible for spreading paratyphoid, tuberculosis, meningitis and mastitis. They are also a cause of the greatly feared "hospitalism", the passing on of diseases within hospitals. There is even reason to suspect that they transmit polio viruses and infective hepatitis.

## 3. Rat control, an imperative of environmental protection

*Environmental protection is now generally accepted to mean how we can prevent our living space being contaminated by chemicals, exhaust gases and refuse products. Although these are certainly very real and urgent problems, we must also not forget those forms of environmental pollution which have threatened man and his existence for centuries, and which are today more or less taken for granted because they have become so familiar, or even because those affected are responsible for creating them. It is scarcely conceivable that our civilized society tolerates the presence of rats within its midst, which as a threat to the health of man and animals ranks equally with automobile exhaust fumes and effluents. What are the main types of damage caused by these rodents?*

Most of us dislike rats either because they fill us with disgust or because they are financially damaging as contaminators of valuable produce. Rats can be very costly indeed to the farmer. In reality, however, the major importance of the rat as an economic pest is far exceeded by its significance as a vector of infectious diseases.

*What are the main diseases transmitted by rats?*

We hardly need mention the plague which was spread by fleas on rats, and which around the year 1330 annihilated one third of Europe's population within three years and which is still liable to be introduced at any time from the tropics. Today it is much more relevant and therefore of greater concern that rats bring Salmonella, the pathogens of paratyphus, into the pantry when they enter our dwellings during their nocturnal forays from the sewers. Or that Weil's disease, a particularly unpleasant form of jaundice, is transmitted by the urine of rats. Contracting this infection when bathing outdoors is all too easy, since up to forty per cent of rats can harbour the pathogen, which remains infectious for prolonged periods in a moist environment. Rat droppings can contain Entamoeba, the dysentery pathogen, and tapeworms, and the bite of a diseased rat can transmit rabies to man and domestic animals.

*We do not need to list the large number of pathogens and parasites spread by rats and the vermin they carry: The few examples just mentioned clearly demonstrate the epidemics which lie in wait wherever ignorance, indifference or false economy allow rats free rein to contaminate our environment. This is particularly so wherever rats, emerging from their subterranean haunts, take up residence above ground, inevitably bringing with them all the germs they have picked up in the sewers. Making their way out of ruptured pipelines, they clamber to the surface or climb up soil pipes, through the water traps of toilets and so enter our houses directly. These are by no means rare occurrences. There are of course different species of rat?*

Although the black rat, which makes its home mainly in the upper storeys of buildings and in attics, has virtually disappeared from most parts of Germany, the brown or common house rat is still widespread. This creature prefers to live near water and, as an omnivore, finds food everywhere. Leftovers of meat on rubbish dumps are devoured just as eagerly as stored grain or the revolting waste in the sewers. Being something of a "gourmet", it greatly prefers first class food which it is very skilled in pilfering from larders, food stores or even camping tents. Thus it is typical "city vermin", which often travels great distances each day in its search for food. The brown rat can also sustain itself outdoors, and colonies of rats are known to exist whose inhabitants live all year round without direct contact with man. In winter, they often descend in swarms upon field barns and turnip clamps. Individual rats which detach themselves from such outdoor populations because of the usually limited food supply, represent a constant danger to the environment; they often recolonize farms which have just been cleared of rats at an astonishingly rapid rate.

*What does the common house rat look like and how does it behave?*

Common house rats are greyish-brown in colour and have powerful, squat bodies. Although much less nimble in their movements than black rats, they can still climb, jump and swim with great skill. Obstacles to their advance are gnawed away unless the material can resist their glass-hard teeth, or if a smooth surface provides no opportunity for gnawing. Caustic bait is of no use, because the bitten material usually does not come into contact with the mucous membranes of their mouth. Not counting their long, hairless tail, fully grown brown rats measure about 25 centimetres, and can reach a weight of more than 500 grams.

*What is known of their biology and behaviour?*

These rats usually live in large colonies or packs, whose members are all related to each other. The individual animals watch over each other and recognize the other members of the pack by their common odour. Outside rats which enter the territory of another pack are attacked and often killed. Rats rear their young with great care. Since several dams frequently litter in a communal nest, very large litters can grow up without losses. Litters of twelve are no rarity, and one rat has even been observed to litter 19 young. Since the females of this rodent species can litter three to four times in a single year and since the young rats themselves are mature enough to breed when only three months old, a truly fearsome growth potential exists which is held in check only by the inadequate availability of food supplies.

*Why are rats so difficult to control?*

It is not only their vast reproductive potential which makes it so difficult to get rid of these unwelcome guests. Their caution when faced with anything new and their excellent learning ability only too often allows them to outwit man's efforts at control. They also have an almost unbelievable ability which is without parallel anywhere in the animal kingdom: Rats can pass on experience to their progeny. It has been proved that a pack of rats can still refuse to accept a certain type of poison bait long after new generations have replaced those which first had the life-endangering experience with this bait.

*Rodent pests and rats in particular are thus a source of grave public health problems and economic damage. How can man rid himself of this plague?*

Rat control of course has a long history. Even in the Middle Ages, a specific profession was dedicated to the control of rats and mice. The Pied Piper of Hamelin on the Weser is world-famous. In keeping with the times, the methods employed by these rat-catchers were different from our modern techniques, and were frequently based on mystical ideas. Until very recently, measures taken against rats had at best yielded partial success, since too little was known about the biology and behaviour of these pests. A real change for the better only came with the introduction of modern control methods which made use of new chemical and biological knowledge.

*New and effective means were therefore found which afforded improved prospects of control?*

At first fast acting poisons were used which were still accompanied by undesirable side effects such as bait shyness induced by the rats' warning instinct. Domestic animals also died accidentally when poisoned rats were eaten by dogs, cats or birds of prey.

*Incomplete and unsatisfactory results were thus the first step towards destroying these rodent pests. How did things go on from there?*

It was only after the Second World War that the decisive breakthrough occurred with the invention of the coumarin compounds, which did not have the disadvantages we have mentioned. These control agents, prepared in the form of suitable bait mixtures, are readily eaten by rodent pests and provide permanent and effective rat control.

*Over the last few years, many large-scale rat control operations have been carried out in the cities on the Rhine and Ruhr. How are such large-scale operations carried out and what do we mean by rat eradication?*

The only generally binding legal basis for the control of rats is embodied in § 13 of the Federal Law on Epidemics enacted in 1961. This legislation however provides only for single operations, and obliges the landowner to undertake at his own cost appropriate measures to eradicate rats on his property. Experience has shown however that this is not sufficient to keep a locality free from rats. Areas which have just been cleared are usually repopulated very rapidly by rats which, coming from neighbouring areas or from sewers, repossess the cleared area.

*Have any lessons been drawn from this experience?*

Over the last few years, there has been an increasing tendency to carry out "large-scale rat control operations". These coordinated projects cover an entire rural area, community or city and comprise a number of separate, coordinated stages. Noted pest-control companies having a sufficiently large staff of trained operatives are usually contracted to carry out this work. Firstly they make a "survey of infestation" in which every piece of land containing buildings is investigated for rat infestation. This is followed by the actual "control compaign". In this phase, separate teams advance not only against the rats in the properties previously identified as "infested", but also against those which live on open ground, banks of rivers and canals, rubbish dumps and similar places and also in the sewer system. It is important for all the control teams to advance at an equal rate to prevent the rats re-occupying the areas which have just been cleared. On completion of this work, a "guarantee period" immediately commences. This usually lasts for two years.

*What is the purpose of this?*

The purpose of the guarantee period is to maintain the success of the control action and, if possible, improve it still further. In this way, notifications of re-infestation are to prevented from increasing once again.

*We must therefore regard the rat as a highly dangerous environmental pest with which we live in close contact, whether we are aware of it or not. It is a highly aggressive creature greatly skilled in the arts of survival. It is obvious to everyone that something must be done. Yet do we really have a chance of ridding ourselves of these pests once and for all?*

As long ago as the fifties, an extensive pilot project carried out in North Rhine-Westphalia demonstrated that, using the newly developed coumarin-containing bait, rats can be quickly and completely eradicated. Since this time, this experience has also been applied and expanded in large-scale operations in some regions of Germany such as Baden-Württemberg, Bavaria, Bremen, Hamburg, Hessen, Lower Saxony, Rhineland Palatinate, Saarland and Schleswig-Holstein. Many European countries beyond the borders of the Federal Republic of Germany such as Belgium, Bulgaria, Italy, the Netherlands, Spain and Hungary and even Egypt have also adopted this method of large-scale rat control.

*What form does this control take?*

Control agents containing coumarin cause rats to die painlessly and without symptoms, and their warning instinct is not alerted and thus cannot help them. Even the most experienced rats have no chance of survival. Control operations performed in a professional manner yield total success both in large areas such as entire cities or rural districts, and on single lots of ground. Large-scale eradication presents great advantages. Only this approach is beneficial to the community as a whole and eliminates rats from our environment. Large-scale operations are also more economic than the uncoordinated efforts of individuals; finally, only concerted programmes offer the prospect of solving the rat problem over the long term.

*In the context of environmental protection policy, the Federal Government is currently examining ways and means of redeveloping inner city areas. These endeavours are aimed at improving the quality of life in densely populated areas. Measures being considered for this purpose are the removal of atmospheric pollution, regeneration of contaminated streams and rivers by cleaning of waste waters, solving refuse disposal problems and above all targeted, large-scale rat control programmes.*

*A major aspect of the environmental programme of the Federal Republic, which is concerned with waste disposal by means of refuse incineration, large-scale dumps and other methods of non-hazardous refuse disposal, is to prevent the landscape being spoiled by pests and vermin encouraged by environmental pollution, as a means of protecting and preserving the health of the population.*

## *4. The importance of wood preservation in the building industry, agriculture and forestry*

*Wood has always been a popular and versatile building material. It is easy to machine, noise-insulating and is widely used because, given the many different kinds of wood, it has not yet been surpassed by any other material. Wood however requires care and protection, both against weathering and pests. What should we know about wood protection?*

When we think of wood protection, we think firstly of protecting windows, doors, window-sills and wood panelling against adverse weather conditions such as wet and heat. A number of wood protectants such as tar and carbolineum which were formerly used, and also modern chemical impregnants, have proved their worth as preservatives while also affording protection against fungal infection and attack by pests. Since wood is not a dead material but, as we say, is always "working", modern wood protectants which allow the wood to breathe and exchange moisture are of great assistance in modern practices of wood protection.

*We mentioned wood being attacked by pests. Which are the main culprits in this respect?*

Chief among the insect pests which attack wood as a construction material are the house longhorn beetle and the so-called woodworms.

*What is the house longhorn beetle?*

The house longhorn beetle is the best known wood beetle which attacks wood in buildings. In summer, these small black beetles with their large feelers can be observed in wooden beams. Hidden in the rafters are white larvae which can clearly be heard chewing their way through the wood when the house is quiet. As soon as the presence of these pests is detected, the building inspection authorities must be notified immediately.

*And the woodworms?*

Infestation with woodworms is apparent from small, circular holes and expelled sawdust. Woodworms are the larvae of the death watch or furniture beetle, of the genus Anobia. In addition to the attack by insects, the wood in buildings is damaged by dry rot.

*What exactly is dry rot?*

Dry rot is a fungus. It attacks wood which has become moist. Affected wood shows lengthwise and transverse cracks, crumbles away and has a musty smell. The mycelium of the fungus spreads rapidly throughout the wood and destroys it.

*How is it controlled?*

The first step consists in eliminating the source of the moisture and removing the visibly affected wood. The wood which remains and the newly installed wood is treated with a specific wood protectant which gives permanent protection against renewed attack.

*So much for protection of wood already inside buildings. Stored wood which has been cut in a forest, transported, machined and then put into storage must also be protected from spoilage or pests?*

Stored wood is dormant capital. It must also be protected from damage by fungi and insects.

The best known pests in this respect are the various species of bark beetle which infest not only felled trees but also commerical timber. The most important of these are the bark-breeding and wood-breeding bark beetles. Infestation, which is apparent from the feeding galleries of the larvae, reduces the value of the wood. Control measures are applied in the spring using a special product.

*Chemical wood protection is thus practised wherever wood grows, is stored, has been or is to be machined, and is constantly necessary to ensure that this valuable and versatile material grows to its full quality in the forests through the exercise of forestry skills, and is subsequently preserved by means of wood protection.*

## *5. Stored product protection in arable farming and horticulture*

*Protecting stores has always been important for all types of food. While in the individual household or farm stocks are laid up in the summer and autumn, as a means of getting through winter and spring until the new harvest, on the national and global economic scale long-term stockpiling is necessary. Why is this necessary?*

Stockpiling on a worldwide scale is necessary above all as a means of ensuring that sufficient stocks are available for years with poor harvests caused by drought or other adverse circumstances, as part of a strategy for preventing widespread famine.

*Such comprehensive stored product protection must be extremely costly. What main activities are involved?*

A basic distinction should be made between preventive or indirect, and direct protection of stored products. With apples for example, the fungi which cause rotting if introduced with the fruit into cold storage must be controlled on the tree; this is preventive or indirect stored product protection. When the produce is in cold storage, direct protection must be given by ensuring clean conditions and by means of extremely precise humidity and temperature control so that the fruit retains its table quality.

*How important is stored product protection in potato cultivation?*

The same applies for potatoes as for apples. Timely spraying must be performed in the field to prevent Phytophthora or late blight from entering the tuber. This indirect stored product protection is vital for maintaining the health of the tubers during storage, whereas direct protection is applied during winter storage by suppressing germs and controlling the climate in the storehouses.

*What other kinds of stored product protection are possible for highly perishable fruit?*

There are many different ways of prolonging the keeping quality of fruit. These include drying, preserving in jars and tins or deep-freeze preservation. All species of fruit are also made consumable over prolonged periods by processing them into fruit juices. Other possibilities are preserving in salt and vinegar for cucumbers or the storage of cabbage, carrots and garden produce in special clamps.

*Stockpiling is important not only for man's food but also for animal feedstuffs. What means are employed to protect these products during storage?*

Stockpiling in summer for the winter and in good years as an insurance against poor years is done in various ways. Chief among these is drying, as is practised for example with hay, straw and potato or sliced beets, but also for other coarse food and also for species of cereal. Preservation can also take the form of ensilaging of maize, beet leaves and other green fodder plants. The storage of fodder beet and Swedish turnips in clamps continues to play an important role.

## *6. Illustrations of pests*

The following pages 159 to 163 show illustrations of the Chicago Corn Exchange and the major pests discussed in Sections VI and VII.

Corn exchanges are important trading institutions for the world grain trade, and protective measures are indispensable for the storage and transport of cereals. The 44 storey and 162 metre high Board of Trade Building in Chicago illustrated above houses the world's largest grain exchange. It was completed in 1930, the same year which witnessed the collapse of the international grain market due to overproduction in the world economic crisis. At the summit of the building stands the 9.75 metre high statue of the Roman corn and earth goddess Ceres, the goddess of growing vegetation. In 1932 the poet Gottfried Benn, in an article entitled "Does Carleton deserve a Memorial?" described the grain exchange and the crisis in Chicago and the tragic dialectic which exists between shortage and superfluity, from which not even grain cereal is exempt.

Grain weevils (Sitophilus granarius), flightless weevils measuring up to 5 mm in length, attacking cereal. Development from the egg to the weevil occurs inside the cereal grain.

Grain weevil (magnified) on damaged wheat.

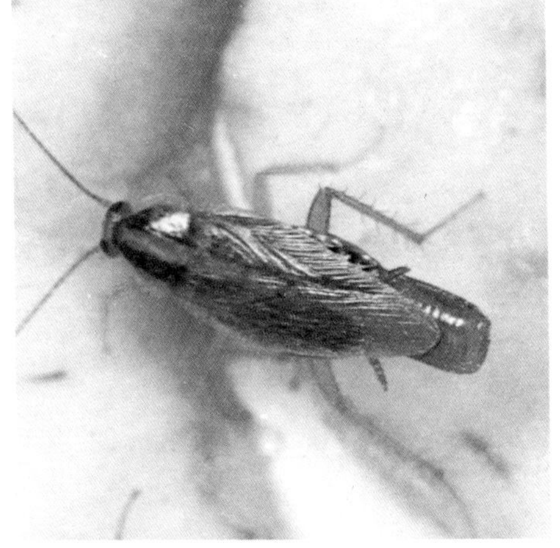

Female of the German cockroach (Blattella germanica) with egg capsule.

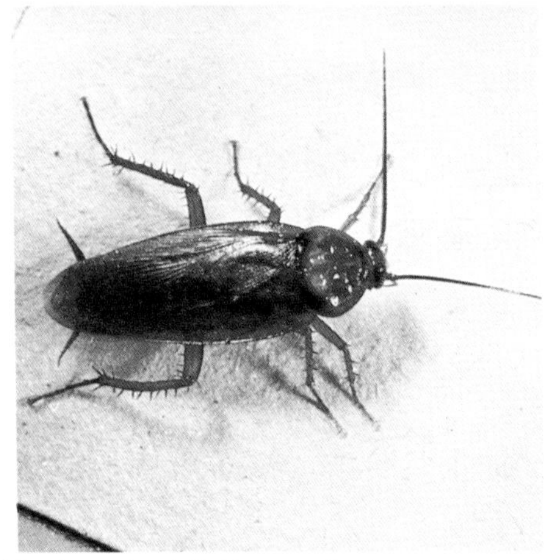

American cockroach (Periplaneta americana).

Oriental cockroach (Blatta orientalis) with egg capsule.

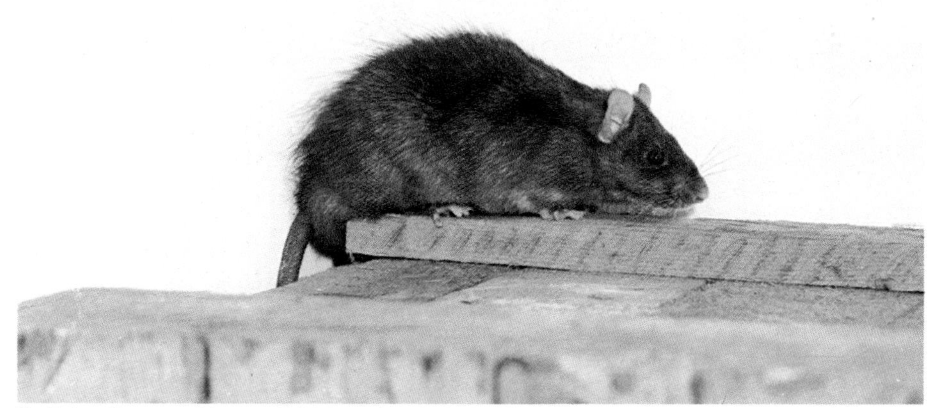

The black rat (Rattus rattus) is a pest which infests attics and animal stabling. It breeds less quickly than the brown rat, by which it has largely been displaced.

The brown or common house rat (Rattus norvegicus) has a high reproduction rate, colonizes open ground and buildings and transmits many deadly diseases (typhus, cholera, dysentery, plague).

The house mouse (Mus musculus domesticus) has a high rate of reproduction, infests dry rooms and transmits diseases.

The field mouse (Microtus arvalis) is a pest at home in fields and fruit orchards. It breeds in vast numbers after drought periods.

Larva of the house longhorn beetle, which needs 3 to 6 years to reach adulthood and destroys the wood of roof timbering.

Wood pest: adult house longhorn beetle (Hylotrupes bajulus).

Larva of the classical "woodworm", which takes 2 to 10 years to reach adulthood and destroys furniture.

Wood pest: common death watch beetle (Anobium punctatum) adult stage of the "woodworm".

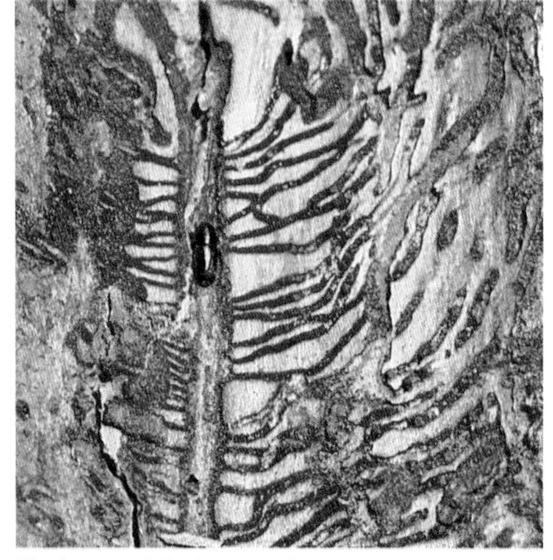

Wood pest: attack by the engraver beetle (Ips typographus), which destroys wood in storage and while still growing.

Damage caused by dry rot (Serpula lacrymans), the most destructive "building fungus" for pine wood.

The pheasant damages the seed in maize crops.

The rook damages the germinating and emerging cereal plants.

The starling is a harvest pest particularly injurious to cherries and grapevine.

When present in large numbers, the blackbird attacks fruit, vegetables and grapevine.

Several species of thrush damage pre-harvest crops in orchards and vineyards.

The tree sparrow appears in large flocks and feeds on cereal crops at the milk ripeness stage.

## VII. Agriculture, forestry and horticulture under ecological aspects

Agriculture, forestry and horticulture determine the character of our countryside and, together with industrial and metropolitan areas, make up our environment.

Of the total area of the Federal Republic, 55 per cent are used for agriculture and horticulture, 30 per cent are covered by woods and forests, about 4 per cent consist of moorland, wasteland and water and 11 per cent are utilized for urban development transport and industrial buildings. Agriculture, forests and water therefore account for almost 90 per cent of the territory of the Federal Republic.

This is a high proportion for an industrialized nation. Considering the high population density in the area of industrial concentration, the agricultural landscape has great importance as environment for the cities.

In 1981, the number of inhabitants per square kilometre was 33 on world average, only 12 in the USSR, 24 in the USA and no less than 163 in the European Community. Within the area which now makes up the Federal Republic of Germany, in 1870 there were already 82, in 1935 170 and in 1980 no less than 248 inhabitants per square kilometre. By comparison, the Netherlands currently have 346 and Japan 314 inhabitants per square kilometre. The population density has therefore trebled within a century. Over this same period, the area of land used for agriculture has decreased, with building development and traffic systems covering land at a faster rate than moorland, heathland or land on the North Sea coast can be reclaimed.

A particular problem arises from the concentration of population within the cities, which was intensified by the incorporation of rural communities when a number of boundaries were re-drawn. Between 1950 and 1980, the proportion of residential population in villages with less than 2000 inhabitants in the Federal Republic declined from 27.5 to 3.7 per cent, whereas the proportion of those living in towns and cities with at least 20,000 inhabitants increased over the same period from 43.0 to 59.8 per cent. Today, 17 per cent of the population live in cities of more than 500,000 inhabitants and only 0.7 per cent in villages with less than 500 inhabitants.

These changes have had an impact on the leisure habits of the population. At the ever-lengthening weekends, on holidays and in their leisure time, people living in built-up areas go in search of rest and recreation in the agricultural countryside surrounding the major conurbations. Vacations on farms or, to be more accurate, in the heart of the countryside, are becoming ever more popular, since private cars give holidaymakers increasing independence from public transportation.

As this trend has increased, however, the proportion of farmers in the overall population has decreased. Whereas 45 per cent of the world's economically active population are still employed in agriculture, in the Federal Republic this proportion has meanwhile declined to 5.3 per cent. Since 1960 alone, the proportion of persons employed in agriculture and forestry has dropped from 14 to almost 5 per cent. These figures show that an ever-shrinking number of the economically active population are engaged in providing not only food but also a recreational amenity for the population as a whole. In our country, one farmer, or expressed in more general terms, someone employed full-time in agriculture, not only provides the daily bread for 43 people, but also helps create a healthier environment.

Agriculture and forestry thus play a vital part in caring for and maintaining the countryside. In our industrial age, so inimical to the interests of agriculture, it often happens that agricultural land is no longer farmed, falls into disuse for socio-economic reasons and ultimately becomes a wasteland. The individual farmer should be given incentives in the form of tax relief and public subsidies so that marginal farms are kept in operation, to prevent communities which are at a natural disadvantage from dying out. Only in this way can we prevent the gradual erosion of the infrastructure of precisely those areas which often perform a specially valuable recreational function for the city dweller.

The position of agriculture within the national economy and in the rural population of human society as a whole is constantly changing. The agricultural sector however has always been, and always will be, a valuable part of the economy as a whole. Up to a hundred years ago, the saying: "The farmer's wealth is the people's health" still had great meaning in this country. The proverb still holds true for the developing countries, since in agrarian economies the weal and woe of the national economy depends decisively on the output of agriculture. In the industrialized countries, however, it can justifiably be said: "If industry is booming, prosperity is blooming", a phrase which illustrates the degree to which agriculture depends on the health of industry.

Opinions now differ only in degree regarding the mutual dependencies between industry and agriculture. The importance of agriculture as a producer of food will increase worldwide as the world population continues to grow. Moreover, particularly in the industrialized countries, it will become increasingly significant as a preserver of the countryside and thus a protector of the environment, an additional task which will benefit the population at large.

## *1. The importance of arable farming and forestry for preserving the countryside*

*In view of the changes increasingly being inflicted on the countryside by industry, residential developments and traffic systems, it is more important than ever that people should be given the opportunity to find rest and recreation in a natural setting during their free time and holidays. What is the situation in the Federal Republic in this respect?*

In terms of land use in the countryside of the Federal Republic, agriculture and forestry continue to maintain their dominating position. About 85 per cent of our country consists of woodlands, meadows, pastures and arable land.

*Although the Federal Republic is a highly industrialized country, purely in terms of area, agriculture and forestry occupy a great deal of space. What is the situation in the built-up areas?*

An attentive trip through the industrialized areas, for instance of the Rhine and Ruhr, reveals the great variety of natural scenery and how much of the country is still dedicated to agriculture and forestry. Particularly in these areas it is important to keep agriculture and forestry fully functional, beyond their purely economic significance, as a means of protecting the countryside.

*How important are agriculture and forestry as factors in preserving the countryside?*

This can be well illustrated by considering woodlands. The regenerative effect of woodland derives from its air which is cleansed of dust and smoke, and from the specific woodland climate. Depending on the species of tree, woodland areas can absorb 30 to 70 tons of dust per hectare. The wind blows soot and dust into the woods, where they settle on leaves and twigs, and permeate with the rain into the forest soil, where they are retained. Like the permanent crops in agriculture (for example pome fruit), woodlands also require regular care in the form of soil cultivation, fertilization and crop protection in order to maintain the health and promote the resistance of these ecologically so important plant communities. Deficiency diseases develop in the absence of proper care, since woodlands will not grow without it. For example, magnesium is an important plant nutrient for many species of coniferous tree and must be supplied to prevent damage.

*Because of their beneficial air cleansing effects, woodlands, parks and tree plantings near residential and industrial areas should be preserved, cultivated, extended or re-established by rural and city planners. What influence have woodlands on the water economy?*

Woodlands are known to have a great water storage capacity. The uptake capacity of forest soil pervaded with deep-running roots is estimated at 500 to 2,000 cubic metres of water per hectare.

*Not only woodlands but also meadows, grasslands, gardens and arable lands perform similar functions in maintaining the balance of nature and preserving the natural character of the countryside. Not only water resources, but also the oxygen balance is positively influenced?*

Land use for agricultural and forestry purposes has an extremely positive effect on the oxygen balance. Five large trees or 100 square metres of grassland can for example satisfy the oxygen demand of one person.

*Maintaining the health of crop plants in agriculture and forestry is thus a life-sustaining necessity for us?*

Activities pursued to optimize crop growing and in the sphere of environmental and crop protection to preserve the health of cultivated plants have not only economic aspects: All these cultivation measures are also important aids to protecting the countryside and are thus in the common interest.

## *2. Problems of preserving the countryside*

*Measures for preserving the countryside are intended to prevent damage to the balance of nature and the character of the countryside and to remedy such damage as has already occurred. Preservation of the countryside, occurring either unconsciously or pursued as a deliberate policy, has always been important. Only with the coming of the industrial age, however, have opposing forms of countryside developed. What forms of countryside do we see today?*

Currently existing forms of countryside can be classified as follows according to their fundamental character:

1. urbanized or civilized countryside with housing estates, shopping centres, industrial and transportation facilities;
2. agriculture or production countryside with horticulture, arable farming and forestry, with meadows and pastures, cereal, beet and potato growing and woodlands or man-made forests and
3. leisure or recreational countryside with mountain resorts, health and seaside resorts, sports facilities, nature parks, wild life reserves and national parks.

*The task of countryside preservation is to create a relationship and maintain a balance between these different and to some extent opposed forms of countryside and to prevent disharmonies arising between them. What are the primary requirements for this purpose?*

Preservation of the countryside has the task of alleviating negative effects on man and of promoting positive effects. Let us take as an example the fallowing of economically marginal fields caused by small farmers abandoning the land to work in industry and leaving their farmland, meadows and pastures to lie uncropped when no one wishes to lease them for agricultural use. These areas become overgrown. Even worse, weed seeds are spread by the wind from these overgrown areas to neighbouring farms, gardens and parks.

*Weed control is therefore also important among endeavours to preserve the countryside?*

Official regulations giving precise instructions for the control of weeds were also issued in Germany in previous centuries. Most of these regulations concern the control of thistles and also of coltsfoot, giving exact directions on pulling up, setting alight, scorching in ovens or incinerating. All these methods were extremely laborious. Today, these weeds are eradicated with chemical agents, since mechanical weed removal involves excessively high wage costs.

*Weed control or the suppression of plant growth is very important for environmental care in many spheres?*

In caring for and maintaining transportation facilities, for example railways, roads and airports, the prevention of weed growth is vitally important. Especially in our own climatic conditions, weeds proliferate to such an extent that everything would very soon be overgrown unless plant growth was suppressed or prevented by means of continuous control measures.

*The care and maintenance of railway lines, motorways, roads, sports grounds and airports is a major item of public expenditure because of the associated high labour costs. Chemical weed control has greatly rationalized these activities and substantially reduced the workforce required. Just to give a general idea: What transportation areas in the Federal Republic require this kind of attention to keep them functioning satisfactorily?*

A total of 31,500 kilometres of railway lines must be cared for, 7,500 kilometres of motorways, roads totalling more than 480,000 kilometres, representing an area of almost 1.2 million hectares. Public parks and gardens as well as cemeteries, sports grounds and airports cover about 360,000 hectares in the Federal Republic.

*This amounts to 1.5 million hectares of useful area for the public transportation and recreation sector. As a comparison, it might be mentioned that useful agricultural land covers an area of 12.2 million hectares. The care of these 1.5 million hectares, used in so many different ways, must be performed primarily according to the purpose for which they are used. What is the task of chemical weed control in this context?*

For highway systems, a distinction should be made between weed control and growth suppression. Weed control is practised to eradicate weeds which grow in from the roadside or which penetrate through and destroy road surfaces and jeopardize their safety. Weed control at roadsides also facilitates rapid water drainage from the road surface. Speed limit and information signs must also be kept clear of weeds so that they are distinguishable at all times. Growth suppression is performed on road slopes and in ditches and also on the central reserves of motorways. This cuts down the need for labour-demanding and hazardous mowing operations.

In the Land North Rhine-Westphalia and in some other Länder of the Federal Republic, regional legislation requires that highways and road slopes be kept clear of weeds by mechanical control measures.

*Chemical weed control thus facilitates and rationalizes work on roads and highways. The risk of workmen being injured in traffic accidents is also reduced. Do these measures also have significance in other areas of the transportation system?*

Weed control is also important in maintaining the functioning and traffic safety in the German Federal Railways (Bundesbahn) and other public and private railway systems. Regular line maintenance programmes are implemented in which points and warning and signalling equipment are given particular attention. Chemical weed control is particularly important in maintaining railway installations, since constant drainage of the trackbed must not be restricted by weed growth, otherwise the track will lose its elasticity.

*As well as safeguarding the functioning of railways and highways, the care of public parks and gardens, cemeteries, sports grounds and airports is a task in itself. Is restricting the growth of weeds also an important aspect of environmental protection in this sphere?*

Here we make a distinction between weed control on paths and squares where all vegetation, including that of moss and lichen, must be removed and selective weed control among ornamental shrubs and bushes, roses and on lawns. Substances are used for this purpose which destroy only the weeds in the upper soil layer, without affecting neighbouring plants and the deeper reaching root networks of ornamental bushes and trees.

*Not only the public parks in cities and rural communities must be cared for and maintained, but also transportation and industrial facilities. What steps are taken to care for the rest of our environment?*

Man's guiding hand is needed throughout our entire countryside, since the original vegetation is woodland and forest, to which we here in Germany are also indebted for our brown coal and coal deposits, and which predominated in earlier geological periods. Continuous care and cultivation of the countryside is also necessary in our nature parks, national parks and wildlife reserves, which also have an important recreational value for man, to prevent undesired changes occurring within the plant community. The protected areas of the Lüneburg Heath are a good example. Without herds of sheep continuously grazing and eating other plant species, the heathland would long ago have reverted to wild woodland. Care of these areas which are not used for farming or forestry should be performed according to the respective useful function and the relevant safety regulations.

## *3. Water as a life-sustaining element*

*Disasters caused by droughts and floods repeatedly demonstrate how important water is for life in general and also for the continued existence and development of plants, animals and man. What actually is water?*

Chemically speaking, water consists of hydrogen and oxygen; its chemical formula is $H_2O$, in other words two hydrogen atoms are chemically combined with one oxygen atom. Depending on the temperature, water occurs in different aggregate states, namely as steam, liquid water and in solid form as ice.

*What other particular properties does water have?*

Water has an excellent capacity for storing and transporting heat. Our climate is decisively influenced by this fact, and we need only think of the Gulf Stream whose warmth is responsible not only for the ice-free waterways and their thriving fish population, but also greatly influences the climate of the continents along which it flows.

Moreover, every hot water heating system utilizes this capacity of water to store and transport heat.

*Water must then also play a major role in the circulatory system of nature?*

Water is the most important solvent in the natural environment. The nutrients vital to plant life are supplied dissolved in water through the soil. These nutrients are taken up through the roots and their translocation through the plants occurs as a result of suction pressure and the high surface tension. If the soil is dry, plants are deprived both of nutrients and life-sustaining water, their growth stagnates and finally they shrivel and die.

*And what is the situation with man?*

Water is essential for man's existence. On no other liquid does our life depend so directly. A man can survive for several weeks without food, but only for a few days without water. This is why it is so important to safeguard water supplies throughout the world.

*How great is water consumption?*

Water consumption per head of population, including industrial consumption, is 200 to 350 litres per day, depending on the region. The massive rise in our water consumption, including in the Federal Republic, has only been possible by maintaining a balanced circulation of water in the natural environment and by creating large water reservoirs. For example, after working brown coal up to a depth of about 500 metres in the Rhineland, water reservoirs are formed which contain more than the total volume of about 1,800 million cubic metres which is held in all of the artificial dams currently existing in the Federal Republic. Experts estimate that in 50 years, the continuously increasing world population will be consuming the total quantity of fresh water in circulation.

*The water circulation in nature however takes the form mainly of precipitation and evaporation. If there is no precipitation, the earth dries up since evaporation still continues. What effects have dry periods on yields in agriculture and horticulture?*

The development of crops is greatly affected by prolonged periods of drought. Depending on the water supply of soils, which is determined by the ground water level, winter humidity and soil quality, pronounced differences are observed. Worst affected are crops grown on lighter soils which are less able to retain water. The situation becomes critical for yield levels if the drought perists into the spring. In vegetable growing, flower and ornamental cultivation and in gardens and public parks, additional irrigation by sprinkling is necessary in dry periods to prevent the various annual and perennial plants from drying out.

*What are the effects of drought on pests?*

Drought and heat encourage the breeding of insect pests. Particularly in beet crops, therefore, damage caused by pests during dry periods in the emergence time of beet plants should be prevented by timely treatment. Special attention should also be paid to controlling aphids not only in beet crops, but also in all other crops during dry periods. Many fungal diseases such as rust are promoted by warm and dry weather.

*To summarize, we can say that prolonged dry periods, which will doubtless also occur in future, bring great disadvantages for farms, gardens and forests. Not only this, but also the droughts which have persisted for many years in the Sahel area of Africa continue to illustrate the importance of water as man's most important "food". Many famines throughout the world have been and continue to be caused by lack of water. And yet an excess of water, such as we see in devastating floods, can also cause incalculable suffering.*

## *4. Influence of climate and weather*

*The influence of climate and weather is decisive for plant growth and crop yields both in agriculture and horticulture. Years without protracted snowfall are followed by years with cold periods or heavy snow. What effects have frost and snow on agriculture and horticulture?*

For winter cereals, cold periods in January and February are only a disadvantage if bare frosts occur, when the protective covering of snow is absent. Snow can however also cause losses if the seed has not been treated properly against fungal diseases and, as often occurs in such cases, snow mould disease (Fusarium nivale) appears and the cereal crops are severely decimated by rotting of the cereal plants.

*What other effects does frost have?*

Periods of frost have a beneficial effect on the structure of the soil, which is after all the foundation and nutrient substrate of plants. Freezing of the soil produces frost tilth, in other words, the increased friability improves the physical properties of the soil.

*Does the cold destroy pests?*

Yes and no. Pests overwintering in their adult stage, such as certain species of aphid like the spruce aphid or the green peach aphid, are decimated by permanent frost. As a rule, however, pests overwintering in the well-protected stages such as egg or pupa are fully capable of surviving even very low temperatures.

*And what is the situation with fungi?*

We can take apple mildew as an example, which overwinters in the terminal buds of the long shoots and only begins to freeze at temperatures below —20 °.

*And how does frost affect weeds?*

Frost periods bring the growth of all species of plants to a standstill and thus also stop weeds from growing. Although in mild winters certain weeds found among crops like winter barley continue their luxuriant growth during the winter months, since they generally have a much lower temperature optimum than cultivated plants, in years of cold or snow weeds are prevented from developing. Mild winters make great demands on the weed control efficacy of herbicides which are applied in autumn for winter cereal.

*How is horticulture affected by cold periods?*

It is important to protect plants which are sensitive to cold, if possible by covering them to keep out the cold and wind. After heavy snowfall, trees and bushes should for example be freed from their load of snow to prevent them breaking.

Fruit plants, and particularly their stems, can be damaged by frosts when exposed to very low temperatures and pronounced temperature variations between day and night. Under certain conditions, particularly in small gardens, a certain measure of protection can be given by limewashing the trees. Pruning should not be carried out during frosts.

*Cold and snow perform certain functions in agriculture and horticulture throughout the year which are specially important in the economy of nature. Late frosts which come after the start of the growing season in spring are particularly damaging. A cold snap towards the end of March injures not only flowers and ornamentals but also fruit species, in some cases severely. Even worse are late frosts in May, on days when the "ice saints", named after the patrons of the three days from May 11 to 13, appear which can seriously injure the blossoms of fruit trees. What are the effects of frost during the blossom stage?*

Night frosts with prolonged sub-zero temperatures during fruit flowering cause serious blossom damage in all species of fruit. In 1976 for example, the late frosts attacked all the varieties during the flowering stage or at the start of flowering, that is from the "pink bud stage" up to "full blossom". The proportion of frozen blossoms differed according to the variety. The severest blossom damage was suffered by the cultivars Stark Earliest, Klarapfel, Mantet, Geheimrat Oldenburg and Roter Boskoop with 100 per cent, followed by James Grieve and Cox Orange with more than 90 per cent. The cultivars Ingrid Marie, MacIntosh, Laxtons Superb, Jonathan and Red Delicious suffered more than 60 per cent blossom frost damage, while Champagner-Renette and Melrose had less than 50 per cent. Gloster is also one of the apple varieties less sensitive to frost.

*Despite the pronounced blossom damage, were the fruit set and yield affected to different degrees in the various cultivars?*

The highest yield losses were suffered by Cox Orange, Roter Boskoop, Laxtons Superb, Stark Earliest and Klarapfel with more than 80 per cent, followed by James Grieve and Golden Pearmain with more than 60 per cent. The lowest yield losses occurred with Melrose and Champagner-Renette. Of the pear varieties, the Vereinsdechant pear was relatively undamaged by frost and gave good yields compared to the other varieties.

*Did the summer drought also adversely affect apple and pear cultivars?*

The effects of the frost during the blossom stage on the fruit set and yield were compounded and aggravated by the long-persisting dry period in March and April with its rain deficit of 75 per cent and in June with a rain deficit of 80 per cent. The longest dry period lasted for 40 days from June 2nd to July 11th 1976. Worst affected by the dry period were the cultivars Cox Orange and Roter Boskoop. Particularly noteworthy was the fact that all cultivars on rootstock M 4 were more severely damaged than those on rootstock M 9. Those which suffered the least damage were Mantet, Melrose, Granny Smith, Champagner-Renette and Geheimrat Oldenburg.

*What effect had the sudden rainfall at the end of July and in August?*

The drought damage was manifested mainly in June in the form of retarded leaf, shoot and fruit growth. The sudden onset of rainfall which then followed at the end of July, caused splitting of the fruit, which affected mainly Cox Orange and Ingrid Marie and which substantially impaired the commercial value of these cultivars.

*Did blossom damage also occur in soft fruit and what effects did it have?*

Of the soft fruit varieties, only currants were damaged by the frost period from April 28 to 30, since the gooseberries had already finished flowering and strawberries, raspberries and blackberries flowered much later.

Major differences were apparent between blackcurrants, redcurrants, whitecurrants and also between the individual varieties. Among the blackcurrants, which were in the "early flower" stage, only the Wellington, Stripta and Westra varieties were undamaged by frost. With the redcurrants and whitecurrants, which were in full blossom during the frost, the blossom damage was less than for the blackcurrant varieties.

*Many years of experience show that frost damage in fruit crops is a very serious occurrence, and that nothing is more important than normal weather for safeguarding our food.*

## 5. Agriculture and the world of birds

*The transformation of the natural countryside into cultivated land continues inexorably, a development which cannot but have consequences for the world of birds. Many ecologists, nature conservationists and especially those concerned with the protection of birds however point an accusing finger at the practice of agrochemistry and by implication at agriculture and horticulture themselves as being chiefly responsible for the depletion of the animal kingdom. There must however be many ways of looking at these problems?*

Nature conservation sees one of its main tasks as protecting the surviving natural countryside from development, intensive use and adverse influences of all kinds. It is concerned to establish valuable areas of the natural landscape as nature reserves and wildlife sanctuaries and so to develop new, ecologically varied protected areas for the animal and plant kingdom. Many species of animal still have their natural biotope on agricultural land where, in the course of time, certain changes in the abundance of species and their relative importance have come about as the landscape has altered.

*Can you give some examples?*

Many species of animal which man has encouraged directly, for example by winter feeding, have now multiplied to such an extent that they have become a liability and are causing damage in agriculture and horticulture, such as the starling, blackbird, wood pigeon, sparrow and others. Many birds, such as the black-headed and laughing gull and magpie, are even driving out endangered species.

*Are there any more specific examples relating to the bird world and agriculture?*

Firstly, perhaps, a few more familiar examples: the pheasant as a seed pest in maize crops and crows as seed pests in wheat. These species of bird damage the emerging seeds by feeding on and playing among them, as a result decimating the cereal crops. The farmer tries to protect the seed by treating it with bird repellents to drive off these animals.

*These are the seed pests among the bird species; what about birds as harvest pests?*

In cereal crops, particularly in wheat and barley, the sparrow is a major harvest pest, since it descends in large flocks on the cereals during their state of milk ripeness and, feeding with extreme voraciousness, destroys up to 50 per cent of the harvest. They can be driven away only to a limited extent by means of optical and acoustic bird repellent devices.

*Which birds cause most damage to fruit and horticultural crops?*

The bird species which wreak most havoc in fruit crops are the starling, blackbird, bullfinch and the fieldfare, which greatly damage cherry and apple harvests, sometimes to the point of total ruin. A similar situation obtains in vegetable crops, in which pigeons are also a major pest and can completely devastate harvests such as lettuce.

*What defensive measures can be taken?*

Defensive measures against species of birds which act as seed and harvest pests in agriculture and horticulture are possible only up to a certain point and are defined by the legislator. The individual farmer can attempt to reduce harvest losses caused by bird pests by applying seed protectants and by using optical, acoustic and mechanical repellent devices. Measures which are possible on small areas, such as spreading nets over endangered crops, are not suitable in every situation, especially not for large-scale crops.

*The aim of bird and nature protection should therefore be to preserve the indigenous bird population with its many different species, to help maintain the biological balance and prevent individual species of bird from achieving dominance and thereby developing into pests.*

## *6. Meadows and pastures in the natural landscape*

*Meadows and pastures are an important feature of the natural scenery of Germany. Meadows and pastures are generally thought of as being natural vegetation. In our climatic regions, however, grassland is anything but original, since it usually covers areas formerly occupied by woodland. This is why, when a farmer no longer cares for and cultivates grassland, it reverts in the course of time to natural woodland. How much of the Federal Republic is covered by grassland?*

Meadows and pastures cover almost 5 million hectares in the Federal Republic. By comparison, land used for arable farming occupies 7.3 million hectares.

*The farmer knows that grassland requires as much care as arable land if it is to yield maximum benefit. What activities are necessary to achieve this?*

Depending on whether the land is used as meadow or pasture, fertilization or cultivation takes priority. In recent years, when timely care of meadows and pastures was neglected due to lack of workforce, weeds began to spread far and wide, reducing the economic viability of grassland use and in particular the value of fertilization measures.

*Meadows and pastures are however not monocultures of certain species of grass or clo-*

*ver, but communities of plants made up of many different species of grass, clover and herbs. Do we also find weeds in meadows and pastures?*

Weeds in meadows and pastures are plants which, when present in large numbers, have adverse effects on useful animals, grass swards and the economy of grassland use. Different types of weeds are found in different grassland areas, for example in waterlogged ground, shadowed areas at forest margins, acidified soil, or where land is used incorrectly, for instance when mowing is carried out too late or when pastures are grazed too heavily or too late and where fertilizers are applied in an unbalanced manner.

*Which weeds have proved particularly troublesome in grasslands?*

In recent years, the worst culprits have been the large-leaved dock species, particularly blunt-leaved and curly dock, also known as ox-tongue, which have developed into a serious problem in meadows and pastures. The dock species compete for space and nutrients with the other grassland grasses and plants. Because of their high seed propagation, they spread unchecked. The proliferation of dock weeds is frequently caused by overfertilization with liquid or semiliquid manure. Since mechanical control has proved unsuccessful or is too demanding, chemical dock control should be performed as single plant or broadcast treatment, depending on the intensity of infestation, in order to improve the economy of grassland use.

*What is the most favourable time for control?*

On meadows after the first or second crop, on pastures after removing the grazing animals and clear-cutting, when the dock has reached a height of about 20 centimetres. Only those agents should be used for control which have been approved by the Federal Biological Research Centre.

*So much for the agricultural aspects of meadows and pastures. How important are grasslands as part of our natural scenery?*

Throughout the land, meadows and pastures provide the basis for livestock husbandry and dairying. However, grassland is also an important feature of the landscape. As leisure time increases and the countryside becomes increasingly urbanized, meadows and pastures acquire a major recreation value equal to that of woodlands. For this reason municipal and local councils create parks and extensive lawns within residential areas. Sports and games lawns are also an important aspect of urban planning.

## *7. Problems of environmental and crop protection*

*The subject of environmental protection has become a major public issue. Aspects of this discussion include the refuse problem, automobile exhaust gases in the cities, preservation of woods, streams, rivers, lakes and oceans, to name but a few. Crop protection surely belongs to this complex of problems?*

Protection of the environment and public health is a wide ranging problem, also covering for instance semi-luxury goods which, if abused, can severely damage the health. As we can see from the general discussion of these issues, whereas everything in the field of environmental protection is still in a state of flux and progress is achieved only slowly, in crop protection concern about the possible toxicity of these products has always aroused strong feelings. Manufacturers and health and crop protection authorities have cooperated for many years to secure maximum protection for users and consumers alike.

*At this point, we might perhaps mention the specific measures taken by the legislator?*

In addition to the Foodstuffs Law with its order on tolerance levels, the Crop Protection Law which was passed by the Bundestag in 1968 and the Foodstuffs and Utensils Law of 1974 legally regulate the entire practice of crop protection in arable farming and horticulture, giving first priority to protecting the consumer.

*The law therefore states that the consumer is to be supplied with perfect quality horticultural and agricultural produce from the German countryside. What crop protection activities does the legislator consider to be necessary?*

The most important crop protection measures are defence against insect pests, the control of plant diseases such as fruit scab, and halting the growth of weeds. The correct way of using the individual products recommended for these purposes is precisely defined for each application in the instructions for use and in the official registration documents for the relevant product.

*Application of crop protectants in accordance with instructions guarantees harvest produce free from residues, if the safety intervals between application and harvest specified by the federal authorities are observed. What do we know about the effects of crop protection on the soil and environment?*

Every soil is a complicated system whose characteristics are determined by the grain sizes of the soil particles and their composition, and by the content of organic substance. Also, the microflora and fauna and the water supply of the soil greatly influence its value as a growing location for plants. Types of soil differ greatly, so that for example heavy loamy soil and light sandy soil vary considerably in their behaviour. Official registration of crop protectants now also includes testing of how these compounds behave in the soil. The crop protectants so far approved, when applied correctly, have not been found to have any adverse effects on the soil. Furthermore, the legislator, through the agency of the Federal Biological Research Centre and the Federal Office of Health, would not grant approval and release for such products to be applied.

*Do crop protectants harm game animals?*

When used correctly and in accordance with the statutory provisions, no damage occurs. On the contrary, the number of game animals and consequently the game density is continuously increasing. Many institutes in different countries are researching these problems, so that numerous studies are available on game animal mortality. It may be interesting to mention that about 300,000 deer, roe and hares perish every year in traffic accidents in the Federal Republic.

*How is the bird world affected?*

Several important points can be mentioned in this respect. Countryside subject to increasing building development and traffic density, intensified land use and which is disturbed by tourism and traffic, sometimes no longer offers many species of animal and especially birds the conditions they need to survive. Bird protection stations such as the Essen Bird Protection Station in North Rhine-Westphalia, were established some time ago in different parts of the Federal Republic, and are intensively engaged in assessing the influence of ecological changes on the bird world.

*Environmental and crop protection are causally related to each other, and horticulture and agriculture are important factors in preserving our countryside and thus indispensable for preserving our environment.*

## VIII. Types of garden and their significance.

Gardening is one of man's oldest activities. Long before man began to domesticate animals and took up the shepherd's and nomad's life, he cultivated plants. In these primitive times, while the man went hunting, the woman would search for grains and roots for their daily food. As she prepared the meal in front of the cave, some grains and roots would spill over onto the ground, eventually took root and developed into new plants. This may have gone unnoticed for a long time, and it was a great turning point when man finally began to sow the grains around the cave and harvest them later, to save himself the laborious work of searching for and collecting the wild-growing grains, herbs and roots. And when animals began to destroy these plants during the night, the cave dweller would protect the beds by fencing or "yarding" them off with twigs or stakes, thereby creating the garden. This work, as our researches have shown, was carried out by women, who were thus in effect the inventors of horticulture. It is therefore no accident that, perpetuating this ancient tradition, the garden and its produce belonged by law to the farmer's wife even beyond the Middle Ages.

Only later, when man became more numerous, and stocks of food had to be laid up in large quantities for winter and times of shortage, did it become necessary to make the transition from horticulture to farming. In this way, agriculture came into being as an offshoot of horticulture.

For most of the Germanic tribes, however, the garden as "private property", as a source of food and vegetables for each family, remained apart from communal land use and was the woman's special preserve. The custom in these primitive times whereby each family always cultivated its own garden for food explains modern man's propensity, persisting like an ancient instinct, to tend a garden or at least a few flowers of his own.

It was not only for economic reasons, however, that the garden was cultivated as a source of food for the family, but also because of man's yearning to create in his garden a small earthly paradise, a "Garden of Eden" as described in the second chapter of the first Book of Moses: "fertile and well-irrigated, full of useful and splendid plants, a sanctuary of beauty and tranquillity."

Princes and burghers, knights and monks repeatedly strove to give these longings earthly shape and to transform their gardens into an image of paradise. Along the banks of the Yangtze-Kiang and the Indus, in the narrow, desert-bordered oasis of the eastern Mediterranean, the home of the ancient advanced civilizations, the first flowering gardens came into existence which we know were not cultivated for economic reasons only.

These gardens were however not only places of earthly delight, not only a symbol of princely dignity and power but also images of supernatural reality. In gardens, gods were worshipped and the dead were laid to rest. The rulers of Assyria and Babylon also used their gardens as visible proof to their subjects of the geographical extent of their domain: Plants from all parts of their empire, from the mountains and valleys and from the coasts, from warm and cold regions were collected in the palace gardens. Descriptions of gardens handed down from antiquity thus confine themselves to listing exotic plants. Today's gardeners frequently also like to grow plants not indigenous to their own location, but which, carefully nurtured, must be protected from heat and cold.

Garden architecture has undergone many changes down the ages. The gardens of the Egyptians had a strictly symmetrical layout, their design elements were trees arranged in rows, flowers and arbours. The Babylonians laid out their gardens in the form of terraces and these fabled "hanging gardens" were at that time one of the wonders of the world; the Assyrians had hunting and animal parks resembling the natural countryside, and the Persians established woodland animal parks and terraced gardens. The Greeks, because of their high population density, had paved, colonnaded courtyard gardens containing pot plants in front of their dwelling houses, and also public gardens in the form of groves of trees sourrounding temples, palaces and gymnasia. The Romans, like the Greeks, had courtyard gardens in their city dwellings and more extensive gardens outside the city, laid out in strictly architectural form and integrated into the landscape as a "setting" for their country houses. The gardens of Islam, influenced by the late Hellenic period and the Persians, served as a spatial complement to the house, and included ponds, tendril-bedecked pergolas, large, shady trees, tiled pathways and flowering shrubs appropriate to the climate, an art spread by the Moors as far as Granada in Spain and by the Mongols as far as India. The gardens of China, by contrast, are a symbolic reflection in miniature of the natural landscape down to the tiniest detail: water, still, falling and flowing; stones and mountains, shrubs of all sizes and species, mosses, wilderness-like plant communities; decorative elements include bridges, tea-houses, lanterns and water jars. The flora of China, whose development was not disturbed by an Ice Age, provided the necessary variety for these gardens.

The garden design of the western world, which had its inception in the Middle Ages, was conceived and functioned on a geometrical pattern. Gardens were often enclosed by buildings such as monasteries and cloisters and were used for breeding and cultivating useful and medicinal plants, and were more suited to the contemplative life than to the practice of the fine arts. In Italy of the Renaissance and Baroque, garden architecture was an important element of cultural and artistic expression. Albertus Magnus, writing in the 13th century, describes the layout of an ornamental garden, and Raphael (1483—1520) personally designed gardens. With waterfalls, ponds, fountains, pergolas, neatly trimmed box-tree hedges, evergreen shrubs, separately arranged cypresses and pines, the architectural perspectivistic garden was created which, making use of the natural contours of the ground, enclosed villas usually situated on hillsides. During the reign of Louis XIV (1643—1715), thanks to the genius of the landscape gardener André le Nôtre (1613—1700), France took the lead in garden design. His designs were strictly geometrical-axial, and everything in his ornamental gardens was related to the buildings, strictly demarcated from the natural surroundings, and lent perspectives by means of prospects emphasized by avenues and moats. The palace gardens which have been preserved in many countries, in Versailles, Brühl, Würzburg, Nymphenburg or Hampton Court bear witness to the splendour of these grounds.

Finally, in 18th century England, oriental garden design began to exert its first influcences on the European school. The ideal of this design was to achieve a naturally picturesque garden in which the influence of man's guiding hand was no longer apparent. Design was effected through the creation of spaces by means of groups of trees, informally arranged shrubs and spacious lawns. The boundaries of the garden flowed over into the natural landscape, and cities such as Berlin, Hanover, Karlsruhe, Kassel and Munich owe many of their most pleasing features, which have continued to influence present-day planning practices, to the integration of open countryside into garden design. Throughout the 20th century, the formal elements of these three historical garden styles have persisted alongside each other: The architecturally spaced garden, deriving from the gardens from the Renaissance, the geometrical-perspectivistic garden, orginating from the Baroque, and the landscaped garden traceable both to the English park and the Oriental miniature garden.

Besides useful and ornamental gardens, monastery gardens and, at a later stage, botanical gardens have always had a special importance. Monasteries were the main repositories of western culture in the early Middle Ages. The monks, who had taken a vow of prayer, manual labour and study following the rule of Saint Benedict, in carrying on the cultural tradition of antiquity also acquired much knowledge about garden cultivation which they passed on to later ages. The growing of vegetables, fruit and medicinal plants was practised in the Benedictine and later also the Cistercian monasteries, which also became centres of supply for medicines. The famous monastery plan from the year 820, preserved in the library of St. Gallen, indicates the presence of several gardens: the cloister courtyard, the arboretum which also served as a cemetery, the spice and medicinal herb garden beside the dispensary and the vegetable garden. The cloister, situated to the south of the main church, with its encircling arcades and plant-filled courtyard, is reminiscent of the peristyle of antiquity. We may imagine its surface divided by intersecting paths and covered with lawn or ivy. The centrepiece of such simple, monastic gardens was usually a well or a bed of specially beautiful plants having symbolic significance. The arboretum was also used as a cemetery, a dual function which at the same time suggests a symbolic association. The lawn, in which the narrow graves of the monks can be discerned, may have symbolized the fields of the heavenly paradise, and the growth cycle of the fruit trees, the alternation of winter dormancy, flowering and fruit was perceived as an image of birth, death and resurrection. The "boumgarto", the tree fruit garden which was invariably found near every monastery, was also used for outdoor recreation, and would be visited by the monks in summer to enjoy the beauties of nature and to pray for the dead. Finally, the "Wurzgertlein", the medicinal herb garden, in which spices, medicinal and flowering plants grew side by side, was very important for the healing arts of the age, and from which, as early as the 14th century, the first medicinal-botanical garden was developed by Matthaeus Sylvaticus (1277—1342) in Salerno. As long ago as 50 A.D., the Greek doctor Pedanius Dioskorides (first century A.D.) described about 600 medicinal plants.

Whereas the Benedictines built their monasteries in the mountains, the Cistercians, an order founded at the end of the 11th century at the Benedictine reform monastery of Cîteaux, preferred wooded valleys. These monks too, by establishing fruit and vegetable gardens and the model farms, known as "outwork", belonging to the monastery, contributed to progress in horticulture and agriculture. East German colonization extending as far as the Vistula in the 12th and 13th centuries owed much to the efforts of these religious orders.

The most celebrated "monastery gardener" however is the Augustine abbot Gregor Mendel (1822—1884) who, through his cross-fertilization experiments with red and white flowering pea plants in the monastery garden at Brünn more than 100 years ago, discovered the laws of inheritance, making it possible for the first time to breed new, higher-yielding species of cultivated plants and breeds of domestic animal, thereby revolutionizing horticulture and agriculture. This was the culmination of centuries of work with plants performed by monks in their monasteries who in this way passed on and propagated the cultivation methods for our crops, although from the start of the 19th century, with the arrival of the scientific era, this work had already been taken over by governmental and private agricultural experimental stations and farms.

In our own age, the garden has an even wider range of functions than in former times. It is an ornamental, recreational and useful garden simultaneously. It also serves in many different ways for leisure activities. The public parks and gardens of our cities, rural communities and institutions and the national parks also have an important green belt function for the built-up industrial areas. The domestic garden of the small and amateur gardener also supplies families with fresh fruit and vegetables and with flowers. The nature reserves in the Federal Republic of Germany cover an area of more than 50,000 square kilometres, which are protected and cared for by the forestry authorities. National parks account for more than 4,000 square kilometres. Public parks and recreation areas as well as sports grounds cover about 75,000 hectares, and small and domestic gardens almost 50,000 hectares. On all of these areas, constant care, observation and preservation of flowers, shrubs and trees is an important factor in maintaining of the amenity value of gardens and natural scenery.

## *1. Decorative and useful gardens*

*In our region of the Rhine and Ruhr, we find not only intensive commercial horticulture, but also many flower and vegetable gardens everywhere being tended by small and amateur gardeners. What is the situation in the built-up areas?*

Almost every second civil servant and blue-collar household possesses a garden with fruit and vegetables. And every third white-collar and four tenths of self-employed households pursue this hobby which keeps the cooking pot filled. Freelancers evidently have little time for this pursuit: Only fifteen per cent cultivate fruit and vegetables on their own patch of ground. The pleasures of an ornamental garden are enjoyed by every fifth blue-collar and white-collar family, and every fourth civil servant family; thirty per cent of the self-employed and fifteen per cent of freelancers also have a garden. The latter rate the beauty of a garden higher than its usefulness. The pleasure which all gardeners take in tending their garden and in the gardening arts is at the same time an expression of their positive feeling for life.

*How does the small gardener decide which form his garden is to take?*

In laying out the garden, the choice of plants is a question both of personal preference and actual need. Depending on the gardener's wishes and preferences, ornamental plants, fruit or vegetables will predominate.

*Does the small gardener face any cultivation problems, particularly in protecting his plants?*

His main problem will probably arise from the mixed cultivation of different crops and from the fact that the garden is an outdoor dwelling, as it were the "green room".

*He therefore faces two basic problems, firstly the need to use pesticides with a broad spectrum of action because of the mixture of different crops, and secondly the requirement for products presenting as little health hazard as possible to man and domestic animals. What particular aspects must be considered?*

For the gardening enthusiast, a range of pesticides for different applications have been approved by the legislator, the most important aspect of which, apart from efficacy and plant safety, is their non-hazardous nature. All products are suitable for the small gardener which not only have reliable action but which also are not subject to the Poisons Order, such as fungicides and weed control agents. For the control of insects, manufacturers offer low-toxicity preparations and products with short safety intervals.

*Apart from chemical crop protection, what other ways of keeping down diseases and pests are available to the small gardener?*

Methods which continue to be popular are collecting the pests, or pruning of apples and roses for mildew control and the use of sticky trap bands for winter moth control.

Not to be underestimated for the containment of diseases and pests, however, are methods of cultivation, since plants are more vulnerable to such damage in unfavourable environmental and nutritional conditions.

*How important is "integrated crop protection" for the small gardener and how do we define these scientific and practical endeavours?*

Integrated crop protection, reduced to a simple formula, is "as little crop protection as possible and as much as necessary". Important aspects of this approach are optimal care and cultivation of the soil, balanced fertilization, observance of crop rotation and the careful choice of varieties, taking account of resistance to disease and being sure to purchase healthy seeds and plants. Chemical crop protectants should be applied as soon as attack is detected and not when the crops have already suffered some degree of damage.

*All cultivation methods increase the pleasure offered by a garden, which has always been the special province of women. What is the modern housewife's attitude to her own garden?*

Gardens are cultivated today not only to supply the family with fresh fruit and vegetables, but are also used for constructive leisure purposes. As in earlier times, the garden also offers an ideal playground for growing children and gives them the opportunity to develop in healthy, natural sourroundings. Every tree and bush also helps to maintain the "green lung" of our cities, thereby actively helping to protect the environment.

## 2. *Roses as garden ornaments*

*The garden rose, whose aesthetic value lies in its harmony of colour, shape and perfume and its long flowering period, is now a firmly established favourite among garden and interior ornaments. It is the undisputed queen among flowers. What significance did the rose have in former times?*

The garden rose was prized in ancient Babylon, and hybrid garden roses in Greece are mentioned by Archilochos (650 B.C). The Germanic peoples used the wild rose as enclosures for their holy shrines. The crusaders brought hybrid roses, such as the damask rose, to central Europe where they were cultivated in monastery gardens for many centuries. The rose also plays an important role in Christian symbolism, particularly in painting and architecture. The circle divided by the five-leaved rose blossom, in the form of the "rose window", became the central motif of Gothic architecture.

*Which species of rose are cultivated today?*

Among today's garden roses, we distinguish between wild roses and cultivated roses, which include dwarf, tea, polyantha, climbing and park roses. Together with dwarf roses and tea roses, the polyanthas or many-flowered roses have become the most popular bedding roses in our gardens because of their bushy growth and their long flowering period. They are however less suitable as cut flowers. The most popular climbing roses are the long-flowering varieties. The park rose is a shrub rose which can reach a height of up to 2 metres.

*Do roses make any special demands?*

Roses require deep soil rich in humus and nutrients in a sunny location. They can be planted both in autumn and in spring. Annual earthing of roses before the start of winter is important as a protection against frost and desiccation.

*What other types of care are important for roses?*

Roses require great care and attention if they are to give pleasure as a permantent crop over many years. They are attacked by many diseases and pests, and annual crop protection measures are thus essential.

*What disease mainly attacks roses?*

The most prevalent disease among our roses is known as powdery mildew. The leaves become covered with a white, powdery coating. The younger shoots and leaves in particular are attacked, but the flower is also affected. The leaves become stunted and at times show reddish discolouration. This disease is caused by a fungus. Its occurrence and the intensity of infection depends on the weather, and the variety of rose and type of rootstock are also factors. Weakly developed plants in a poor nutritional condition are unfortunately at great risk, and roses growing in very light, sandy or cold and wet soils are attacked more frequently.

*Do any other fungal diseases cause damage to roses?*

In late summer and autumn, the black spot disease generally appears. The leaves begin to show large, brown to violet-black, round to star-shaped spots. Premature yellowing of the leaves and leaf drop result. The entire plant growth is stunted. The third most important leaf disease in roses is rust. On the underside of the leaves we find pin-sized, dusting pustules; in summer these are orange-coloured and in autumn they appear black. This fungus is also visible on the twigs in spring in the form of dusting, orange-red swellings, the spores.

*How are these diseases controlled?*

Control is applied by means of regular treatment with an officially approved fungicide which is effective against all three diseases. The treatment must be commenced as soon as the first signs of attack become apparent. It is important that all parts of the plant, but particularly the newly developed parts, are thoroughly wetted by the spray formulation. During the period of most vigorous shooting, spraying should be performed every eight days, and with heavy infection the first two treatments should be performed within four days of each other.

*What insect pests particularly damage roses?*

Like almost all plants, roses too are attacked by aphids. The pattern of damage is always the same. The aphids pierce the plants, suck out the juice and inject toxins into the plants. The damage takes the form of yellow spots, curling and rolling of the leaves and twisting of the shoot tips. The rose aphid is leaf-green, spotted, meat-red or lemon-yellow, and lightly powdered. Both winged and wingless stages are known. Many colonies of rose aphids remain on the plants throughout the summer. The familiar rose mosaic virus is transmitted by these pests.

*Do any other pests attack roses?*

Particularly worthy of mention is the rose leafhopper. The damage caused to roses by leafhoppers is manifested as a whitish speckling on the upper surface of the leaves. On the leaf undersides, we find yellowish to light green insects whose presence is easily identified since they can readily be made to take flight. Leafhoppers also damage roses by their sucking activities.

Various species of caterpillar, such as the winter moth, also damage roses by devouring the foliage.

*How is control exercised?*

Damage is prevented by means of timely treatment with special compounds for controlling aphids and leafhoppers and with a contact poison against caterpillar species.

*Mechanical weed control in roses is very difficult during their growth period, because, as the proverb says, there is "no rose without thorns". What possibilities exist in this respect?*

The care of roses can be made easier by means of chemical weed control. Products suitable for this purpose are applied in the spring to weed-free soil. The soil surface should be friable, so that the preparations are precisely distributed. If the soil is sufficiently moist, these agents prevent the emergence of weeds. After application, however, the soil should not be worked during the growing season since otherwise weed seeds are displaced from deeper soil layers to the top soil where they germinate. Precise dosing and correct application of these agents is also important.

*Careful tending of roses in the garden is essential if they are to keep flowering into the autumn and flourish over many years.*

## 3. Lawns as the centrepiece of garden design

*Lawns frequently have pride of place both in domestic gardens and public parks. Well-kept lawns convey to the observer a feeling of the harmony of nature and an impression of peacefulness and spaciousness, even on a small scale. Trees standing alone amid lawns create a particularly charming atmosphere and all species of plants, especially summer blooms, come into their own in flower beds bordering these green areas. Does the laying and care of lawns make any particular demands as regards location?*

Several important rules must be observed for laying or maintaining a densely growing, permanent lawn. The area of the garden which is to be sown should receive as little shadow as possible from houses, walls and large trees. Any weeds which are present should be removed by hoeing or tilling before the seed is planted. The sowing area should be worked thoroughly to a good depth to prevent waterlogging. A suitable grass mixture can be made up by garden centres, the formulation depending on how the lawn is to be used and the type of soil. The seed should be sown on a solid and friable seedbed and should then be pressed down by rolling or with the aid of footboards. As long ago as the 13th century, Albertus Magnus* described the laying of an ornamental lawn.

*What measures should be taken after sowing?*

After sowing, a dense turf should be encouraged through regular care and cultivation activities such as fertilization, irrigation and mowing. Lawn weeds usually have a large rooting capacity and are thus able to appropriate the nutrients in the soil; moreover, they remain largely unaffected by mowing but tend to flourish less, the more carefully the lawn is tended. Annual seed-propagated weeds tend to appear mainly in the year of sowing, but these can be eradicated simply by regular mowing. At a later stage, broad-leaved weeds on lawns can be destroyed by applying a hormone-based weed killer. The lawn will be particularly at risk from becoming overgrown with broad-leaved species of weeds if it is not cut regularly.

*Regular cutting is therefore the most important way of caring for a lawn. Mosses frequently flourish in lawns and destroy the turf. What countermeasures can be taken?*

---

* See page 230

Mosses on lawns grow mainly in wet locations. Soil compression or shadowing by overhanging branches are another frequent cause. In these areas, where dew remains on the ground for prolonged periods, small, unobtrusive hand-sized patches of moss begin to form. Especially in acidic soils and soils weakened by nitrogen deficiency, mosses then spread rapidly and choke the grass. Permanent control of mosses without removing these causes will therefore be extremely difficult. A number of moss control agents are available commercially.

*Another troublesome nuisance on lawns are the so-called fairy rings. How do these originate?*

Circles of mushrooms frequently appear on ornamental lawns. These mostly take the form of turf "fairy-rings". The spores of these fungi are carried by the wind. On the part of the lawn where the fungus spore begins to grow, the fungal mycelium spreads out in the shape of a star at a soil depth of up to 25 centimetres. Depending on the weather, the organs of reproduction, the mushrooms, are pushed upwards. These fungi then form the "fairy rings" and are responsible for disseminating the spores. The fungal mycelium continues to spread outwards in the soil when the weather offers favourable conditions.

*And how can they be controlled?*

Because of the deep-lying fungal mycelium and its sideways spread, control of these fairy rings is not without its problems and successful treatment is a difficult business. The results of treatment are often only apparent in the following year. A specially recommended fungicide should be sprayed as control agent. Before applying treatment, it is important that the soil should be sufficiently moistened to a depth of 25 centimetres by rainfall or artificial irrigation. This should be checked beforehand by examining a spadeful of soil. The colonized strips and a surrounding area within a radius of 2 metres should be treated. 5 litres of the prepared formulation should be used for each square metre.

*Although lawns are permanent areas of greenery in gardens and public parks, without regular care they deteriorate rapidly and become unsightly. Can you briefly summarize the most important types of care once again?*

First and foremost, regular mowing of the lawn during the long growth period. Not to be forgotten is fertilization, which should be performed at regular intervals. Also important is to prevent waterlogging and, in prolonged dry periods, to water the lawn in the evening. Timely control measures should be undertaken to keep down voles and moles and to eradicate weeds and "fairy-rings".

*The "English lawn", which has developed from the landscape gardens and parks which originated in Great Britain, is a very special form of lawn achieved by keeping the grass short, for instance by sheep grazing or mechanical mowers. The other form is the meadow, which was important particularly in former times as a tree meadow, being used for the twin purposes of fruit growing and mowing for green fodder and hay. Yet the meadow is also cultured vegetation which can only be maintained if it is mown twice each year, otherwise it becomes overgrown with woodland. Smaller lawns are not suitable for use as meadows, since such surfaces cannot be used continuously for walking and playing.*

## *4. Water as design element in the garden*

*The garden is an important asset to all sections of the population, useful to some for leisure purposes while for others offering a welcome refuge from humdrum occupations. Whereas gardens were once used chiefly for growing fruit and vegetables for the home kitchen, today, replete with flowers, ornamental shrubs and bushes, lawns, fountains, ponds or swimming pools, they have become the focal point of family life in the summer months. Water in particular offers many opportunities for creative garden design. How can water be integrated into the design of a garden?*

Garden pools take many different forms, ranging from the collecting basin for rain water and the pool containing aquatic plants to the children's paddling pool and the swimming pool. Finally, the fountain provides the romantic plashing of water on summer evenings. Yet water in the garden also needs to be cared for.

*How is this best done?*

Wherever flowing water is not available, the freshness and biological activity of the water must be maintained by replenishing, circulation and cleaning. In swimming and paddling pools, this is done by filtering and recirculating the water, and by adding chlorinated substances or new non-chlorinated products to prevent the water becoming spoilt by algae formation or clouding. These additives also prevent bacteria and fungi from breading. In pools containing plants, feed water or circulation by means of fountains promotes oxygen enrichment and thus the biological activity of the water, which is important particularly if it contains toy fish.

*The pool is only one part of the garden, beside which we usually find the terrace or garden seat, surrounded by lawns, flowers and ornamental shrubs. As swimming becomes increasingly popular as a leisure sport, at once a relaxing and health promoting activity, more and more private swimming pools are being installed in gardens. Pure, clear water is doubtless essential for this purpose. How is this achieved?*

Comprehensive care of water includes disinfection of bathing water and algae control. Apart from algae, mould fungi and water bacteria can also occur if insufficient care is given.

*How are swimming pools best cared for?*

With swimming pools, we distinguish between pretreatment and aftertreatment. The empty pool should be thoroughly cleaned and then disinfected with a long-acting solution of a special product based on a quaternery ammonia compound. The pool is then rinsed out with clear water and filled. Immediately after filling, the same preparation is added to the bathing water in the recommended quantities. Chlorinated products with chlorine stabilizers are also used for disinfection. During the bathing season, mechanical filtration of the water should be accompanied by regular use of the necessary additive at the recommended intervals.

*What rules must be observed in caring for ornamental pools and fish ponds?*

In fish ponds, the necessary cleaning out of algae or other contaminants can only be performed mechanically or by replacing the water. Chemical algae control is out of the question, since when the algae die, hydrogen sulphate is formed and oxygen removed from the water, thereby indirectly harming the fish.

*And what methods should be applied in caring for ornamental pools?*

In ornamental pools, the same methods of algae control can be used as for swimming pools, without damaging the plants growing at the edge of the pool. If any underwater plants are present, chemical algae control is not recommended.

*Algae, particularly in damp periods, tend to form a slippery and slimy layer on terraces and paved pathways. What can the amateur gardener or housewife do about this?*

Control of algae on paved pathways and terraces should preferably be of a preventive nature. At regular intervals, an algae control agent in the prescribed solution should be sprayed or applied with a watering can, using a formulation dose of not less than 1/2 litre per square metre. It is important to apply products which do not damage adjacent lawns or flower beds.

*Proven methods thus now exist for keeping swimming and ornamental pools in gardens and also paved pathways and terraces permanently clean. With all of these measures, it is essential to comply with the application instructions to protect man, animals and plants from hazard. Every gardening enthusiast can obtain detailed information on these measures from his local garden centre.*

## 5. Preserving the health of conifers

*Over the past few years, infestation with spruce aphids in our gardens and public parks has greatly increased, necessitating several control measures throughout the year. What is the reason for this?*

The mild weather in recent years without periods of pronounced cold has greatly encouraged the activity of this aphid species, since aphids also survive in winter at low temperatures. If heavy snowfall and severe frosts occur during wintertime, the adults cannot survive, and the aphids have to hatch again from their eggs in spring. Special vigilance is therefore needed when the growing period begins. Trees mainly attacked are the sitka spruce and in this country, particularly the Colorado spruce and the Colorado blue spruce. Also affected are the Norway spruce and the Serbian or omorika spruce.

*Is the damage easy to recognize?*

The aphids concentrate their sucking activities on the completed needles in the lower, shadowed part of the trees. The needles become spotted and drop prematurely. Attack spreads from below and from the inside of the tree and continues upwards and outwards. The possible extent of the damage thus cannot be identified when the attack first begins.

*What is the life cycle of this aphid species?*

The spruce or sitka spruce aphid lives on the different species of spruce without changing hosts. It overwinters as a winter egg or in mild zones as a wingless aphid and propagates up to late autumn by viviparity of the young aphids.

*What can be done to prevent this attack?*

The most effective means of control is timely spraying in the spring with late winter insecticidal sprays containing mineral oil. During the rest of the year, when the temperatures are higher and shooting begins, a systemic insecticide should be used.

*How can the gardening enthusiast identify the attack?*

The presence of attack should best be looked for on the lower twigs in the interior of the tree. If appropriate, the branches should be struck vigorously and the aphids collected on a piece of white cardboard held below the branches to check for attack. Many years of experience have shown that in our climatic zone, treatment must be given several times each year.

*What should we know about controlling the Eastern spruce gall aphid?*

The overwintering adult insects, which initiate the coming generations of the Eastern spruce gall aphid, can occasionally be found on the tips of twigs of spruce trees, mostly of the Norway spruce, on the underside of the twigs near the buds. These gall aphids are covered with white waxy wool. They are responsible for the pineapple shaped galls, which later become wood-hard and brown, which disfigure the trees when present in large numbers.

*What means of control are available?*

The Eastern spruce gall aphid is controlled in spring by applying late winter insecticidal sprays containing mineral oil. The twigs must be very thoroughly wetted, particularly from below, since the mites are extremely well protected by the white waxy wool which grows ever thicker. Repeated treatment after shooting with a product specific to gall-forming aphids enhances the success of control.

*Pest control in conifers is important to preserve the health of these valuable trees both in nurseries and conifer forests. The amateur gardener must also protect the valuable conifers in his garden, since attack by pests can damage these trees to the point of total needle drop and perishing of the plants. When applying these measures, it is important to comply with the Order on the Protection of Bees, in other words, flowering plants in adjacent beds must not be wetted by the spray formulation.*

## 6. Flowers and ornamental plants

*Not everyone has a garden, but everyone enjoys the sight of flowers and ornamental plants. With rising standards of living, expectations in this respect have also increased. Specially cut flowers, windows decorated with pot plants, gardens filled with a large variety of plants are now an important factor in maintaining our quality of life. Over the past 20 years, annual sales of flowers and ornamentals have increased from about 10 DM to 110 DM per head of population.*

*The cultivation of flowers and ornamentals has recently undergone a considerable increase in the Federal Republic. The cultivation area under glass is 3,000 hectares and outdoors 4,000 hectares. This produce is also imported in substantial quantities from neighbouring countries, as the requirement for flowers and ornamentals as decoration for private dwellings and gardens, but also public parks and gardens in rural communities and cities continues to grow. Where do we find most of the growing centres for flower and ornamental plants?*

The location of these special enterprises is governed less by climatic and soil conditions than by the presence of marketing and sales outlets. Cultivation is thus mainly concentrated on the outskirts of built-up areas.

*The production of flowers and ornamentals under glass is highly intensive and requires much capital . What is the current situation?*

Because production is so costly, the manager of horticultural enterprises must organize his production techniques as far as possible to avoid losses of revenue and to guarantee profitability. At present, the very existence of under glass cultivation is threatened by the energy crisis and high fuel oil prices and is experiencing intense competition from more cheaply producing countries abroad.

*The oil crisis has had far-reaching consequences for under glass cultivation. As result, large sales are more important than ever to maintain the profitability of flower and ornamental cultivation. However it is not only the producer and dealer who, subject to different considerations and constraints relating to the production and marketing of the produce he offers, determines the state of the market, but also and to an even greater extent the purchaser and the demand he generates. Which flowers and ornamental plants enjoy special popularity?*

Flowers which are especially favoured are carnations and chrysanthemums, as well as roses, tulips and frisias. Anthurias and orchids have recently also enjoyed increasing popularity. Among the pot plants, particularly favoured are begonia elatior hybrids, pot chrysanthemums, azaleas, ericaceae, cyclamen and green and foliage plants. Popular balcony and garden plants among the summer blooms are geraniums, petunias and fuchsias, and for autumn and winter planting asters and pansies.

*The cultivation of flowers and ornamental plants on a commercial and amateur basis is both labour and capital demanding. Gardens must therefore be tended with particular care. How significant is crop protection in this context?*

The importance of crop protection as a production factor increases the more intensively growing is practised. The application of crop protection measures for flowers and ornamental plants is therefore specially important. The prime concern is to control the numerous insect pests; in greenhouses and flower shops, spider mites, aphids and white fly are pests which must be treated immediately and, with persisting attack, on a regular basis.

Also important is the control of fungal diseases such as mildew and botrytis or leaf and stem rot as well as various other leaf spot diseases and soil fungi.

*What aspects of crop protection should claim the gardener's particular attention?*

As well as the effects of the compounds applied, plant tolerance is a major problem in view of the large number of species and varieties of plants which are cultivated. As is generally the case in plant cultivation, the early development stage is decisively important, particularly in flowers and ornamentals. Accordingly, preventive crop protection must be given special emphasis.

*The multiplicity of species and types of flowers and ornamentals which we see today derives from the exchange of flora between all climatic zones of the earth. Consequently, they make many different demands on location and climate. The commercial and amateur gardener must therefore possess wide specialized knowledge to guarantee the healthy growth of his plants.*

## 7. Culinary herbs*

*Throughout the ages, the kitchen garden has been used to grow both vegetables and fruit and culinary herbs and spices. The value of our food depends not only on the nutrients it contains. Also important is the appetizing taste of food, its pleasant aroma and attractive appearance. The interplay of all these factors is essential for the wholesomeness of our food and also for our well-being. The culinary arts must play an important part in man's nutrition?*

One of the greatest skills involved in the culinary arts is to prepare food in such a way that most of its nourishing constituents are preserved and its appetizing taste enhanced. Mastery of cooking skills is essential for this purpose. These enable us to serve our food in a variety of appetizing ways. Tasty food needs to be prepared in such a way that the natural aromatic and gustatory substances are preserved or first made accessible. Spices should heighten, but not swamp the native flavour of the dish.

*What in fact are spices?*

Spices are parts of plants which we add to our food and which through their active ingredients influence its aroma, taste or colour, making it more attractive and wholesome. The most important active ingredients in our culinary herbs and spices are ethereal oils, bitters, tanning agents, glycosides, alkaloids, resins, ferments, proteins, fats, oils, vitamins, minerals and colourants.

*What spices are known to us?*

Spice plants can be divided into two groups according to the way they are used: The so-called true spices which are added in desiccated form to food, which include pepper, cinnamon and cloves, and the vegetable spices or spice herbs which are used mainly in their fresh form in the kitchen.

The distinction between spices and food is therefore not a strict one. Many plants can be used equally well as pure spices and as vegetables. Celery, leaks

* Vegetable and fruit species and spice and medicinal plants are described in Section II "Food crops in agriculture and horticulture".

and onions for example serve both purposes. Salt, sugar und vinegar do not come under the heading of "spices", but in culinary terms belong to the group of taste inducing substances.

*Spices and herbs must have played a significant role since ancient times?*

The history of culinary herbs and spices is closely associated with the history of medicine and pharmacy. We cannot state with certainty how long plants or their parts have been used as spices. Since in most cases they also have medicinal properties, it can be assumed that they were also used to treat diseases.

The most ancient body of knowledge relating to such plants dates from the third millenium B.C. and is contained in the cuneiform writings of the Sumerians of Mesopotamia. From ancient Egyptian inscriptions we also know that coriander and mint were cultivated in Egypt from 1200 to 600 B.C. Spice gardens and spice yards are mentioned in the Old Testament. We even find instructions for their cultivation.

*What was the situation in the Middle Ages?*

The Benedictine monks did much to propagate the use of culinary herbs and spices. From their affiliates in the Mediterranean region, they brought them to this country and planted them in their monastery gardens. From within these confines, they soon spread throughout the whole of Central Europe.

Indian and Indonesian spices were brought by the Arabs to Southern Europe in the early Middle Ages. During the crusades, many Europeans became acquainted with and learned the value of oriental spices. Thereafter, a lively trade in spices developed. The most important trading ports were Genoa, Naples and above all Venice.

*Why did the tropical spices, and particularly pepper, gain such rapid acceptance in Europe at this time?*

The rapid spread of spices in the late Middle Ages was favoured by the circumstance that at this time there were few ways of keeping meat and fish fresh for prolonged periods. To make them palatable at all, it was necessary to disguise their taste and smell with the strongest of spices. Domestic herb cultivation suffered under the increasing import of tropical spices. Nevertheless, in the 16th and 17th centuries, seed fennel, marjoram, holy thistle, anise and coriander were grown extensively throughout Central Europe.

*What is the situation today?*

In recent years, views on what constitutes healthy nutrition have changed. Given modern man's mainly sedentary lifestyle with its lack of physical exercise, it is now thought that high-calorie foods with few vitamins, such as sugar and fats, can harm the human organism. This imbalance must therefore be compensated by offering vitamin-rich food, fresh vegetables, salads and culinary herbs and spices.

*What importance has the "herb patch in the garden"?*

Only those spice plants should be grown in the domestic garden which are used fresh every day in the kitchen, such as parsley, chives, chervil, celery, dill, lovage and marjoram.

Grain spices such as anise seed, caraway and coriander are of course most conveniently purchased from the dealer, since they can be cultivated more cheaply and in equally good quality on a larger scale.

In the domestic garden, it is naturally also possible to grow those herbs for which there is a personal preference. Here too it is possible to meet the plants' special demands for light and moisture. Fresh herbs are always more aromatic than those which are dried, deep frozen or salted.

*Finally, what practical tips can be given on how to use spices?*

There is no generally valid rule as to how spices should be used. Seasoning is a matter of habit and preference. Proper seasoning is not a question of quality, but rather the combination of suitable spices: They should enhance and refine, but never alter the original taste of food.

## *8. Illustrations from the garden*

Pages 194 to 197, which relate to Section VIII, contain illustrations of the palace garden at Brühl as an example of Baroque garden style, species of roses and also diseases and pests on garden plants.

The garden parterre, laid out in 1730 and reconstructed 200 years later, part of the extensive Baroque gardens and parks of Schloß Augustusburg in Brühl, the former summer residence of the Elector of Cologne, in the late Baroque style.

The rose, as queen of flowers, is an adornment to the garden, but the various rose species require great care and attention.

Rose mildew, caused by the fungus Sphaerotheca pannosa, covers everything with a powdery coating.

Black spot on roses is caused by the fungus Marssonina rosae. This causes leaf drop.

Rust on roses is caused by the fungus Phragmidium mucronatum.

Rose aphids suck the leaves, peduncles and buds which then die.

Heavy infestation with rose leafhoppers causes leaf drop.

The common pine aphid can also be found at the base of the short, two-needled shoots, which die due to their sucking activity.

The Eastern spruce gall aphid causes formation of galls in which the aphids develop.

The sitka spruce aphid (Liosomaphis abietina) is a sucking pest which greatly damages the needles.

# IX. Foundations of food production

Whereas in former times agriculture was the principal occupation of the population and was practised to supply individual requirements, in the industrial age agriculture is one element within the national economy based on division of labour. In earlier times, the farmer's family produced the food and drink they needed themselves; most of their own clothing, household equipment and implements were also manufactured on the farm. Urban households were also much more self-sufficient than they are today. Agriculture was only a source of raw produce for food and clothing, and its processing, preparation and preservation was done by the urban housewife and household staff. At the beginning of the 19th century, 80 per cent of the economically active population were still engaged in agriculture, 8 per cent in the trades and 12 per cent in the service sector. Today, only 5 per cent of economically active persons are engaged in agriculture and forestry, 50 per cent are employed in industry and 45 per cent are active in the trades and service industries.

This process of industrialization has also produced a situation in which agriculture can no longer be regarded as the sole source of food supply. Many branches of the economy are now wholly or partly engaged in satisfying the population's demand for food. Today, most of the produce which leaves a farm consists of raw materials which only become suitable for consumption after further processing and preparation. However, agricultural production can only commence when essential operating resources such as agricultural machinery, fertilizers and animal feedstuffs, fuels and crop protectants are purchased from other sectors of the national economy and when a range of services such as customer advice, credits and after sales service are utilized.

The increasing interdependence of agriculture and other areas of the national economy has led to the evolution, between the farm and urban household, of a constantly growing sector concerned with the preparation, processing and distribution of agricultural raw products through the food industry, catering and trades, a development which is manifested most clearly in the decreasing proportion of producers who participate in the price to the final consumer. This extension of the marketing sector is also encouraged by the functional depletion of urban catering which in extreme cases has become nothing more than a facility for warming up convenience foods. As in agriculture, so in the urban household, this surrender of functions has been accompanied by a release of formerly employed work force for other areas of the economy.

The interdependence of the various branches of the national economy is now studied with the aid of input-output analysis, a system developed by the American political economist Wassily Leontief (*1906). The principle underlying this approach is that in all branches of the national economy, the value or qualitiy of processed resources (input) is equal to the quantity of goods produced (output). These interdependencies have been calculated for many different branches of the economy and countries and have also been established for the interrelationship of agriculture and the other areas of national production in the Federal Republic. We are interested particularly in the input relationship of the chemical industry with agriculture. For the business year 1980/81 for example, at a gross production value for agriculture of 52.1 thousand million DM in the Federal Republic, deliveries from the chemical industry to agriculture were valued at 5.5 thousand million DM. After crop protectants to the value of 800 million DM, this total is made up primarily by fertilizers.

The foundations of food production for the growing population in the 19th century were substantially improved by advances in science. Progress in the different fields of agriculture throughout the world contributed greatly to this process. One of the greatest of these achievements was the discovery by Justus von Liebig (1803—1873) that plant nutrition is not taken from humus, in other words parts of plants rotting in the soil, but from nitrogen, potassium, phosphoric acid and other minerals which the plant takes up from the earth through its roots and converts to sugar, starch, protein and fat through photosynthesis in its leaves. The use of mineral fertilizers has led to yield increases in all cultivated crops. Thus in Japan, where the consumption of mineral fertilizer is higher than in Western European countries, rice yields currently run at 5.6 tons per hectare. In India, Indonesia and Burma, however, the rice yields are only 2 to 3 tons per hectare, since mineral fertilizer is used to a much lesser extent.

In addition to increasing yields per unit area through the use of mineral fertilizers, which was introduced in 19th century Europe in an attempt to banish hunger, in America at this time another development had been in progress. This was the introduction of mechanization into agricultural production. Through the use of steel ploughs, mowing machines and automatic harvesters, farming of large areas became possible. The American wheat empire however was only built up when in 1865 the protective tariffs in England were abolished and wheat could enter Europe unhindered. France at this period was also unable to feed its population without American wheat.

Together with fertilization and the introduction of mechanization, plant breeding also helped to continuously increase food production. The breeding of new varieties of wheat however not only raised yields per unit area, but also made it possible, for example, to cultivate spring wheat in Canada which ripened in 100 days, taking advantage of the short growing period. Plant breeding has completely transformed the map of the world, since no month now passes without a wheat harvest somewhere in the world: In January, Australia, New Zealand and Argentina gather in a harvest; in February and March, India and Uruguay; in April North Africa, Mexico and Persia; in May Spain, China, Florida and Texas; in June California, Italy, Southern France and Japan; in July the Ukraine and Canada; in August England, Norway, Sweden, Denmark, Germany, Belgium and Holland; in September Scotland; in October Russia; in November Peru and South Africa and in December finally, Abyssinia, the country which we can regard as the original homeland of wheat. By using his reason, man has become capable of supplying himself with food anywhere in the world. Like wheat, other plants such as potatoes and maize have been spread over the face of the earth by man's creative hand.

Before long, however, the vast monocultures of wheat, potatoes and rice, to name but a few, suffered setbacks. Fungal diseases and pests threatened to destroy entire harvests and in some cases brought cultivation of the affected crops to a complete halt. Very soon, therefore, at the end of the 19th century, intensive research was initiated to identify the cause of the diseases and define means for their control. Today, chemical crop protection is used to secure yields and quality in crop growing.

This is the situation in which we find ourselves today. Anyone who does not protect his seed corn by dressing, anyone who does not spray his apples, potatoes and beets in good time, will only harvest what the pests leave behind. Even today, no less than 25 to 35 per cent of potential world harvests are lost because of insect pests, plant diseases and weed infestation.

Every specialized discipline within agricultural production is dependent on having new findings first tested in experimental stations under controllable conditions, before they can be recommended and generally introduced in practice.

Today's agricultural experimental stations, which are now more or less taken for granted, were however only established within the last 100 to 150 years. Their founding coincided with the inception of the scientific age in Europe at the beginning of the 19th century. In former centuries, new crops and methods for their cultivation were introduced by way of monastery, palace and botanical gardens. Far-sighted personalities, world travellers, learned academics and princes were the pioneers of progress. Often, hardship was the most effective teacher, and yet for example the introduction of potatoes to Europe, despite precise instructions for their cultivation, encountered numerous difficulties and much time passed until they ceased to be a rarity from the botanical garden and were accepted as an important staple food.

The ending of the old three-crop rotation system by cropping the fallow land in summer with clover, fodder or root crops through the introduction of the modern crop rotation on arable land, combined with the discovery of mineral fertilization and the beginning of monocultivation of important crops such as cereals, sugar cane or cotton on extensive, continuous areas in different regions of the earth, brought with it a systematization of agrarian production as a whole. Albrecht Thaer, Heinrich von Thünen und Justus von Liebig, to name but three of the grand old men of agricultural research, laid the groundwork for a worldwide, increasingly specialized and interlinked science of agriculture.

Disputes between scholars, for instance regarding the theory of plant nutrition — now the humus, now the mineral theory — increasingly established the experiment as the chief method of proving the validity of a principle. *Argumentum et experimentum,* proof and experiment, was demanded by Roger Bacon as long ago as the 13th century. This scholar recognized the value and importance of *"scientia experimentalis",* experimental science, as research in the natural sciences was known at that period. The experiment — as referred to by Johann Wolfgang von Goethe in one of his essays — became the "mediator between subject and object" or, as expressed in the writings of Leonardo da Vinci, science should prove its conclusions by means of a decisive experiment.

Whereas a physical or chemical experiment can be performed under strictly controllable and above all repeatable conditions, an agricultural experiment must take account of many different factors, such as soil and weather behaviour, which can influence the experimental findings. The most important principle of experimental method for agricultural science is therefore: One experiment proves nothing, only corresponding results from several parallel experiments create the basis for meaningful results. The repetition of an experiment in space and time, that is in several locations or in several successive years, is thus essential if far-reaching conclusions are to be drawn from the results. This fact cannot be repeated often or emphatically enough.

The development of modern agriculture is therefore inconceiveable without the experiment. It may sound strange that one of the most important initiators of modern experimental crop cultivation research, Matthieu Tillet, a French scholar, in attempting to prove that bunt of wheat is transmitted by fungal spores, was obliged to convince the sceptical scientific world by means of experiments which were conducted on a chessboard pattern with numerous repetitions.

This realization that examples provide a stimulus, that experiments deliver proof and encourage imitation has led to the establishment of numerous experimental stations and farms over the last hundred years, which have become important connecting links between theoretical science and its practical application.

Today's principles of food production are based on many years of scientific study throughout the world. New knowledge and recommendations can now only become generally adopted in practical agriculture if their correctness has first been subjected to rigorous investigation in experimental trials.

## *1. Types of farm management*

*Today's strained food situation in many developing countries raises the question as to why it is not possible, as we in the industrialized world are doing, for these countries to close the gaps in their food supply by increasing their agricultural production. What are the most important principles for achieving high yields and for intensive crop production?*

Feeding the growing population in many parts of the world, in the industrialized and developing countries, would not be possible without the fundamental changes in the principles of agrarian production which have occurred over the last 150 years.

*What is the nature of these changes?*

High yield increases first became possible with the introduction of agrochemistry. In other words: Scientific discoveries from the field of chemistry have revolutionized fertilization and the protection of plants against various kinds of environmental damage.

*Can you expand on this?*

The principles of cereal production which were formerly applied, involving the intercalation of a fallow period, were based on the law of statics. To maintain the fertility of the soil, more should not be extracted than is returned to it. The available commercial fertilizers such as stable manure, semi-liquid and liquid manure set natural limits to these endeavours. The first progress came when fallow ground was cropped in the summer with clover, known as the "green fallow", for growing feedstuffs or green manure plants. The major advance however is associated with the name of Justus von Liebig who, by introducing mineral fertilization with lime, potassium salts and phosphates as well as nitrogen fertilizers, was able to compensate through balanced fertilization for high rates of nutrient withdrawal from the soil resulting from high yields.

*This must also have set many other changes in motion?*

Mineral fertilization set the pace for a general reform and intensification of agricultural production. Advances in plant breeding and mechanization including sprinkling and irrigation should particularly be mentioned. Over the past few decades, chemical crop protection has become an increasingly essential factor in safeguarding harvests.

*Although in spite of these tremendous advances and high yield increases we have not yet succeeded in banishing hunger from the world, this form of intensive agricultural production continues to attract criticism from various quarters. What alternative forms of agricultural production could be possible today?*

As in all spheres of activity, in agriculture too we find trends and counter-trends. Today's agricultural production, which is based on the scientific principles of plant nutrition through mineral fertilization and the preservation of plants by chemical crop protection, and can now be regarded as at once the classical and the progressive approach, is faced with the alternative "biological-dynamic" approach to farming.

*What is the essence of this method of farming?*

This method of farming derives from the doctrines of the philosopher Rudolf Steiner, who, influenced among other things by the unhappy aftermath of the First World War, appealed for what he described as a "tripartite organization of the social organism". According to this system, economic life should be organized on a basis of complete freedom with the state, producer and consumer coexisting independently. The principles of this system of mangement as they relate to agriculture were first expounded by Rudolf Steiner in a series of lectures given over Whitsun 1924 at the Koberwitz estate of Count Keyserlingk near Breslau. According to these ideas, the cultivation of food for man, animals and plants depends not so much on chemical-material relationships, but rather and to a much greater degree on the dynamic effects of forces and radiation. Steiner distinguishes between cosmic forces which draw plants upwards and influence primarily the quality of products of the soil, and terrestrial forces which broaden the leaf and influence the yield level.

*How are these forces to be used?*

These forces are to be utilized for the development of plants with the aid of accumulators or biological-dynamic products and of fertilizers and crop protectants, which should be applied whenever necessary to promote yields or quality. Planting of crops should also take into account the movements of the planets. For instance, cereal species are full moon plants which need to be sown under the light of a full moon.

*Did this theory of farming find any practical acceptance?*

After the First World War, a number of relatively large farms embraced this new theory in an attempt to cut down their expenditure on materials such as fertilizers and crop protectants, and so to reduce their indebtedness.

For ideological reasons, this mode of farming was declared to be "farming according to the laws of nature" in the "Third Reich" in 1940. This approach envisaged that, after the victorious conclusion of the war, the European-Asiatic economic area would be farmed according to the principles of agrochemistry to secure food supplies and, in the so-called "Old Reich", the biological-dynamic method would be applied. Farmers were to be assisted in changing over to this method in the "Old Reich" by means of tax relief, higher prices for agricultural produce and other forms of financial subsidy.

*How is this approach regarded today?*

A comparison of yields obtained in biological-dynamic and agrochemical farming shows that, in biological-dynamic farming without mineral fertilization and crop protection, lower yields are achieved, for example 25 to 45 per cent less wheat, 35 to 50 per cent less potatoes and 30 to 50 per cent less sugar beet. Even for rye, an undemanding species of cereal, the yield loss is 20 to 40 per cent. Despite a higher labour input for the care and cultivation of crops, biological farming produces distinctly lower yields and therefore higher prices must be charged for these biological harvest products for economic reasons.

*What other systems of "biological" farming are there?*

Another form is the organic-biological cultivation method championed by Müller-Rusch. Cosmic influences play no part in this system.

This approach is also characterized by a general rejection of the methods of agrochemistry and thus of the practice of mineral fertilization and chemical crop protection.

*And what is the quality of the harvested produce?*

Long-term comparative studies have shown that no differences in quality exist between products of normal and "biological" farming.

In the strained food supply situation, in which one third of the world population is suffering from malnutrition or starving, everything humanly possible must be done to ease this distress and to increase agricultural yields by all available means. It is thus urgently necessary to utilize all new knowledge and scientific advances in agricultural production. No viable alternatives to this are known at the present time.

## 2. History of agriculture and arable farming

*Man and his development depend to a great extent on his living space, in other words his environment, which is largely determined by the prevailing climate. Although wars, conflicts between human beings, proverbially spark off many developments, man's deeds and actions have been equally influenced by climatic conditions. Has climate also determined the development and spread of agriculture in our own region as the basis of our food supply?*

Following upon the era of the hunters and gatherers, which had persisted for

500,000 years in the Palaeolithic and Mesolithic Ages, after the end of the last Ice Age, which lasted from 75 000 to 8000 B.C., the first farming culture developed in Central Europe around 5000 B.C. Named after the typical strip-like decorations of the clay vessels typical of this culture, it is known as the age of the "band ceramicists". Within a short time and to an astonishingly uniform extent, these tribes colonized areas of loess soil extending from Moravia to the Southern Netherlands and as far as the Paris basin.

*What crops were grown here during this period 7000 years ago?*

Excavations in Cologne-Lindenthal commenced in 1929 and the investigations conducted over the last 10 years in the loess area of the Aldenhoven plateau around Jülich have yielded fundamental knowledge about the band ceramic culture in Germany. Excavations in these and other areas have revealed the following food plants grown in that period: One-grained wheat, emmer wheat, two-grained spelt, poly-rowed barley in the form of naked barley and spelt, peas, lentils, wheat, flax, millet, poppy, rye, spelt and oats. Also interesting is that the weeds we know today were also present at that time, such as brome grass, white goosefoot, black bindweed, dock-leaved persicaria, redshank and knotgrass. Also present were nipplewort, chamomile, cleavers, foxtail, chickweed, fumitory and pennycress as well as hempnettle and field thistle.

*So an astonishingly large number of food plants were cultivated at the start of the arable farming period in Central Europe. Many of the weed species we know today, some of which were also used for food or other purposes in this period, have therefore been found in the band ceramicist settlements. What kinds of fruit and other useful plants were found?*

Altogether, six species of wild fruit were found, namely apple, raspberry, hazelnut, cornel cherry, wild rose and wild grapevine, and other useful plants which have been identified include dyeing plants for dyeing linen and wool, dyer's mignonette, a species of Reseda, which was used for yellow, white goosefoot for red, dwarf elder for blue and marsh bedstraw for red and yellow. Dyer's woad, known to us from the "Waidmarkt" or woad market in Cologne, which was used for dyeing textiles blue up until modern times, is only known to have been used in Central Europe from the time of the Roman Empire.

*Crops were therefore grown in this period not only for food and clothing, as is demonstrated by flax growing, but also for other purposes, as we may conclude for instance from the dyeing plants. How did the farming areas of this period come into existence?*

The band ceramicists, the peoples of the Neolithic period, were the first colonists of Central Europe. They originated from the Danube area in South East Europe. On arriving in Central Europe they radically remodelled the land they found by clearing the forests, and, in a relatively short time, agricultural land with animal husbandry was created.

*What was the climate at this time?*

At the time when arable farming was first established, warm summers and winters with heavy rainfall prevailed for a period of 3500 years, a climate favourable for arable farming. Following this, from 4000 to 3500 B.C., came a period of extremely heavy rainfall from which the legend of the great flood originates. Particularly significant at this time was the "optimal climate" of the Roman period, a time of warmth and low rainfall from 300 B.C. to 400 A.D., during which numerous cultivated plants and weeds from the Mediterranean area and in particular vine growing were introduced into the Roman provinces of Germania.

*At the turn of the era, arable farming in our region thus became more intensive?*

Following the time when the soil was worked and weeds controlled by means of hoeing, in the Bronze Age the wooden hook plough drawn by a team of oxen entered the service of crop growing and, in the Iron Age, the iron ploughshare. Where formerly crops had been cultivated in 'celtic fields' measuring 1000 to 2000 square metres, in the Roman period farms of up to 90 hectares were established in the German territories with individual field sections larger than before. The most significant invention of this period however was the mouldboard plough, which first made it possible to turn the soil to free it from weeds. For almost 2000 years now, the mouldboard plough has been the most important soil working implement in the humid climatic regions, not least because of its effectiveness in controlling weeds.

*What was the situation in the Middle Ages?*

Following the favourable farming period of the Roman Age, from 400 to 750 A.D., there followed several centuries of cold climate with heavy rainfall, as result of which agriculture suffered reverses. Harvests were no longer sufficient to meet the demand for food and the migration of the Germanic peoples to the south began. After this, from 800 to 1200, came a very favourable period, known as the "Middle Ages optimum", with mean annual temperatures which were 1 to 1.5 ° C higher than today, as result of which vine growing spread to northwest Europe and England. This period was particularly propitious for agriculture.

*What developments in agriculture which occurred from 800, the time of Charlemagne, can be regarded as particularly important?*

The general introduction of the three-crop rotation with division of the land into three fields, which were planted with winter barley and summer barley, the third field always being left fallow, led to an intensification of agriculture. The fallow period was introduced as a year of rest and regeneration of the soil, during which mechanical weed control was performed several times.

An especially significant advance around the year 1000 was the introduction of the horse as draught animal into agriculture. The horse was superior to the ox by virtue of its speed and endurance. Field work could therefore be carried out more quickly and on time, soil cultivation was improved and the iron harrow, which was invented around this time, could be used for weed control.

Particularly worthy of mention are the agricultural and horticultural model farms of the Cistercians established in the 12th century. This religious order in particular exerted a decisively positive influence on arable farming and horticulture in our territories over a period of 600 to 700 years.

*How did the climate and its influence on arable farming develop in the Middle Ages and in the modern era?*

Further developments in agriculture from 1200 were not favoured by climatic conditions, and working the land became more difficult. The period from 1200 to 1400 is regarded as the climatic turning point of the late Middle Ages with its high rainfall and storms and land erosion on the North Sea Coast caused by storm tides. The years around 1350 were catastrophic with their cold summers, crop failures and migration from the land, intensified by the outbreak of plague in Europe. Also to be mentioned is the period from 1550 to 1700, referred to historically as the "Lesser Ice Age" with mean temperatures 1 ° C lower than today. The severe winters experienced at this time are depicted for example in the paintings of Breughel. This era also witnessed the first great wave of emigration to the newly discovered continents.

*Man was oppressed by wars and plagues throughout this time, and the yeoman farmer was also affected by these events, although exceptions such as the "Weser Renaissance", an expression of prosperity deriving from successful cereal cultivation with high incomes in times of rising prices, were still possible. Only with the coming of the modern era, however, did general improvements come about in every sphere?*

Agricultural development over the subsequent centuries up to the present time is characterized by innovations. The ending of the agricultural conceptions of the Middle Ages, with its compulsory rotation and three-field farming, and the agricultural reforms of the 18th and 19th century, radically altered farming techniques. The new land use and crop rotation system, using fallow land by growing clover as a "green fallow" in summer and cultivating root crops such as beets and potatoes or growing fodder plants, spread from Flanders and England throughout the whole of Europe. Frederick the Great also endeavoured to introduce the English system of intensive crop rotation farming. While in the 19th century scientific discoveries such as the principles of plant nutrition became widely accepted and introduced into practical agriculture, the requirement of profitability of the individual farm and the various branches of agriculture as a function of climate and location, advocated by Johann Heinrich von Thünen, was adopted as the central tenet of economic activity.

*Arable farming has thus been the basis of food production in our region for 7000 years. From the very beginning, the farmer has attempted, allowing for climate and location, to produce food for himself and others. Technical advances in today's economy which is based on division of labour have led to a high level of development of agriculture in the industrialized countries. It must however be remembered that in many countries throughout the world, agriculture is still at a stage of development equivalent to that which we practised in ages long past, and beyond which we have greatly progressed.*

# X. Developments and tasks in agriculture

The most epoch-making events in world development are generally considered to be the first and second "industrial revolution": the first through the introduction of the "machine" in the 18th and 19th centuries, and the second in the second half of the 20th century in the form of "automation" in all areas of industrial production and daily life.

Another event in human history has however had much more far-reaching consequences, namely the "neolithic revolution", or the transition to cultivating useful plants. The last ice age ended about 10 000 years ago. At this time, in the early Neolithic period, the age of man began, when probably somewhere in the Near East, the change from collecting to cultivating specially valuable plants must have occurred. With the cultivation of useful plants, a fundamentally new period in man's development began. Up to that time, man's fate and very existence had depended on what edible things he was able to find on his lengthy hunting expeditions. Even the so-called "harvest peoples" only understood how to use what the earth offered them when conditions were particularly favourable and without any intervention on their own part, and they were merely consumers, beneficiaries of what nature produced spontaneously. The cultivation of useful plants and their tending introduced a completely new element into the history of life on earth: For the first time, a being appeared, namely Homo sapiens, who consciously and systematically produced the food he needed. By eliminating the competition from other plant species which disturbed the yield development of the plants he desired, by cultivating the soil and finally by spreading ash from his fires and animal manure, he greating increased the yields of the wild plants. While in the palaeolithic period the population density is believed to have been 1 person per 50 to 100 square kilometres, in the neolithic period this number rose to 1 to 2 people per square kilometre. The "neolithic revolution", the systematic cultivation of useful plants, therefore led to a hundred or perhaps thousand-fold increase in the earth's population during this period, due to the dramatic improvement in food supply. The major significance of this event can be judged from the fact that the first "industrial revolution" in the 19th century in the major industries of Europe resulted in an only 10-fold increase in the population.

The original wild plants underwent a basic change over the millenia, in that the best plants were always chosen and thus a form of "selection" took place, which culminated in modern breeding methods based on the laws of inheritance discovered by Gregor Mendel. The cultivated plant differs essentially from the original wild plant by virtue of its "Gigas growth" and its "allometric growth". Gigas forms are plants in which the organs to be harvested have become greatly enlarged as result of selection by man, as for example apples, cucumbers and beans, and also cereal grains, which are much larger than those of wild plants. The same also applies to the vegetative organs, and so for example the leaves of many cultivated forms of cabbage are greatly enlarged compared to those of wild cabbage. A similar situation obtains with root crops. Gigas growth thus occurs in all organs of the plant, and Charles Darwin discovered Gigas growth to be the most important characteristic of cultivated plants. Not only Gigas growth, but also "allometric growth" of cultivated plants is decisive for today's high yield levels; in other words, the organs of plants desired by man show better growth than the other plant organs. This principle of allometric growth even results in a situation where the desired parts of the crop to be harvested also develop better than the unwanted parts. Thus for example in wild tomatoes the fruit coat or pericarp and the partition of the fruit valves are very thin, but in cultivated tomatoes these parts are highly developed as fruit flesh.

In addition to Gigas growth and allometric growth, another fundamental characteristic of the cultivated plant is its more or less reduced "vitality" compared to the wild plant. The consequence of this is the inability of many cultivated plants to survive outside the artificial environment created for them by man and without man's direct assistance. The loss of its natural means of protection, such as bitter substances, awns and thorns exposes the cultivated plant to attack from enemies which the wild plant had been able to repel by virtue of these defensive features. Finally, the reduced vitality of cultivated plants is attributable not least to the fact that abnormalities and pathological features, in other words signs of disease, have served as the selection characteristic in plants, as for example the fleshy exuberance of the fruit set in cauliflower.

From all these considerations, it becomes apparent how important crop protection is for present-day cultivation of our crops, as a means of warding off diseases, pests and food competitors with the aid of mechanical and chemical measures applied by the farmer, or in other words, the crop producer. Whereas in past millenia and centuries man confined himself to collecting pests, a method still employed in underdeveloped countries, and to pulling up weeds, the competitors for food, in order to increase and safeguard the yields from crops, nowadays more modern and labour-saving methods are applied. Over the past 75 years, the most important of these methods has been chemical crop protection. The diseases, pests or weeds which threaten the plants are controlled by spraying an active chemical substance in aqueous solution or by dusting. The most important requirement for this treatment is that the preparations used should control the pests reliably and durably, without harming the development of the plant and without representing any health hazard for man, either when the agent is applied or when the harvested produce is subsequently consumed. The vital importance of crop protection today can be judged from the fact that at present about 25 to 35 per cent of the potential world harvest is still being destroyed by pests, diseases and weeds, and for many different reasons. The most important of these is the lack of specialist training: The highest yields and most intensive crop protection measures are found in the highly developed industrialized countries.

With reference to modern crop protection it should not go unmentioned that the large yield increases have only been possible due to the results of research pursued by the chemical industry throughout the world over the last three decades. For instance, it was only after the Second World War that the organophosphate compounds were introduced onto the market as crop protectants. The possibilities which modern organic chemistry has also opened up for crop protection are evident from the fact alone that the structural formula developed by Gerhard Schrader, an active basic principle of all organophosphate compounds, has given access to 25 million substituents potentially useful as insecticides.

The results achieved by crop protection research play a major role in increasing the profitability of individual agricultural and horticultural enterprises by raising yields and securing harvests, while at the same time safeguarding world food supplies.

The numerous publications of UNO and its organizations such as the WHO and FAO repeatedly emphasize how difficult it will be to secure food supplies for the constantly increasing world population over the next few decades.

The rapid development which occurred in all fields of science in the 19th century also brought many new problems in its wake. Thanks to medicine and social hygiene, infant mortality was drastically reduced and life expectancy raised. The consequence was an explosive increase in population which betweeen 1850 and 1950, that is in one hundred years, resulted in a doubling of the earth's population from 1250 to 2500 million. Population scientists estimate that this figure will have increased to 6500 million by the year 2000, so that over these 50 years the world population will have increased two to three times.

In past millenia, the earth's population density was much lower. At the time of Christ's birth the world population was 160 million which by 900 A.D., that is in 900 years, had increased to 320 million. In 1700, 600 million people inhabited the earth, in other words, the population had doubled once more within 800 years; the next doubling, that is the increase to 1200 million people, by the year 1850, occurred within a space of only 150 years.

The low population growth in the Middle Ages was a consequence of the epidemics, such as cholera and plague, which carried off at least one quarter of the world population. Allied to this were devastating famines which not only claimed many victims but which also repeatedly provided tinder for political revolution. Many national disasters were agricultural disasters. Every disproportion between food supply and demand compels the use of extraordinary measures. The destruction of the European potato harvest in 1845/46 by a fungal disease, Phytophtora or downy mildew, resulted in a famine of indescribable dimensions. On the heels of the famine came epidemics which dispatched one million people over the next five years. The consequence of this was a massive wave of emigration to North America.

In the 17th century, the great philosopher Leibniz (1646—1716) was still teaching that the true power and wealth of a state resides in the size of its population, since where men are, there too substance and power are to be found. At the beginning of the 19th century, however, the English clergyman and political economist Robert Malthus (1766—1834) kindled fears about the effects of overpopulation. Mankind would starve, he claimed, if families would in future have more than two childen, since the means of subsistence could not keep pace with the rising population. His slogan was: No more children than mortalities. The soil, Malthus stressed, became more impoverished with each harvest, and dreadful famines would be the inescapable consequence.

Many events, such as the wave of migration from Europe just mentioned, seemed to bear out Malthus' views, with the result that his pupil, the philosopher of liberalism John Stuart Mill (1806—1873) was able to proclaim: There is no civilization which is able to supply the needs of a greater number of persons as well as it can a small number. Nature responds to overpopulation by inflicting the punishment of hunger.

100 to 150 years have passed since this time, and it has become evident that it is not hunger or deprivation which checks the excessive growth of population, but rather prosperity, its exact opposite. When families and peoples rise from illiteracy and poverty to a state of education and prosperity, their readiness and ability to practice

family planning increases. The enormous rise in the world population over the past centuries which has nonetheless taken place, is attributable to the development process of the peoples, known as the population cycle, which proceeds in four phases: In the original state, a high birth rate is compensated by a high mortality rate, so that the population rise is extremely low. With the introduction of medicine and hygiene, the mortality rate decreases while the birth rate remains at its high level, so that population numbers increase rapidly for about 130 years. With increasing enlightenment and school education, the mortality rate falls again, but at the same time the birth rate drops sharply, with the result that the population rise declines drastically. Finally, low mortality and birth rates persist in a state of balance, and the population then increases only very slowly, if at all.

This last-described state has already been reached in all Western European countries, and the Slavic peoples are now also entering the phase in which the population rise is slowing down greatly. A decisive factor in reaching this stage of slowing increase is the overcoming of illiteracy and the rationalization of all areas of life. Experience to date suggests, therefore, that the rapid growth of population numbers will only come to a standstill when a state of prosperity and education has been achieved by all peoples.

Agriculture throughout the world must therefore prepare itself to satisfy a further demand for food which by the year 2000 will substantially exceed present levels.

In the phase of the continuing population rise over the next few decades, it will without doubt be possible to meet the demand for food through the coordinated use of fertilization, plant breeding, automation, irrigation and crop protection. An important factor in achieving this will be to raise existing standards of education, since of 350 million families currently engaged in agriculture throughout the world, 250 million possess only a hoe or a wooden hook plough with which to work the soil, and thus are still at a state of development familiar to us from descriptions of ancient Egypt.

Peoples which had attained a higher level of culture incidentally always had a highly developed agriculture. The fall of Rome was due in no small measure to a neglect of arable farming. National disasters have often been agricultural disasters. Unfortunately, only hunger and war really bring this fact home to man. The French thinker Henri Fabre is therefore justified when he states: "History celebrates the battlefields on which death befalls us, but it does not speak of the cornfields by which we live; it knows the names of royal children born out of wedlock, but it is not able to speak to us of the origin of wheat. — What a progress of human folly!"

## *1. Problems of agricultural production*

*The primary requirement for the production of food is agricultural farmland. Results of recent studies reveal that the earth possesses about 3200 million hectares of agricultural land. Half of this, the higher-yielding readily cultivated half, is already in agricultural use. For the other half, high capital investment for irrigation, ground clearance, fertilization, crop protection and other cultivation measures will be needed if it is to be used in a similar manner. Where do reserves exist and what do they cost to develop?*

The average cost of cultivation in unpopulated areas runs to about 5000 DM per hectare. According to a report of the FAO, the world food organization, cultivating new land is uneconomical, even considering the existing food demand: In Southern Asia, some countries of East Asia, in the Middle East and in North Africa and in certain areas of Latin America and Africa, often only limited possibilities exist of extending cultivable land. In the dry regions it can even become necessary to return land which does not give very high yields to pasture use. Although large tracts of land which could be cultivated exist in Latin America and the southern Sahara, the cost of reclamation is so high that it is more economical to cultivate land already in use more intensively.

*How can this more intensive land use be put into practice?*

With today's level of technical development and considering the further advances in agricultural science which can be expected, additional production increases are possible in intensive farming, particularly by stabilizing yields.

*What is meant by this?*

In addition to further increasing yields in individual cases, it should above all be attempted, through the consistent application of knowledge in the fields of fertilization, plant breeding and crop protection, to compensate for yield fluctuations, which is not always successful due to climatic influences. Nevertheless, in this way it would be possible to stabilize agricultural production and generally increase average and general yield levels. There is after all a difference between a cereal yield of 8 tons per hectare on the individual farm and as a national average.

*The question presents itself as to how many people could theoretically be fed on earth if man were prepared to pay the high cost of reclaiming all the land which could be used for arable farming, and to produce as much food as humanly possible?*

This is a question which, given the shortages which continue to characterize the world food supply situation, is decisively important. On the basis of the current average requirement of 0.4 hectares of agricultural land, which is regarded as sufficient to feed one person with a low proportion of food of animal origin, we can sum the situation up as follows:

For the current population of 4,700 million people, the existing agricultural land per person worldwide is about 1 hectare. This includes arable land, forests and grassland. It should however be remembered that this includes all the pastureland in the world, which accounts for 60 to 70 per cent of land used for agriculture. Worldwide, 0.3 hectares of arable land are available per person. To feed the entire world population to the standard currently enjoyed by the population of the USA, 0.9 hectares per person are necessary, in other words as much as the currently existing total area of agricultural land, and also much more potentially cultivable or farmable land than the total area which exists on earth.

*The demands of the individual person on the available types of food also cannot continue to grow indefinitely, particularly in view of the continuing rapid rise in world population. This is impossible firstly because of the limited availability of agricultural land in the world and secondly because of the costs involved?*

Beween 1950 and 1975, it proved possible to increase world food production by 40 to 50 per cent. To achieve this, it was necessary to substantially increase annual expenditure on tractors, fertilizers and crop protectants. The next increase in production by the same percentage will cost a great deal more.

*Increasing the output of agriculture therefore also depends on growth in other areas of the economy. The increase in energy costs not only affects horticultural crops under glass. Its effects are also not confined to the use of tractors for ploughing, sowing and harvesting, since it also has consequences for the production of essential operating resources such as machinery, fertilizers and crop protectants. The future problems of agricultural production and thus of securing food supplies against a background of rising world population are inextricably linked to the economic problems which arise from the constantly changing political constellations.*

## 2. *Agriculture and the future*

*The future of our world depends equally on ponderables and imponderables. The creative spirit of man, applied with diligence and perseverence, will in future also be decisive for the continued existence of this world. However, man should be prevented from unleashing more wars and bringing down want and misery upon the head of mankind. What are the tasks which face agriculture in the future?*

Achieving the prosperity and satisfaction of all mankind offers the best chance of bringing peace to the world. Adequate supply with food in all climatic zones is the task which faces agriculture and horticulture in all countries. To realize this goal, the preconditions must be created for increasing agricultural production in the areas of high population density throughout the world, where the greatest population increase is currently taking place and is also to be expected in the future.

*What scope for cultivation exists in these warm climates?*

The essential requirement for improving agricultural production is to ensure an adequate supply of water. Only if farmland is irrigated can harvests be increased, since water is the vital element for all life and growth. As soon as the water supply has been secured by means of irrigation projects, the farmer can successfully cultivate food plants. The droughts and crop failures which repeatedly occur in many countries serve to remind us of the special significance of water in crop growing.

*Climatic conditions vary greatly throughout the world, however, even if we consider only the regions with arable farming and animal husbandry?*

Even in Germany, rainfall in agricultural cropping areas fluctuates between 400 and 1200 mm per year. The areas with the highest rainfall in the world are in India and Hawaii, with over 12 000 mm per year. As long as 60 years ago, Montandon presented an analysis of the disasters due to earthquakes, volcanic eruptions, floods, famines and pests and concluded that lack of water was the main problem. Dry tracts of land with low rainfall amounting to less than 250 mm per year therefore predominate throughout the world.

*Are the long-persisting droughts such as we have seen in Africa or Australia more a problem of recent times?*

Drought periods of shorter or longer duration have occurred throughout the ages, and even the land around the Nile would not have been fertile without the recurring annual floods caused by the rainfall in the Abyssinian uplands.

In this connection we might think of the rain monument erected in our own century in one of the world's lowest rainfall zones with 8 mm of rain per year. Almost half a century ago, a monument of this kind was erected in the town of Pirados in Chile in the form of a large granite block shaped like a raindrop, which bears the following inscription: "On 25th December 1936, the first rain fell here for 91 years". The drought problem has therefore existed at all times.

Unfortunately, the desert regions are spreading. In Africa alone, about 100,000 hectares of cultivated land are lost every year to the enroaching desert. Over the last 50 years, the Sahara has swallowed up over 1 million square kilometres of farmland and grassland. About 30 million people live in this area, and are threatened by the advancing desert. Almost half the countries of the earth have deserts within their borders. A global plan of action is to be put into effect by UNO to halt the spread of this desolation and the loss of land.

*Over the last few centuries, numerous large-scale water storage projects have been implemented in the form of dams and reservoirs, with the aim both of improving the water supply for agriculture and of generating energy in the form of electricity for irrigation and cultivation purposes. What such measures have been undertaken?*

Many examples from Germany and the rest of the world can be quoted, since water is also stored to secure drinking water supplies.

An international futuristic scheme was developed by Sörgel, an engineer from Munich, as long ago as 1927. His Atlantropa project involved separating the Atlantic Ocean and the Mediterranean Sea by means of an earth-fill dam at Gibraltar. After the water level in the Mediterranean had been lowered by evaporation and withdrawal of water, the water flowing in from the Atlantic would be utilized in power stations to generate electricity to desalinate the sea water and irrigate the Sahara over an area of 6 million square kilometres. So far, however, this project has remained only a utopian vision. The principle of using different levels for water storage and energy generation is the world's oldest irrigation technique and finds application even in the smallest cistern.

*Additional sprinkling or irrigation is thus a vitally important yield promoting measure in many areas, without which all other efforts will remain fruitless. What measures apart from securing the water supply will be decisive for ensuring adequate food production in the future?*

In addition to water supply, conservation of the soil as a growing location for crop plants is a vital factor. In particular, all soil conservation measures must be aimed at preventing erosion or removal of soil by wind or water. However, many aspects of the land use systems successfully implemented for centuries in the moderate climatic zones are not automatically suitable for use in countries with warm climates.

The method of minimal soil cultivation with band tillage for drilling crops, leaving the intermediate strips unworked, effectively reduces levels of erosion. In the USA, the soil conservation service has achieved excellent results in combating wind and water erosion by means of minimum tillage and permanent soil coverage.

*Optimal techniques of water supply and soil conservation will therefore be fundamental for the future of farming. What other production factors have priority in this respect?*

The selection of high-yielding species and cultivars of crop plants will continue to be essential for increasing yields. Also very important is the securing of optimal food supply by selecting fertilizers appropriate to the location and crop. Crop protection will be decisively important in the future, when the concern will be not only to safeguard yields in the face of attack by diseases, pests and weeds, but also to increase the harvest quantity per unit area by ensuring good plant development and preserving the assimilation surface, in other words, the green parts of plants. Crop protection and plant breeding must endeavour in the future, by means of joint research activities, to improve utilization of sunlight by the green plant. By these means, the sun's energy will be converted more efficiently into useful food for man.

*The population increase cannot be expected to cease over the next few decades. If a famine of major proportions is to be avoided, more food than hitherto must be produced in the regions of the world where the population is rising to ensure adequate nourishment. This will however only be possible if land already under cultivation is used more intensively than before, since in most cases new farmland can only be newly cultivated and developed at the cost of high investment.*

# Epilogue

Over the course of two decades a large number of talks have been broadcast by radio which are to be regarded as a cohesive series of discussions. These programmes were intended not only to inform the listener, whether an agricultural producer or a consumer of food, about topical subjects in farming and the food economy in the widest sense, but also to encourage reflection upon these issues so that daily events could be appreciated within their historical and cultural context.

The purpose behind these broadcasts was to promote an understanding not only of our own problems in farming and food supply, but also those facing our neighbours throughout the world.

The modern world economy, characterized by advances in communications technology, has led to the creation of a system of close interdependence between all the peoples of the earth.

Johann Heinrich von Thünen (1783—1850), the prominent agriculturalist and political economist, writing before 1850, at a time when the Cologne-Minden railway had just entered service, described the influence of modern transportation as follows:

*"A great and beneficial consequence of the invention of railways is that the princes, rightly recognizing that their future prosperity, power and influence will depend on the existence of a railway network covering their territory, have no time to wage war but, if they do not wish to be subject to their neighbours, must expend all their efforts in creating the railway network.*

*At some future time, however, when, due to the close dependencies created by the railway, the prosperity of each nation will depend on that of its neighbours, the peoples themselves will no longer endure, will no longer tolerate war."*

This vision of the future cherished by the great political economist has regrettably still not been fulfilled today. Neither modern transportation nor communications have brought about international understanding, and agriculture, although providing the potential for peaceful utilization of the world's resources, is repeatedly made into a political bone of contention.

Immanuel Kant (1724—1804) as a philosopher and advocate of peace referred in his essay "Perpetual Peace" to the fact that wars are irreconcileable with reason and demanded a universal peace treaty between all peoples. In the context of cultural history, for Kant the art of cultivating "no longer recognizable species of grass, cereals" and in particular "the multiplication and improvement of fruit species through transplantation and grafting" is possible only in already established states with secure land ownership and where agriculture is linked to trade, through which the peoples "were first brought into a peaceful relationship towards each other and hence, even with those more distant, into a state of harmony, community and peaceful coexistence".

World trade is an essential guarantor of the peaceful coexistence of peoples and, using the many different means of transportation, is responsible for the exchange of goods and fills gaps in supply, particularly of food.

The overpopulation of this world with peoples of different nations and races, and thus their need for food, is continuing unchecked. Agricultural development has now been in progress for five to ten thousand years. Again and again it has proved possible to provide bread for all. And yet famines still occur, above all because climatic factors limit or even prevent the production of food from plants either through droughts or floods. Over a period of thousands of years, the "evolution" of food plants has repeatedly produced cultivated plants adapted to the climate, or man has introduced cultivated plants from one climatic zone or region of the earth to another. Politically based agrarian revolutions, by contrast, have always turned back the clock.

In former times, hunger in Europe was a cause of emigration to other countries and regions of the earth. Only in recent times have we witnessed the world political phenomenon of the European Community producing enough food to satisfy its own demand.

The task for the future is to guarantee the continued peaceful development of farming as the basis of our food supply, with the aid of new knowledge from research and development, to the benefit of mankind in all the countries of the earth.

# Literature references

## Foreword incl. Preface

Blum, J. [Ed.] (1982): Die bäuerliche Welt. Geschichte und Kultur in sieben Jahrhunderten. Verlag C.H. Beck, München, 246 p.

Fleischmann, W. (1919): Capitulare de villis vel curtis imperii Caroli Magni oder Die Landgüterordnung Karls des Großen, newly translated, with explanations. Landw. Jahrbücher, 53rd annual volume, pp. 1—76.

Kruif, P. de (1928): Bezwinger des Hungers (The hunger fighters). Willi Weismann-Verlag, München, 286 p., 3rd Edn., 1947.

Krzymowski, R. (1961): Geschichte der deutschen Landwirtschaft. 3rd Edn. Duncker & Humblot, Berlin, 441 p.

Kulischer, J. (1965): Allgemeine Wirtschaftsgeschichte des Mittelalters und der Neuzeit. Vol. I. 351 p., Vol. II. 553 p., 3rd Edn. Verlag R. Oldenbourg, München und Wien.

Museum für Deutsche Volkskunde (1978): Das Bild vom Bauern. Vorstellungen und Wirklichkeit vom 16. Jahrhundert bis zur Gegenwart. 2nd Edn. Editor: Museum für Deutsche Volkskunde, Berlin. Staatliche Museen Preußischer Kulturbesitz, 160 p.

Noth, M. (1954): Geschichte Israels. 2nd Edn. Verlag Vandenhoeck & Ruprecht, 435 p.

Prentice, E. P. (1939): Hunger and History. The influence of hunger on human history. 1st Edn. Harper & Brothers, New York, 1939. 2nd Edn. Caxton Printers Ltd. Caldwell, Idaho, 1951, 269 p.

Rothenberger, K.-H. (1980): Die Hungerjahre nach dem Zweiten Weltkrieg. Harald Boldt Verlag, 265 p.

Sorauer, P. (1866): Die nächste Aufgabe der Akklimatisation. Zeitschrift für Akklimatisation, Organ des Akklimatisations-Verein in Berlin, New Series, Vol. 4, pp. 82—94.

Stein, E. (1966): Hungrige speisen. Editor: Deutsches Brotmuseum e.V., Ulm/Donau, 148 p.

Wehnelt, B., s. Kolbe, W. and G. Haug (1979): A review of 65 years of Bayer Agrochemicals Division (1914—1979) and 50 volumes of Pflanzenschutz-Nachrichten (1922—1979). Pflanzenschutz-Nachrichten Bayer, 32nd (50th) annual volume, pp. 201—550 (English edition). — Biographie Wehnelt cf. pp. 474—475, facsimile "Kornkäferbekämpfung im alten Orient", 1934, pp. 549—553 (cf. also p. 248 of this book).

## Introduction

Abel, W. (1970): Conrad von Heresbach (1496—1576). In: Franz, G. and H. Haushofer [Ed.]: Große Landwirte. DLG-Verlag, Frankfurt (Main), pp. 4—18.

Benn, G. (1948): Drei alte Männer. Gespräche. Limes Verlag, Wiesbaden, 44 p., 2nd Edn., 1955.

Beutler, C. and F. Irsigler (1980): Konrad Heresbach (1496—1576). In: Rheinische Lebensbilder, Vol. 8, pp. 81—104. Rheinland-Verlag GmbH, Köln.

Bundesministerium für Ernährung, Landwirtschaft und Forsten (1982): Statistisches Jahrbuch über Ernährung, Landwirtschaft und Forsten der Bundesrepublik Deutschland 1982. Landwirtschaftsverlag GmbH, Münster-Hiltrup, 424 p.

Clostermann, G.: Persönliche Mitteilungen und Gespräche (1959—1983). Wesel-Bislich, Neuhollandshof.

Columella (1st century A.D.): Über Landwirtschaft. Ein Lehr- und Handbuch der gesamten Acker- und Viehwirtschaft aus dem 1. Jahrhundert u. Z. Ahrens, K. (Ed.), Akademie-Verlag, Berlin, 466 p., 1976.

FAO (1981): FAO Trade Yearbook 1980. Vol. 34. Editor: Food and Agriculture Organization of the United Nations, Rome, 359 p.

— (1982): FAO Production Yearbook 1981. Vol. 35. Editor: Food and Agriculture Organization of the United Nations, Rome, 306 p.

Först, W. [Ed.] (1973—1982): Beiträge zur Geschichte und Gegenwart des WDR. Annalen des Westdeutschen Rundfunks, Vol. 1—5. G. Grote'sche Verlagsbuchhandlung KG and Verlag W. Kohlhammer GmbH., Place of publication Cologne.

Fraas, C. (1865): Geschichte der Landbau- und Forstwissenschaft. Literarisch-artistische Anstalt der J.G. Cottaschen Buchhandlung, München, 668 p. Reprint: Johnson Reprint Corporation, New York, 1965.

Fraile, E. M. y (1939): Landwirtschaftlicher Unterricht und Propaganda. Rundfunk und Lichtbild im Dienst der Landwirtschaft. XVIII. Internationaler Landwirtschaftskongreß Dresden, June 6th—12th 1939, Section II, pp. 33—60. Reichsnährstand Verlags-Ges.m.b.H. Berlin.

Graff, O. (1957): Dünger und Düngung bei Konrad Heresbach. Landbau-Forschung Völkenrode 7, pp. 75—77.
Hashagen, J., Narr, K.J., Rees, W. and E. Strutz (1958): Bergische Geschichte. Editor: Bergischer Geschichtsverein, 630 p.
Hay, G. [Ed.] (1975): Literatur und Rundfunk 1923—1933. Verlag Dr. H. A. Gerstenberg, Hildesheim, 407 p.
Heresbach, K. (1570): Vier Bücher über Landwirtschaft (Rei Rusticae Libri Quatuor). Vol. I: Vom Landbau (De Re Rustica). Verlag J. Birckmann, Cologne. — Reprint of the Latin edition with German translation and critical commentary. Translator: H. Dreitzel, Ed.: W. Abel. Verlag Anton Hain KG, Meisenheim, 1970.
— (1577): Fovre bookes of husbrandy. English translation by Barnaby Googe. Reprint: Da Capo Press, New York and Theatrum Orbis Terrarum, Amsterdam, 1971.
— (Ed.: Blusch, J., 1977): Handbüchlein der Thereutik, das heißt über Jagd, Vogelfang und Fischerei (Thereuticas Compendium). Critical edition and German translation with introduction. Boppard.
Hirzel, S. (1895): Der Dialog. Ein literarhistorischer Versuch. Verlag S. Hirzel, Leipzig.
Kolbe, W. (1977): Guide to Höfchen Experimental Station. 7th Edn. Issued by Bayer Pflanzenschutz Leverkusen, 79 p.
Kuhlmey, G. (1943): Konrad Heresbach, Prinzenerzieher und Staatsmann am Klevischen Hof. Verlag O. Kolp, Mettmann, 39 p.
Langethal, E. C. (1854): Geschichte der teutschen Landwirthschaft. Vols. I and II. Verlag Friedrich Luden, Jena, 558 p.
Lebermann, B. (1906): Die pädagogischen Anschauungen Conrad Heresbachs. Dissertation Universität Würzburg, 145 p.
Rotthauwe, A. (1972): Heilige Händler und Zweifarbige Tücher. Bericht und Bild zum vergangenen Wesel. Editor: Willibrordi-Dombau-Verein e.V., Wesel, 236 p.
Rotthauwe, H. (1975): Konrad von Heresbach in Mehr. In: Land an Rhein und Issel und die Böse Sieben. Editor: Amt Haldern, pp. 239—241.
Schönneshöfer, B. (1908): Geschichte des Bergischen Landes. Buchdruckerei und Verlagsbuchhandlung A. Martin & Grüttefien G.m.b.H., Elberfeld, 601 p., Reprint: Verlag Ute Kierdorf, Remscheid, 1981.
Siegel, C. (1978): Die Reportage. J. B. Metzlersche Verlagsbuchhandlung, Stuttgart, 146 p.
Soeldner, H. (1974): Sie hören den Landfunk. Verlagsgesellschaft Neureuter & Wolf m.b.H., München, 240 p.
Statistisches Bundesamt (1982): Statistisches Jahrbuch 1982 für die Bundesrepublik Deutschland. Verlag W. Kohlhammer GmbH, Stuttgart and Mainz, 780 p.
Stempel, W. (1983): Der Willibrordidom in Wesel. Große Baudenkmäler, Issue 347. Deutscher Kunstverlag München und Berlin, 16 p.
Thiel, H. (1954): Konrad Heresbach; Die Zeit, der Mensch, das Werk. In: Thiel, H. (Ed.): 1050 Jahre Mettmann. Stadt und Land in Vergangenheit und Gegenwart, pp. 84—108. Aloys Henn Verlag, Ratingen, 235 p.
— (1966): Heresbach — Freund des Landlebens. Mit einer Würdigung der Schrift über den Landbau. Unsere Bergische Heimat, Heimatkundliche Monats-Beilage zum General-Anzeiger der Stadt Wuppertal. Mitteilungsblatt des Bergischen Geschichtsvereins, 15th annual volume, May 1966.
— (1966): Pferdeliebhaber und Jagdkenner. Translation from the writings of Konrad von Heresbach. Unsere Bergische Heimat, Mitteilungsblatt des Bergischen Geschichtsvereins, Wuppertal, 15th annual volume, September 1966.
Wolff, J. (1969): Ryswickshof in Mehr. Heimatkalender für den Kreis Rees 1969, pp. 85—89.
Wolters, A. (1867): Konrad von Heresbach und der Clevische Hof zu seiner Zeit nach neuen Quellen geschildert. Ein Beitrag zur Geschichte des Reformationszeitalters und seines Humanismus. Issued by Bergischer Geschichtsverein. Printed and published by Sam. Lucas, Elberfeld, 276 p.

## I. World food supply and the limits of food production

Abel, W. (1966): Agrarkrisen und Agrarkonjunktur. Verlag Paul Parey, Hamburg und Berlin, 301 p.
Adrian, W. (1959): So wurde aus Brot Halm und Glut. Getreideanbau, Getreideverarbeitung und Bäckerei der Vorzeit. 2nd Edn. Ceres-Verlag, Bielefeld, 120 p.
Bayer, D. (1966): O gib mir Brot. Die Hungerjahre 1816 und 1817 in Württemberg und Baden. Editor: Deutsches Brotmuseum e.V., Ulm/Donau, 132 p.

Beheim-Schwarzbach, H. (1866): Beitrag zur Kenntnis des Ackerbaues der Römer. Reprint: Dr. M. Sändig oHG., Wiesbaden, 142 p., 1968.
Benn, G. (1932): Gebührt Carleton ein Denkmal? In: Gesammelte Werke, Vol. I, pp. 201—210, 1959, Limes-Verlag, Wiesbaden.
Cramer, H. H. (1967): Plant protection and world crop production. Pflanzenschutz-Nachrichten Bayer 20, pp. 1—524 (English Edition).
Eiselen, W. (1966): Brot gegen Hunger. Catalogue of the exhibition "Brot gegen Hunger", April 1966. Editor: Deutsches Brotmuseum e.V., Ulm/Donau, Fürsteneckerstraße 17.
Harsany, P. (1967): Free bread for every man. An essay on world hunger and production requirements. Academic Publishing Co., Montreal, 111 p.
Heinrichs, J. (1969): Hunger und Zukunft. Aspekte des Welternährungsproblems. Verlag Vandenhoeck und Ruprecht. Göttingen, 88 p.
Jacob, H. E. (1954): 6000 Jahre Brot. Rowohlt Verlag, Hamburg, 502 p.
Malthus, T. R. (1820): Principles of political economy. In Diehl, K. and P. Mombert (Ed.): Ausgewählte Lesestücke zum Studium der politischen Ökonomie. G. Braunsche Hofbuchdruckerei und Verlag, Karlsruhe i. B., 1913.
Morgulis, S. (1923): Hunger und Unterernährung. Eine biologische und soziologische Studie. Verlag J. Springer, Berlin.
Plate, R. (1950): Der Weltgetreidemarkt nach dem Zweiten Weltkrieg. Lage und Aussichten. Verlag Paul Parey, Berlin and Hamburg, 233 p.
Rohrlich, M. (1960): Brot — ewiges Motiv künstlichen Schaffens. Verlag Moritz Schäfer, Detmold, 79 p.
Schröder, R. and W. Steller (1959): Gefärbtes oder gesegnetes Brot? Droste-Verlag, Düsseldorf, 96 p.
Urff, W. von (1982): Nahrungsmittelhilfe — ein Beitrag zur Überwindung von Hunger in der Dritten Welt? Bayerisches Landw. Jahrbuch, 59th annual volume, pp. 899—905.
Vereinigung Deutscher Wissenschaftler (1968): Welternährungskrise oder Ist eine Hungerkatastrophe unausweichlich? Rowohlt Verlag, Hamburg, 123 p.
Währen, M. (n.d.): Das Brot in den Stimmen der Völker. 300 Zitate, Sprichwörter, Redensarten aus fünf Jahrtausenden. Verlag des Schweizerischen Bäcker-Konditorenmeister-Verbandes, Bern, 71 p.
— (n.d.): Brot seit Jahrtausenden. Die Brotformen und Bäckerei im Wandel der Zeiten. Verlag des Schweizerischen Bäcker- und Konditorenmeisterverbandes, Bern, 106 p.
Zischka, A. (1938): Brot für zwei Milliarden Menschen. Wilhelm Goldmann-Verlag, Leipzig, 344 p.

## II. Food crops in agriculture and horticulture

Bary, A. de (1853): Untersuchungen über die Brandpilze und die durch sie verursachten Krankheiten der Pflanzen mit Rücksicht auf das Getreide und andere Nutzpflanzen. Verlag von G. W. F. Müller, Berlin.
Becker-Dillingen, J. (1956): Handbuch des gesamten Gemüsebaues. Verlag Paul Parey, Berlin und Hamburg, 755 p.
Conert, H. J. (1967): Nutzpflanzen in Farben. Otto Maier Verlag, Ravensburg, 247 p.
Crüger, G. (1972): Pflanzenschutz im Gemüsebau. Verlag Eugen Ulmer, Stuttgart, 320 p.
Damaschke, A. (1929): Geschichte der Nationalökonomie. Vol. I., 14th Edn. Verlag Gustav Fischer, Jena, 455 p.
Dodge, B. S. (1963): Pflanzen die die Welt verändern. Verlag F. A. Brockhaus, Wiesbaden, 223 p.
Esdorn, I. and H. Pirson (1973): Die Nutzpflanzen der Tropen und Subtropen in der Weltwirtschaft. Gustav Fischer Verlag, Stuttgart, 170 p.
Fischbeck, G., Heyland, K.-U. and N. Knauer (1975): Spezieller Pflanzenbau. Verlag Eugen Ulmer, Stuttgart, 336 p.
Franke, G. (1976): Nutzpflanzen der Tropen und Subtropen. Vols. I—III. S. Hirzel Verlag, Leipzig, 1345 p.
Franke, G. and A. Pfeiffer (1964): Kakao, A. Ziemsen Verlag, Wittenberg, 122 p.
Geisler, G. (1980): Pflanzenbau. Ein Lehrbuch — Biologische Grundlagen und Technik. Verlag Paul Parey, Berlin und Hamburg, 474 p.
Geisler, G. (1983): Ertragsphysiologie von Kulturarten des gemäßigten Klimas. Verlag Paul Parey, Berlin und Hamburg, 205 p.
Gerhardt, M. (1950): Friedrich von Bodelschwingh. Ein Lebensbild aus der deutschen Kirchengeschichte.

Vol. I Werden und Reifen. Verlag v. Bodelschwinghsche Anstalten, Bielefeld-Bethel. Die Lehrzeit bei Koppe im Oderbruch 1849—1851, pp. 85—95.

Harrison, S. G., Masefield, G. B. and M. Wallis (1975): The Oxford Book of Food Plants. Oxford University Press, 206 p.

Heddergott, H. (1982): Taschenbuch des Pflanzenarztes, 31st series. Der aktuelle Helfer zur Erkennung und Bekämpfung von Krankheiten und Schädlingen an Kulturpflanzen und Vorräten sowie zur Ausschaltung von Unkräutern. Established by Professor F.-W. Maier-Bode. Landwirtschaftsverlag GmbH, Münster-Hiltrup, 699 p.

Heinze, K. (1974/78/83): Leitfaden der Schädlingsbekämpfung. 4th Edn. Vol. I: Schädlinge und Krankheiten im Gemüsebau. Vol. II. Schädlinge und Krankheiten im Obst- und Weinbau. Vol. III: Schädlinge und Krankheiten im Ackerbau. Vol. IV: Vorratsschutz. Established by H. W. Frickhinger. Wissenschaftliche Verlagsgesellschaft mbH., Stuttgart.

Hilkenbäumer, F. (1964): Obstbau. Grundlagen, Anbau und Betrieb. 4th Edn. Verlag Paul Parey, Berlin und Hamburg, 348 p.

— (1973): Schnitt der Obstgehölze. Verlag J. Neumann-Neudamm, Melsungen-Basel-Wien, 144 p.

Hoffmann, G. M., Nienhaus, F., Schönbeck, F., Weltzien, H. C. and H. Wilbert (1976): Lehrbuch der Phytomedizin. Verlag Paul Parey, Berlin and Hamburg, 490 p.

Hoffmann, G. M. and H. Schmutterer (1983): Parasitäre Krankheiten und Schädlinge an landwirtschaftlichen Kulturpflanzen. Verlag Eugen Ulmer, Stuttgart, 488 p.

Jacob, H. E. (1951): Sage und Siegeszug des Kaffees. Rowohlt Verlag, Hamburg, 366 p.

Kaspers, H., and W. Kolbe, (1971): Biology, economic importance and control of cereal powdery mildew Erysiphe graminis DC. Pflanzenschutz-Nachrichten Bayer 24, pp. 327—362 (English edition).

Keipert, K. (1981): Beerenobst. Angebaute Arten und Wildfrüchte. Verlag Eugen Ulmer, Stuttgart, 337 p.

Klapp, E. (1967): Lehrbuch des Acker- und Pflanzenbaues. 6th Edn. Verlag Paul Parey, Berlin und Hamburg, 603 p.

Klasen, M. (1982): Sommerweizen muß die Lücken füllen. Landwirtschaftliche Zeitschrift Rheinland, 149th annual volume, pp. 16—18.

— (1982): Der Hafer enttäuschte nicht. Landwirtschaftliche Zeitschrift Rheinland, 149th annual volume, pp. 68—70.

— (1982): Mehrere Faktoren begünstigen den Erfolg. Landwirtschaftliche Zeitschrift Rheinland, 149th annual volume, pp. 974—975.

— (1982): So bleibt die Wintergerste gesund. Landwirtschaftliche Zeitschrift Rheinland, 149th annual volume, pp. 1960—1962.

— (1982): Der Roggen kann sich sehen lassen. Landwirtschaftliche Zeitschrift Rheinland, 149th annual volume, pp. 2061—2063.

— (1982): Die Winterweizensorten haben es geschafft. Landwirtschaftliche Zeitschrift Rheinland, 149th annual volume, pp. 2112—2114.

— (1983): Anbautechnik und Sortenübersicht. 4th Edn. Publ.: Landwirtschaftskammer Rheinland, Gruppe Landbau und Rheinischer Saatbauverband, 20 p.

Kolbe, W. (1958): Studies on the control of mangold fly. Höfchen-Briefe 11, pp. 37—70 (English edition).

— (1966): Untersuchungen über das Auftreten und die Bekämpfung des Apfelschorfs. Erwerbs-Obstbau 8, pp. 225—229.

— (1967): Untersuchungen über die Befallsstärke, Ertragsbeeinflussung und Bekämpfung des Apfelmehltaus. Erwerbs-Obstbau 9, pp. 90—97.

— (1971): Einfluß der Botrytisbekämpfung auf Ertrag und Fruchtqualität im Erdbeerbau. Erwerbs-Obstbau 13, pp. 193—196.

— (1973): Befallsstärke, Bekämpfung und Ertragsbeeinflussung von Botrytis cinerea als Fruchtfäule- und Rutenschäden-Erreger bei Himbeersorten. Erwerbs-Obstbau 15, pp. 17—21.

— (1976): Untersuchungen über die Bekämpfung pilzlicher Erkrankungen im Strauchbeerenobstbau. Erwerbs-Obstbau 18, pp. 40—43.

— (1978): Über Auftreten, Lebensweise und Bekämpfung der Obstbaumspinnmilbe im Kernobstbau. Erwerbs-Obstbau 20, pp. 140—143.

— (1980): Untersuchungen über Auftreten und Bekämpfung des Apfelmehltaus. Erwerbs-Obstbau 22, pp. 29—32.

— (1981): Überlegungen zur Schorf- und Mehltaubekämpfung im Obstbau. Obstbau 12, pp. 486—489.

— (1982): Versuche zur Botrytisbekämpfung im Erdbeerbau unter Berücksichtigung von Anbautechnik, Sortenwahl und Witterung. Erwerbs-Obstbau 24, pp. 149—154.

— (1983): Versuche zur Schorfbekämpfung im Apfelanbau und Prüfung der Nebenwirkungen gegen Mehltau und Obstbaumkrebs. Erwerbs-Obstbau 25, pp. 198—203.

Kurzrock, R. [Ed.] (1979): Tropische Landwirtschaft. Forschung und Information, Vol. 25.Publication series of the Rias-Funkuniversität. Colloquium-Verlag, Berlin, 156 p.

Lippmann, E. O. v. (1925): Geschichte der Rübe (Beta) als Kulturpflanze von den ältesten Zeiten an bis zum Erscheinen von Achard's Hauptwerke (1809). Springer-Verlag, Berlin. New impression Dr. M. Sändig, oHG, Wiesbaden, 184 p. and supplement 67 p., 1971.

Petersen, A. (1981): Die Gräser als Kulturpflanzen und Unkräuter auf Wiese, Weide und Acker. 5th Edn. Akademie-Verlag, Berlin, 280 p.

Rehm, S. and G. Espig (1976): Die Kulturpflanzen der Tropen und Subtropen. Verlag Eugen Ulmer, Stuttgart, 496 p.

Steineck, H. (1981): Pilze im Garten. 2nd Edn., Verlag Eugen Ulmer, Stuttgart, 148 p.

— (1982): Champignonkultur. 7th Edn., Verlag Eugen Ulmer, Stuttgart, 133 p.

Vollmer, F.-J. (1982): Die Wintergerste im integrierten Pflanzenbau. Landwirtschaftliche Zeitschrift Rheinland, 149th annual volume, pp. 2103—2104.

Winner, C.: Zuckerrübenbau. DLG-Verlag, Frankfurt (Main), 308 p.

Winter, F. et al (1974): Lucas' Anleitung zum Obstbau. 29th Edn. Verlag Eugen Ulmer, Stuttgart, 522 p.

## III. Changes in agriculture and crop cultivation

Bittermann, E. (1956): Die landwirtschaftliche Produktion in Deutschland 1800—1950. Kühn-Archiv 70, pp. 1—149.

Bundesministerium für Ernährung, Landwirtschaft und Forsten [Ed.)] (1982): Alternativen im Landbau. Seminar. Landwirtschaftsverlag Münster-Hiltrup, 291 p.

Dohne, E., Feldmann, F. and H.-J. Kämmerling (1969): Landtechnik, Vol. I. Feldwirtschaft. Aufgaben und Bauarten der Landmaschinen. Arbeitsverfahren. Verlag Eugen Ulmer, Stuttgart, 318 p.

Franz, G. (1969): Die Geschichte der Landtechnik im 20. Jahrhundert. DLG-Verlags-GmbH, Frankfurt/Main, 449 p.

Fruwirth, C. (1923): Die Industrie der Nahrungs- und Genußmittel. 1. Die Landwirtschaft. In Geitel, M. [Ed.]: Der Siegeslauf der Technik, Vol. II, pp. 379—462. Union Deutsche Verlagsgesellschaft, Stuttgart, Berlin, Leipzig.

Haushofer, H. (1963): Die deutsche Landwirtschaft im technischen Zeitalter. Deutsche Agrargeschichte, Vol. V. Verlag Eugen Ulmer, Stuttgart, 290 p.

Henning, F.-W. (1978): Das industrialisierte Deutschland 1914—1976. 4th Edn. Verlag F. Schöningh, Paderborn, 292 p.

— (1978/79): Landwirtschaft und ländliche Gesellschaft in Deutschland. Vol. 1: 800—1750, Vol. 2: 1750—1976. Verlag F. Schöningh, Paderborn, 602 p.

Hesse, H. A. (1972): Berufe im Wandel. Ein Beitrag zur Soziologie des Berufs, der Berufspolitik und des Berufsrechts. Ferdinand Enke Verlag, Stuttgart, 203 p.

Jentzsch, E.-G. (1979): Energie und Ernährung in der Dritten Welt. Publ.: Deutsche Welthungerhilfe, Bonn, 100 p.

Kolbe, W. (1980): Pflanzenkur und Obstbau im Wandel. Erwerbs-Obstbau 22, 183—187.

— (1980): Entwicklung des Pflanzenschutzes im Obstbau. Obstbau 5, pp. 389—393.

Kuhnen, F.: Agrarreform — ein Weltproblem. Publ.: Deutsche Welthungerhilfe, Bonn, 150 p.

Lenk, H. und S. Moser [Ed.] (1973): Technik. Technologie. Philosophische Perspektiven. Verlag Dokumentation, Pullach bei München, 247 p.

Müller, F. (1897): Einträglicher Obstbau in Verbindung mit rationellem Grasbau. Publ. by steierm. Volksbildungsverein. Graz, 148 p.

Niehaus, H. (1948): Der Bauer in der Wirtschafts- und Gesellschaftsordnung. Sammlung Agrarwirtschaft und Agrarpolitik, Issue 12, 70 p. Westdeutscher Verlag, Köln und Opladen.

O'Daniel, W. (1978): Von der Bodenbearbeitung zur Bodenpflege in Kernobstanlagen. Berichte über Landwirtschaft 56, pp. 515—524.

Pimentel, D. (1980): Handbook of energy utilization in agriculture. CRC Press, Inc. Boca Raton, Florida, 475 p.

Schwerz, J. N. von (1836): Beschreibung der Landwirthschaft in Westfalen und Rheinpreußen. Zweiter Theil (Rheinpreußen). Hoffmann'sche Verlagsbuchhandlung, Stuttgart, 307 p. Facsimile Rheinischer Landwirtschafts-Verlag G.m.b.H. Bonn, 1980.

## IV. Agrochemistry as a production factor

Börner, H. (1978): Pflanzenkrankheiten und Pflanzenschutz. Verlag Eugen Ulmer, Stuttgart, 419 p.

Büchel, K. H. (1977): Pflanzenschutz und Schädlingsbekämpfung. Georg Thieme Verlag, Stuttgart, 200 p.

— (1983): Die Zukunft der Chemie in der Landwirtschaft. Berichte über Landwirtschaft, Vol. 61, pp. 382—399.

Cramer, H.-H. (1978): Zur Problematik des Pflanzenschutzes in der modernen Landwirtschaft. Der Chemieunterricht, 9th annual volume, Issue 3, pp. 3—40.

Haug, G. (1976): Pflanzenschutz-Forschung der Industrie. In Wegler, R. (Ed.): Chemie der Pflanzenschutz- und Schädlingsbekämpfungsmittel, Vol. 3, pp. 57—84. Springer-Verlag, Berlin—Heidelberg—New York.

Heitefuß, R. (1975): Pflanzenschutz, Grundlagen der praktischen Phytomedizin. Georg Thieme Verlag, Stuttgart, 270 p.

Hörath, H. (1981): Gifte. Eine Einführung in die Gesetz- und Giftkunde. Wissenschaftliche Verlagsgesellschaft mbH, Stuttgart, 187 p.

Industrieverband Pflanzenschutz e.V. (1982): Wirkstoffe in Pflanzenschutz- und Schädlingsbekämpfungsmitteln. Physikalisch-chemische und toxikologische Daten. Published by: Industrieverband Pflanzenschutz e.V., Frankfurt am Main, 375 p.

Kolbe, W. (1969): Die Anwendung von Herbiziden als Maßnahme der Bodenpflege und des Pflanzenschutzes in ihrem Einfluß auf Wuchsleistung, Ertrag und Fruchtqualität im Kernobstbau. Erwerbs-Obstbau 11, pp. 81—86.

— (1970): On the question of chemical weed control in cereals with special consideration to species and varietal tolerance. Pflanzenschutz-Nachrichten Bayer 23, pp. 1—22 (English edition).

— (1975): Über den Einfluß mechanischer und chemischer Unkrautbekämpfung auf den Ertrag unter Berücksichtigung der Sortenverträglichkeit. Zeitschrift für Pflanzenkrankheiten und Pflanzenschutz, Special edition VII, pp. 243—253.

— (1977): Mehrjährige Untersuchungen über die Beziehungen zwischen Unkraut-Deckungsgrad und Mehrertrag bei chemischer Unkrautbekämpfung. Zeitschrift für Pflanzenkrankheiten und Pflanzenschutz, Special edition VIII, pp. 59—67.

— (1977): Studies on the influence of mineral and organic fertilizer dressings on disease incidence in orchards given uniform crop protection treatments (1961—1976). Pflanzenschutz-Nachrichten Bayer 30, pp. 138—152 (English edition).

— (1980) Effect of weed control on grain yield of different winter barley cultivars with reference to sowing time, seed rate and seed size, in long-term trials at Höfchen and Laacherhof Experimental Stations (1968—1980). Pflanzenschutz-Nachrichten Bayer 33, pp. 203—219 (English edition).

— (1982): Einfluß der chemischen Unkrautbekämpfung auf Ertrag und Fruchtqualität im Erdbeerbau. Erwerbs-Obstbau 24, pp. 171—175.

— (1983): Crop production and weed control. A comparative study with reference to long-term trials on 40 crops at Höfchen and Laacherhof Experimental Stations. Pflanzenschutz-Nachrichten Bayer 36, pp. 205—373 (English edition).

Kolbe, W. und F. Hilkenbäumer (1976): Einfluß mineralischer Düngung und von Calciumspritzungen auf den Befall von Lagerkrankheiten an Apfelsorten bei einheitlichen Pflanzenschutzmaßnahmen. Erwerbs-Obstbau 18, pp. 163—165.

Liebig, J. (1840): Die organische Chemie in ihrer Anwendung auf Agrikultur und Physiologie. Verlag von Friedrich Vieweg und Sohn, Braunschweig, 352 p. Reprint: Gerstenberg Verlag, Hildesheim, 1977.

Liebig, J. von (1878): Chemische Briefe. 6nd Edn., Leipzig und Heidelberg, 479 p. Reprint: Georg Olms Verlagsbuchhandlung, Hildesheim, 1967.

Maier-Bode, F. W. (1948): Die drei Stufen der Düngung. Sammlung Agrarwissenschaft und Agrarpolitik, Issue 3, 54 p. Westdeutscher Verlag, Köln und Opladen.

Mayer, K. (1959): 4500 Jahre Pflanzenschutz. Verlag Eugen Ulmer, Stuttgart, 45 p.

Schönbeck, F. (1979): Pflanzenkrankheiten. Einführung in die Phytopathologie. Verlag B. G. Teubner, Stuttgart, 184 p.

Topp, W. (1981): Biologie der Bodenorganismen. Verlag Quelle & Meyer, Heidelberg, 224 p.

Tornow, W. (1972): Chronik der Agrarpolitik und Agrarwirtschaft des Deutschen Reiches von 1933—1945. Berichte über Landwirtschaft, Special edition 188, 193 p. Verlag Paul Parey, Hamburg and Berlin.

Vergil (29 B.C.): Georgica. Landbau. In: Götte J. and M. Götte [Ed.] (1972): Vergil. Sämtliche Werke. Heimeran-Verlag, München, pp. 36—98.

Wegler, R. [Ed.] (1970—1982): Chemie der Pflanzenschutz- und Schädlingsbekämpfungsmittel. Vols. 1—8.

Springer-Verlag, Berlin-Heidelberg-New York.
Whitten, J. L. (1969): Damit wir leben können. Published by: van Nostrand Reinhold Company, New York, 240 p.
Wirth, W., Hecht, G. and C. Gloxhuber (1971): Toxikologie-Fibel. 2nd Edn. Georg Thieme Verlag, Stuttgart, 469 p.

## V. Pests as food competitors

Biedrzynski, E. (1980): Mit Goethe durch das Jahr. Ein Kalender für das Jahr 1981. Artemis-Verlag, Zürich und München, 112 p.
Bodenheimer, F. S. (1928/29): Materialien zur Geschichte der Entomologie bis Linné. Vol. I, 498 p., Vol. II, 486 p. Verlag W. Junk, Berlin.
Döring, W. L. (1835): Die Königin der Blumen oder die höhere Bedeutung der Rose an sich und in Beziehung auf die Gemütswelt nach Naturanschauung, Poesie und Geschichte. Printed by Sam. Lucas, Elberfeld, 748 p.
Fabre, J.-H. (1914): Bilder aus der Insektenwelt. (Authorized translation from "Souvenirs Entomologiques"). Series 1—4. Ed. Kosmos, Gesellschaft der Naturfreunde. Franckh'sche Verlagsbuchhandlung, Stuttgart, 436 p.
— (1950): Aus der Wunderwelt der Instinkte. Westkulturverlag Anton Hain, Meisenheim/Glan, 375 p. Friderich, König von Preußen (1752): Renoviertes und erneuertes Edict, wegen Vertilgung der Heuschrecken oder Sprengsel. Berlin, 4 p.
Guggenheim, K. und A. Portmann [Ed.] (1977): Jean-Henri Fabre. Das offenbare Geheimnis. Suhrkamp Taschenbuch Verlag, 263 p.
Herfs, A. (1949): Tier und Pflanze. Höfchen-Briefe 2 (Special edition), pp. 1—138.
Kolbe, W. (1960): Trial controls of olive fruit fly by means of ®Lebaycid in Crete. Höfchen-Briefe 13, pp. 52—89 (English edition).
— (1968): Ertrags- und Wuchsbeeinflussung, Bekämpfung und Lebensweise wichtiger Blattlausarten im Obstbau. Erwerbs-Obstbau 10, pp. 221—226.
— (1969): Studies on the occurrence of different aphid species as the cause of cereal yield and quality losses. Pflanzenschutz-Nachrichten 22, pp. 171—204 (English edition).
— (1971): Studies on the control of nematodes with ®Terracur P in tree nurseries, fruit crops, vegetables and field crops. Pflanzenschutz-Nachrichten Bayer 24, pp. 431—475 (English edition).
— (1978): Untersuchungen über die Blattlausbekämpfung im Pflanzkartoffelbau. Der Kartoffelbau 29, pp. 322—324.
— (1981): Ergebnisse eines Kartoffel-Nachbauversuches. Der Kartoffelbau 32, pp. 352—353.
— (1982): Ursachen und Verhütung der Vergilbungskrankheit. 30 Jahre Vektorenbekämpfung mit systemischen Insektiziden (1952—1982). Die Zuckerrübe 31, pp. 148—150.
— (1982): Importance of potato blight control exemplified by Höfchen long-term trial (1943—1982), and historical development. Pflanzenschutz-Nachrichten Bayer 35, pp. 247—290 (English edition).
Maria Theresia, Römische Kaiserin (1749): Beschreibung, deren Anno 1747 und 1748 in der Wallachey, und Siebenbürgen eingedrungenen Heuschrecken, und was zu deren Ausrottung für Mittel zu gebrauchen seyen. Wien, 7 p.
Ohnesorge, B. (1976): Tiere als Pflanzenschädlinge. Allgemeine Phytopathologie. Georg Thieme Verlag, Stuttgart, 288 p.
Rudy, H. (1925): Die Wanderheuschrecke *Locusta migratoria.* Sonderbeilage zu Badische Blätter für Schädlingsbekämpfung, Vol. 1, 34 p.

## VI. Storage and protection of food supplies

Andersen, K. Th. (1938): Der Kornkäfer (*Calandra granaria* L.), Biologie und Bekämpfung. Verlag Paul Parey, Berlin.
Heinze, K. (1983): Leitfaden der Schädlingsbekämpfung. IV. Vorrats- und Materialschädlinge (Vorratsschutz). Wissenschaftliche Verlagsgesellschaft Stuttgart, 348 p.
Hermann, G., and S. Hombrecher (1962): Control of rats and mice with ®Racumin 57 products. Pflanzenschutz-Nachrichten Bayer 15, pp. 89—108 (English edition).
Holthusen, H. E. (1981): Chicago. Metropolis am Michigansee. R. Piper & Co. Verlag, München-Zürich, 100 p.

Kemper, H. (1950): Die Haus- und Gesundheitsschädlinge und ihre Bekämpfung. Duncker und Humblot, Berlin, 344 p.
Koegel, A. (1925): Das Ungeziefer, seine wirtschaftliche Bedeutung für die deutsche Nutztierhaltung und die wichtigsten Bekämpfungsmethoden. Verlag Enke, Stuttgart.
— (1925): Die Fliegen als Schädlinge der landwirtschaftlichen Tierhaltung und ihre Bekämpfung. Verlag Paul Parey, Berlin.
Spanuth, H. (1981): Der Rattenfänger von Hameln. Vom Werden und Sinn einer alten Sage. 3rd Edn. Verlag C.W. Niemeyer, Hameln, 144 p.
Wille, J. (1920): Biologie und Bekämpfung der deutschen Schabe (*Phyllodromia germanica* L.). Verlag Paul Parey, Berlin, 140 p.
Zacher, F. (1927): Die Vorrats-. Speicher- und Materialschädlinge und ihre Bekämpfung. Verlag Paul Parey, Berlin, 366 p.
— (1944): Vorratsschutz gegen Schädlinge für Bäcker, Müller und Getreidehändler. Verlag Paul Parey, Berlin.
— (1963): Vierzig Jahre Vorratsschutz in Deutschland. Verlag Duncker & Humblot, Berlin, 143 p.
Zacher, F. und B. Lange (1964): Vorratsschutz gegen Schädlinge. 2nd Edn. Verlag Paul Parey, Berlin und Hamburg, 125 p.
Zinsser, H. (1938): Rats, Lice and History. New York.

## VII. Agriculture, forestry and horticulture under ecological aspects

Bezzel, E. (1982): Vögel in der Kulturlandschaft. Verlag Eugen Ulmer, Stuttgart, 350 p.
Blab, J., Nowak, E., Trautmann, W. and H. Sukopp (1981): Rote Liste der gefährdeten Tiere und Pflanzen in der Bundesrepublik Deutschland. Kilda-Verlag, Greven, 66 p.
Cramer, H.H. (1976): Ökonomisch-ökologische Wechselwirkungen. In Wegler, R. (Ed.): Chemie der Pflanzenschutz- und Schädlingsbekämpfungsmittel, Vol. 3, pp. 39—55. Springer-Verlag, Berlin-Heidelberg-New York.
Deutsche Landwirtschafts-Gesellschaft (1981): Landbewirtschaftung und Ökologie. Zwingen ökologische Ziele zu grundlegenden Änderungen der Bewirtschaftung von Acker — Grünland — Wald? DLG-Verlag, Frankfurt (Main), 160 p.
Erz, W. (1982): Schutz der Tier- und Pflanzenwelt. Ed.: Auswertungs- und Informationsdienst für Ernährung, Landwirtschaft und Forsten (AID) e.V., Bonn, Issue 52, 40 p.
Fischbeck, G., Haushofer, H., Renz, F. and D. Schroeder [Ed.] (1981): Landwirtschaft und Wasserhaushalt. Agrarspectrum, Vol. 1. BLV Verlagsgesellschaft, München, 297 p.
Huber, J. (1982): Die verlorene Unschuld der Ökologie. S. Fischer-Verlag, Frankfurt (Main), 232 p.
Hyams, E. (1956): Der Mensch — ein Parasit der Erde? Kultur und Boden im Wandel der Zeitalter. Eugen Diederichs Verlag, Düsseldorf-Köln, 310 p.
Jakob, K. u.a. (1982): Konfliktfeld "Moderne Agrarproduktion". Beiträge zum Ausgleich ökologischer und landwirtschaftlicher Interessen. DLG-Verlag, Frankfurt (Main), 119 p.
Klausewitz, W., Schäfer, W. und W. Tobias (1973): Umwelt 2000. Published by: Senckenbergische Naturforschende Gesellschaft. Verlag Waldemar Kramer, Frankfurt am Main, 126 p.
Kolbe, W. (1965): Beziehungen zwischen Klima, Obstbau und Pflanzenschutz. Pflanzenschutz-Nachrichten Bayer 18 (Special edition), pp. 138—217.
— (1976): Langjähriger Verlauf der Knospen- und Blütenentwicklung bei Apfel- und Birnensorten im Vergleich zu 1975. Erwerbs-Obstbau 18, pp. 53—55.
— (1977): Einfluß der Jahreswitterung 1976, insbesondere des Blütenfrostes und der Sommertrockenheit, auf den Ertrag der Obstarten und -sorten. Erwerbs-Obstbau 19, pp. 118—120.
— (1979): Seasonal course of top and small fruit developmental stages in relation to annual weather and crop protection measures. Pflanzenschutz-Nachrichten Bayer 32, pp. 93—159 (English edition).
— (1982): Einfluß der Blütenfröste auf den Ertrag der Obstarten und -sorten unter Berücksichtigung der Apfelmehltau-Bekämpfung. Erwerbs-Obstbau 24, pp. 34—41.
Larcher, W. (1976): Ökologie der Pflanzen. Verlag Eugen Ulmer, Stuttgart, 320 p.
Mildenberger, H. (1982): Die Vögel des Rheinlandes. Printed by Rheinischer Landwirtschafts-Verlag G.m.b.H., Bonn. Distributed by: Kilda-Verlag, Greven, 400 p.
Schumakow, I.M., Fedorintschik, N.S. and G.W. Gussew (1976): Biologische Pflanzenschutzmittel. VEB Deutscher Landwirtschaftsverlag, Berlin, 205 p.
Walter, H. (1980): Bekenntnisse eines Ökologen. Gustav Fischer Verlag, Stuttgart, 334 p.

## VIII. Types of garden and their significance

Albertus Magnus (13th Century A.D.): De Vegetabilibus Libri VII. Edited by C. Jessen, Berlin 1867, 752 p. Unchanged reprint Minerva GmbH, Frankfurt a. M., 1982.

Balss, H. (1947): Albertus Magnus als Biologe. Große Naturforscher, Edited by Dr. H. W. Frickhinger, Vol. 1. Wissenschaftliche Verlagsgesellschaft m.b.H., Stuttgart, 305 p.

Boros, G. (1975): Unsere Küchen- und Gewürzkräuter. Verlag Eugen Ulmer, Stuttgart, 123 p.

Clifford, D. (1966): Geschichte der Gartenkunst. Prestel-Verlag, München, 453 p.

Heddergott, H. (1982): Gärtners Pflanzenarzt. Blumen, Zierpflanzen, Landschaft. Landwirtschaftsverlag GmbH, Münster-Hiltrup, 713 p.

Hennebo, D. und A. Hoffmann (1962—1965): Geschichte der Gartenkunst. Vols. 1—3. Broschek-Verlag, Hamburg, 930 p.

Johnson, H. (1975): Das große Buch der Bäume. Ein Führer durch Wälder, Parks und Gärten der Welt. Hallwag Verlag, Bern and Stuttgart, 287 p.

Kordt, W. (1965): Die Gärten von Bruehl. Untersuchungen über die Entstehung und Durchführung des Brühler Parkplans und die Mitwirkung Dominique Girards. Verlag M. Du Mont Schauberg, Köln, 165 p.

Ostlender, H. (1980): Albertus Magnus. 3rd Edn., 56 p. Publ. by: die Dominikaner an St. Andreas, Köln.

Sanders, H., Wiesen, I. and U. H. Krieger (1975): Naturparks in Deutschland. Mairs Geographischer Verlag, Stuttgart, 240 p.

Seifert, A. (1975): Gärtnern, Ackern — ohne Gift. 7th Edn. Biederstein-Verlag, München, 210 p.

## IX. Foundations of food production

Abel, W. (1980): Strukturen und Krisen der spätmittelalterlichen Wirtschaft. Gustav Fischer Verlag, Stuttgart and New York, 132 p.

Aubert, C. (1981): Organischer Landbau. Verlag Eugen Ulmer, Stuttgart, 248 p.

Brugger (1981): Landbau — alternativ und konventionell. Publ. by: Auswertungs- und Informationsdienst für Ernährung, Landwirtschaft und Forsten (AID) e.V., Bonn, Issue 70, 46 p.

Commissie Onderzoek Biologische Landbouwmethoden (1977): Alternatieve Landbouwmethoden. Inventarisatie, evaluatie en aanbevelingen voor onderzoek. Pudoc, Centrum voor Landbouwpublicaties en landbouwdocumentatie, Wageningen, 398 p.

Ennen, E. und W. Janssen (1979): Deutsche Agrargeschichte. Vom Neolithikum bis zur Schwelle des Industriezeitalters. Franz Steiner Verlag GmbH, Wiesbaden, 272 p.

Freckmann, W. (1947): Anthroposophie und Landwirtschaft. Verlag A. Lutzeyer, Bad Oeynhausen, 15 p.

Gimpel, J. (1975): Die industrielle Revolution des Mittelalters. Artemis Verlag, Zürich und München (1980), 280 p.

Glatzel, H. (1977): Sinn und Unsinn in der Diätetik. XII. "Biologisch" oder mineral gedüngt? Die medizinische Welt 28 (new series), pp. 253—260 and pp. 307—311.

Gothau, W. und H. Weyland (1973): Lehrbuch der Paläobotanik. BLV Verlagsgesellschaft, München, 611 p.

Graf, U. (1977): Darstellung verschiedener biologischer Landbaumethoden und Abklärung des Einflusses kosmischer Konstellationen auf das Pflanzenwachstum. Dissertation, Eidgenössische Technische Hochschule Zürich.

Hinrichs, F. (1959): Altenberger Höfe zwischen Wupper und Dhünn. Ein Beitrag zur bergischen Agrargeschichte. Editor: Rhein-Wupper-Kreis, 79 p.

Keyserlingk, A. Graf von (1974): Koberwitz 1924. Geburtsstunde einer neuen Landwirtschaft. Verlag Hilfswerk Elisabeth, Stuttgart, 185 p.

Klein, E. (1969): Geschichte der deutschen Landwirtschaft. Verlag Eugen Ulmer, Stuttgart, 93 p.

Könemann, E. (1940): Reichsminister Darré erklärt sich für den biologischen Landbau. Bebauet die Erde (Organ für biologische Wirtschaftsweise), 16th annual volume, Issue 2.

— (1940): Wie steht es um den biologischen Landbau? Bebauet die Erde (Organ für biologische Wirtschaftsweise), 16th annual volume, Issue 2.

Koepf, H. H. (1979): Was ist biologisch-dynamischer Landbau? 2nd Edn. Philosophisch-Anthroposophischer Verlag, Goetheanum Dornach/Switzerland, 36 p.

— (1980): Landbau natur- und menschengemäß. Methoden und Praxis der biologisch-dynamischen Landwirtschaft. Verlag Freies Geistesleben GmbH, Stuttgart, 270 p.

Lehmann, E. and H. Kummer (1937): Der Schwarzrost, seine Geschichte, seine Biologie und seine Bekämpfung in Verbindung mit der Berberitzenfrage. J. F. Lehmann Verlag, München and Berlin, 584 p.

Neubauer, H. (1931): Über die biologisch-dynamische Wirtschaftsweise. Mitteilungen der deutschen Landwirtschafts-Gesellschaft, 46th annual volume, pp. 634—635.

Pernoud, R. (1979): Überflüssiges Mittelalter? Plädoyer für eine verkannte Epoche. Artemis-Verlag Zürich und München, 170 p.

Pfeiffer, E. E. (1977): Rudolf Steiners landwirtschaftlicher Impuls. In: Krück v. Poturzyn, M. J. (Ed.): Wir erlebten Rudolf Steiner. Verlag Freies Geistesleben GmbH, Stuttgart, pp. 169—187.

Pfeiffer, M. W. (1975): Die landwirtschaftliche Individualität — ein Bild des Menschen, zum Verständnis der Präparate der biologisch-dynamischen Wirtschaftsweise. Author and publisher: M. W. Pfeiffer, Schloß Hamborn, Borchen, 68 p.

Popp, M. (1930): Anthroposophische Landwirtschaft. Zeitschrift für Pflanzenernährung, Düngung und Bodenkunde. Vol. IX, pp. 250—256.

Ribbe, W. (1980): Die Wirtschaftstätigkeit der Zisterzienser im Mittelalter: Agrarwirtschaft. In: Elm, K., Joerißen, P. and H. J. Roth (Ed.): Die Zisterzienser, Ordensleben zwischen Ideal und Wirklichkeit, pp. 203—214. Rheinland-Verlag in Kommission bei Rudolf Habelt Verlag GmbH, Bonn.

Rocznik, K. (1982): Wetter und Klima in Deutschland. S. Hirzel Verlag, Stuttgart, 148 p.

Scharrer, K. (1934): Die biologisch-dynamische Düngung im Lichte der Agrikulturchemie. Chemiker-Zeitung 58, pp. 245—247 and pp. 267—270.

Schaumann, W. (1981): Die biologisch-dynamische Wirtschaftsweise in der Auseinandersetzung mit der Naturwissenschaft unserer Zeit. In: Becker, K. E. and H.-P. Schreiner (Ed.): Anthroposophie heute. Kindler Verlag GmbH, München, pp. 106—134.

Schulz, G. (1943): Goethe und die bäuerliche Welt. 2nd Edn. Goslar, 400 p.

Schwarzbach, M. (1974): Das Klima der Vorzeit. Eine Einführung in die Paläoklimatologie. Ferdinand Enke-Verlag, Stuttgart, 380 p.

Seipp, D., Seipp, E., Großgebauer, A. and G. Hentschel (1983): Keine Angst vor Pflanzenschutz und Düngung. (Ed.): Zentralverband Gartenbau e.V., Bonn, 32 p.

Steiner, R. (1925): Geisteswissenschaftliche Grundlagen zum Gedeihen der Landwirtschaft. Landwirtschaftlicher Kursus. Rudolf Steiner Verlag, Dornach/Switzerland, 6th Edn. 1979, 308 p.

Tillet, M. (1755): Dissertations on the cause of the corruption and smutting of the kernels of wheat in the head and on the means of preventing these untoward circumstances. Reprint: Phytopathological Classics No. 5, American Phytopathological Society Ithaca, N. Y., 1970.

Vetter, H., Kampe, W. and K. Ranfft (1983): Qualität pflanzlicher Nahrungsmittel. Ergebnisse dreijähriger Vergleichsuntersuchungen an Gemüse, Obst und Brot des modernen und alternativen Warenangebots. Author and publisher: Verband Deutscher Landwirtschaftlicher Untersuchungs- und Forschungsanstalten (VDLUFA), Darmstadt, 147 p.

Wehnelt, B. (1943): Die Pflanzenpathologie der deutschen Romantik. Bonner Universitäts-Buchdruckerei Gebr. Scheur, G.m.b.H., 237 p.

Willmann, K. Th. [Ed.] (1981): Steiner, R., Naturgrundlagen der Ernährung. Verlag Freies Geistesleben GmbH, Stuttgart, 171 p.

## X. Developments and tasks in agriculture

Baade, F. (1960): Der Wettlauf zum Jahre 2000. Paradies oder Selbstvernichtung. Gerhard Stalling Verlag, Oldenburg, 272 p.

Ballod, K. (1912): Wieviel Menschen kann die Erde ernähren? Jahrbuch für Gesetzgebung, Verwaltung und Volkswirtschaft, 36th annual volume, pp. 81—102.

Barney, G., o' (1980): Global 2000. Der Bericht an den Präsidenten. Editor: Council on Environmental Quality und US-Außenministerium, Washington DC (German translation). 1508 p.

Bechmann, A., Michelsen, G. [Ed.] (1981): Global Future. Es ist Zeit zu handeln. Dreisam-Verlag, Freiburg i. Br., 190 p.

Bosinger, J. (1925): Der Agrarstaat in Platons Gesetzen. Klio, Beiträge zur alten Geschichte, Supplement 17, 121 p. Reprint: Scienta-Verlag, Aalen, 1963.

Burckhardt, J. (1905): Weltgeschichtliche Betrachtungen. First edition Verlag W. Spemann, Berlin and Stuttgart. Edition Verlag Neske (n.d.).

Chargaff, E. (1979): Das Feuer des Heraklit. Skizzen aus einem Leben vor der Natur. Verlagsgemeinschaft Klett-Cotta, Stuttgart, 290 p.

— (1980): Unbegreifliches Geheimnis. Wissenschaft als Kampf für und gegen die Natur. Verlagsgemeinschaft Klett-Cotta, Stuttgart, 226 p.
Clark, C. (1975): Der Mythos von der Überbevölkerung. Adamas-Verlag, Köln, 148 p.
Collins, J. and F. Moore Lappé (1980): Vom Mythos des Hungers. Die Entlarvung eine Legende: Niemand muß hungern. Fischer Taschenbuch Verlag, 479 p.
Commonwealth Agricultural Bureaux (1980): Perspectives in World Agriculture. Ed.: Commonwealth Agricultural Bureaux, Farnham Royal, Slough England, 532 p.
Darwin, C. (1859): Die Entstehung der Arten: Philipp Reclam Jun., Stuttgart, 693 p., 1963.
FAO (1981): Landwirtschaft 2000. Landwirtschaftsverlag, Münster-Hiltrup, 222 p.
Flechtheim, O. K. (1980): Der Kampf um die Zukunft. Grundlagen der Futurologie. Verlag J. H. W. Dietz Nachf. GmbH, Bonn and Berlin, 432 p.
Jonas, H. (1979): Das Prinzip Verantwortung. Versuch einer Ethik für die technologische Zivilisation. Insel Verlag, Frankfurt a. M., 424 p.
Jungk, R. and H. J. Mundt [Ed.] (1966): Das umstrittene Experiment: Der Mensch. Modelle für eine neue Welt. Verlag Kurt Desch, München, Wien and Basel, 446 p.
Kant, J. (1795): Zum ewigen Frieden. Ein philosophischer Entwurf. Verlag Friedrich Nicoloius, Königsberg. In: Kant, J. Von den Träumen der Vernunft. Fourier Verlag, Wiesbaden, 1979.
Meadows, De., Meadows, Do., Zahn, E. and P. Milling (1972): Die Grenzen des Wachstums. Bericht des Club of Rome zur Lage der Menschheit. Deutsche Verlags-Anstalt, Stuttgart, 180 p.
Metternich, A. (1949): Die Wüste droht. Die gefährdete Nahrungsgrundlage der menschlichen Gesellschaft. Friedrich Trüjen Verlag, Bremen, 275 p.
Montandon, R. (1923): Une carte mondiale de distribution geographique des calamitées. Revue Intern. de la Croix-Rouge 5 (52), pp. 271—344.
Müller, R. (1982): New Genesis. Doubleday & Company, Inc., New York, 192 p.
Niehaus, H. (1976): Den Agrarpolitikern ins Gedächtnis. Wege und Irrwege der Agrarpolitik. Verlag Pflug und Feder, Bonn, 325 p.
Overhage, P. (1977): Die biologische Zukunft der Menschheit. Verlag Josef Knecht, Frankfurt am Main, 240 p.
Paul VI. (1967): Popularum Progressio. Über den Fortschritt der Völker. Paulus-Verlag, Recklinghausen, 45 p.
Peccei, A. (1981): Die Zukunft in unserer Hand. Gedanken und Reflexionen des Präsidenten des Club of Rome. Verlag Fritz Molden, Wien-München-Zürich-New York, 224 p.
Schatz, O. [Ed.] (1981): Brauchen wir eine andere Wissenschaft? X. Salzburger Humanismusgespräch. Verlag Styria, Graz-Wien-Köln, 280 p.
Schell, J. (1982): Das Schicksal der Erde. R. Piper & Co. Verlag, München and Zürich, 268 p.
Schippke, U. (1975): Zukunft. Das Bild der Welt von morgen. Bertelsmann Reinhard Mohn GmbH, Gütersloh, 203 p.
Sörgel, H. (1932): Atlantropa. Verlag Fretz & Wasmuth A. G., Zürich and Verlag Piloty & Loehle, München, 145 p.
— (1938): Die drei großen „A". Amerika, Atlantropa, Asien. Verlag Piloty & Loehle, München, 127 p.
The Brandt Commission (1983): Common Crisis North-South: Cooperation for world recovery. Mit Press, Cambridge Mass., 174 p.
Thünen, J. H. von (1842—1850): Der isolierte Staat in Beziehung auf Landwirtschaft und Nationalökonomie. 2nd and 1st Edn. Leopold's-Universitäts-Buchhandlung. Rostock. Gustav Fischer Verlag, Stuttgart, 4th Edn., 1966.
Tucker, W. (1982): Progress and Privilege. Anchor Press, New York, 314 p.
Weizsäcker, C. F. von (1978): Der Garten des Menschlichen. Beiträge zur geschichtlichen Anthropologie. Carl Hauser Verlag, München-Wien, 612 p.

## Illustration Sources

Colour plate design: M. Elsässer

Colour photographs: Bayer Planzenschutz Leverkusen

Other photographs:

Heresbach portrait, from Wolters (1867), p. 17
Heresbach estate, H.-M. Ulbrich, p. 17
Ryswickshof, Photo Klaus Endermann, Wesel, p. 18
Höfchen Farm, H.-M. Ulbrich, p. 19
Höfchen emblem, StD F. Dippel, p. 19
Spice plant cultivation in Canada (Winnipeg 1983), Dr. W. Kolbe, p. 85
Asparagus harvest, Dr. W. Schiffer, p. 85
Giant Stropharia, Dipl. rer. hort. H. Steinbeck, p. 86
Automatic harvester 1904, from Fruwirth (1923), p. 99
Automatic harvester 1983, H.-M. Ulbrich, p. 100
Edict of Frederick the Great, Archive of Dr. H.-H. Cramer, p. 140—143
Board of Trade Building Chicago 1983, Dr. W. Kolbe, p. 159

Thanks are expressed to the Gerhard-Marcks-Foundation, Bremen, for permission to reproduce the woodcut "The Ploughman".

---

## Acknowledgement

For cooperation and participation in the talks and reports we thank Mrs. I. Pahl-Lelley and Dr. H. Bold, for critical review of the manuscript Dr. Maria Cramer-Middendorf and also Dr. H.-H. Cramer, Dr. G. Haug and Dr. S. Hombrecher, for detailed revisions Mrs. A. Bruns, for corrections Mrs. S. Hohmann, for design Mr. M. Elsässer, for publishing assistance Mr. W. Schüßler and all those who assisted in the preparation and broadcasting of the talks and reports over two decades and in preparing the manuscript and obtaining the photographs and documents.

# Explanations

The abbreviations and terms used in the text are explained below.

### Units of measurement for energy in nutritional physiology

The term calorie used in the text is the large calorie or kilocalorie (kcal), commonly used in nutritional science; 1 kcal = 1000 calories = 4186.8 joules (J) = 4.1868 kilojoules (kJ).

The calorie (calor = heat) is a unit denoting a given quantity of heat. Whereas in engineering 1 calorie (cal) is defined as the amount of heat needed to raise the temperature of 1 g water from 14.5° C to 15.5° C, in nutritional science the heat and energy generating capacity of foods is measured in large calories (kcal). The calorific requirement of man depends on body size, weight and age. The basal metabolism in the fully resting state is 1500 to 1750 calories (cal) and decreases with advancing age. For additional exertion or working metabolism, 400 to 600 calories are needed for light work, 500 to 1000 for moderately hard work and 800 to 1600 for heavy work. The values for women are lower than those for men.

The calorific contents of all foods are expressed in so-called calorimeters, although this physical calorific value is not identical to the physiological value on combustion in the body. Accepted mean values of the physiological caloric values are 9.3 calories for 1 g fat, and 4.1 calories for 1 g carbohydrate and for 1 g protein.

Joules have recently replaced large calories (kcal) as units of caloric value. 1 large calorie or kilocalorie (kcal) is equivalent to 4186.8 joules (J) or 4.186 kilojoules (kJ). 1500 calories (kcal) basal metabolism are equivalent to 6280 kilojoules (kJ).

### Units of measurement for weights

t = ton; 1 t = 10 dt = 1000 kg
dt = deciton; 1 dt = 1 metric centner = 100 kg
kg = kilogram; 1 kg = 1000 grams (g)
$km^2$ = square kilometre; 1 $km^2$ = 1,000,000 $m^2$ = 100 ha
ha = hectare; 1 ha = 10,000 $m^2$

### Abbreviations of organizations

About 14,000 international organizations exist throughout the world, of which the small number mentioned in the text are now explained.

EC = European Community

Headquarters: Brussels, Luxembourg and Strasbourg, 18,000 employees, 10 member countries with 270 million citizens (Belgium, Federal Republic of Germany, Denmark, France, Greece, Great Britain, Ireland, Italy, Luxembourg, Netherlands.)

It was established mainly on the basis of three treaties:

1. Treaty of Paris of the European Community for Coal and Steel (Montanunion) of 18.4.1951 for 50 years; 2. Treaty of Rome of the European Economic Community (EEC) of 25.3.1957 for an unlimited period and 3. European Atomic Community (Euratom) of 25.3.1957.

The EC is the first and only supranational association of European countries and is dedicated to the peace and welfare of Europe. The task of the EC is to guarantee the free traffic of goods with common external tariffs and free passage of persons, services and capital through the creation of a unified economic area of all the member countries with removal of international trade barriers. Since its founding, more than 40,000 orders and directives have been issued to this effect, of which about 3,700 are currently in force.

Countries willing to join are Spain and Portugal. Agreements also exist with third countries such as the five countries of the Eurpoean Free Trade Area (EFTA), with 12 countries bordering the Mediterranean, with the USA, Australia, the People's Republic of China and India and also with the Association of South East Asian Nations (ASEAN) and, according to the Agreement of Lomé (1981) with 60 countries of Africa, the Caribbean and the Pacific (ACP countries).

FAO = Food and Agriculture Organization of the United Nations

Founded: 1945; Headquarters: Rome (Italy), 147 countries are members of the FAO. It is the largest international organization in the world, its aim is the development and promotion of agriculture to secure the world's food supply and hence man's basic needs. The symbol of the FAO is an ear of wheat with the inscriptions FAO and FIAT PANIS (let there be bread). The precursor organization of the FAO was the International Agricultural Institute in Rome founded in 1905.

UNO or UN = United Nations Organization

Founded: 1945; Headquarters: New York (USA), 157 countries are members of UNO.

UNO is dedicated to preserving peace through the proscription of war and the promotion of disarmament, and by guaranteeing personal freedom and upholding human rights. The symbol of the UNO is the globe with olive branches on a light blue ground.

The forerunner organization of UNO was the League of Nations from 1920—1946 with headquarters in Geneva. Germany joined the League of Nations in 1926 and withdrew in 1933. Exclusion of the Soviet Union in 1940 following its invasion of Finland led to the League of Nations being disbanded after the Second World War in 1946.

WHO = World Health Organization of United Nations

Founded: 7.4.1948 (World Health Day), headquarters: Geneva (Switzerland), 155 countries are members of WHO. The aim of WHO is the provision of medical aid to underdeveloped and distressed regions and the control of epidemics (malaria, yellow fever) and advice on matters of health for all member countries. As long ago as 1907, the International Office of Health was founded with headquarters in Paris, whose duties were assumed by WHO including the Medical Agreement on marine, land and air transportation.

**Miscellaneous**

N = nitrogen

Nmin = mineralized nitrogen

The nitrogen supply of plants depends not only on the utilization of the nitrogen supplied by organic and inorganic fertilizer, but also on the mobilization by mineralization and nitrification of the total potential of nitrogen present in the soil, where it is bound in organic and mineral form. About 1 to 3% of the total amount of nitrogen present in our arable soils become available to plants every year through mineralization, which can be equivalent to 20 to 150 kg/ha, an amount which must be taken into account when applying nitrogen fertilizers. According to the Wehrmann method, the amount of mineralized nitrogen (Nmin) found at a depth of up to 100 cm by means of soil analysis performed in spring is used for calculating the respective nitrogen dose. If a dose of 120 kg/ha pure nitrogen is envisaged for the area in question, the amount of mineralized nitrogen present in the soil and thus available to plants is subtracted. If the Nmin value determined by soil analysis is 40 kg/ha, the quantity of mineral fertilizer intended for application should be reduced by this amount. In our example, therefore, only 80 kg/ha pure nitrogen would then be dosed.

## List of names with brief biographies*

Albertus Magnus (1193—1280), p. 179, 185

Theologian (Dominican), philosopher, peacemaker and natural scientist, one of the major thinkers of the Middle Ages who made the philosophical and scientific world view of Aristotle fruitful for Christian theology. His complete works, comprising more than 40 volumes, were written during a varied carreer following a study of theology in Cologne, as lector in the Dominican conventions of Hildesheim, Freiburg i.Br., Regensburg and Strasbourg, as professor at the University of Paris, provincial prior of the German Dominicans, Bishop of Regensburg and as senior lecturer and founder of the "studium generale" in Cologne, later the University, in Germany's then largest city. As a researcher in sciences, he was the first to undertake and describe his observations (experimenta) in a precise and systematic manner.

In the 7th and final book of his botanical works, in which he describes a total of 350 plant species, he observed the transition of plants in agriculture and horticulture from the wild to the cultivated state, the wild plant being improved in cultivation by means of the four processes of fertilization, soil cultivation, sowing and grafting. Fertilizer, referred to as "laetamen" or plant happiness, is used for fertilization and upgrades plants to the cultivated state by improving their nutrition. Soil cultivation creates a more even soil quality, and as a remedy for moist and cold soil he recommended not only dewatering but also admixtures of marl (argila fossa), while in salty water and salty earth it is mainly trees which perish. Moist soils can be improved by growing broad beans. The fields must be fertilized if they are to remain fertile. Aromatic plants such as grapevine and, of the cereals, oats should preferably be cultivated on slopes, and wheat and barley in valleys. In the cultivation of fruit trees, the soil around the trunk must be kept free of weeds, and eggs of caterpillars which eat the leaves must be removed and burned in January. He also writes: If the soil is too moist, the fruits become rotten and from the putrefying mass worms develop which gnaw at the fruits and make them useless.

On the laying of ornamental gardens (viridaria) he writes: "There are certain places which are prepared not for their usefulness or for the production of fruit, but solely for pleasure, which are called

* The list of names states only the page numbers of the text as quotation references and not those of the index of literature references.

ornamental gardens. They are established to give pleasure particularly to two senses, namely those of sight and smell. The eyes enjoy nothing so much as the sight of fine grass which is not too long. The place where the pleasure gardens are to be laid out must therefore first be freed from all roots by digging them out, and then the area must be levelled and wetted thoroughly with boiling water, so that the remains of the roots and the seeds lying hidden in the ground are scorched and can no longer germinate. Then the area must be laid with thin pieces of lawn containing fine grass and then these lawn sections should be firmly pressed in place using broad, wooden hammers and the grass stamped down with the feet until it is scarcely visible or disappears completely. The grass then shoots up with very fine blades and covers the surface like a green cloth".

He is the only scholar in world history who has been titled "The Great". His works are still preserved at the Albertus Magnus Institute in Bonn. In front of Cologne University, founded in 1388, a bronze sculpture created in 1955 by Gerhard Marcks stands in memory of the great Cologne scholar who died in Cologne on 12.11.1280 and whose grave is to be found in the St. Andreas-Kirche.

Archilochos (650 B.C.), p. 183

Greek poet and the first historically definable personality of Europe.

Aristotle (384—322 B.C.), p. 102

Greek philosopher, tutor to Alexander the Great, pupil of Plato, taught in Athens, and died on his farm at Chalkis on Euboea.

Bacon, Roger (1219—1294), p. 200

English theologian (Franciscan) and philosopher with many scientific interests and achievements, who anticipated many inventions of the modern age.

Benn, Gottfried (1886—1957), p. 159

Physician and poet, after studying theology, philology and medicine, medical specialist in Berlin and poet of Expressionism. 1932 member of the Prussian Academy of Arts, 1935 to 1945 political disguise as military doctor, achieving the rank of Colonel (Medical Corps). His essay "Does Carleton deserve a memorial?" published in 1932 deals with the overproduction of cereals in the world economic crisis. In his essay "Goethe and the sciences" also published in 1932 on the centenary of Goethe's death, he examined the view of Goethe as a natural scientist who, in contrast to modern attitudes, considered nature without speculating on its uses. In his Berlin short story "Ptolemy" published in 1947 he described the period of deprivation, cold and hunger in the aftermath of the Second World War.

Berlese, Antonio (1846—1927), p. 137

Italian entomologist, professor of entomology in Portici specializing in applied science, who rose to particular prominence at the beginning of this century by introducing the bait method for the control of fruit flies and locusts, known as the Berlese method. In 1909 he also produced a seminal work on the history of entomology and his major work "Gli Insetti", one of the most important books on insects.

Bodelschwingh, Friedrich von (1831—1910), p. 42

Protestant theologian and director of Bethel asylum near Bielefeld, the largest charitable foundation of the Home Mission. His first occupation was that of farmer and he was trained by Johann Gottlieb Koppe (1782—1863) in Oderbruch in the middle of last century. In 1882, near Bethel, he founded Wilhelmsdorf farming colony (125 hectares) where "vagrants" and unemployed persons found work, shelter and food in return for cultivating wasteland.

Bosch, Carl (1874—1940), p. 103

Chemist and engineer, 1919 Chairman of the Board of Management of Badische Anilin- und Sodafabrik, 1925—1935 Chairman of the Board of Mangement and from 1935 of the Supervisory Board of I.-G. Farbenindustrie Aktiengesellschaft. The name Carl Bosch is associated through the Haber-Bosch process mainly with ammonia synthesis, a process which utilizes the elementary nitrogen in the air on a commercial scale through conversion into soluble nitrogen compounds, making it available as fertilizer. Nobel prize for chemistry 1931.

Boussingault, Jean Baptiste (1802—1887), p. 102

French agricultural chemist, professor of agriculture and analytical chemistry at the Paris Conservatoire des Arts et Métiers. After a twelve year study of metereology and geology in South America, from 1834—1874 he carried out trials on soil fertility, nitrogen fixation in plants and soil and especially in leguminous plants on his agricultural farming establishment in Bechelbronn in Alsace, which he developed into an experimental farm.

Breughel (Brueghel), Pieter the Elder (1525—1569), p. 206

Dutch painter (known as "peasant Breughel"). Known among other things as a landscape painter and for his paintings of the everyday world of peasants, e.g. "Grain Harvest" (1565). His son, Pieter the Younger (1564—1638) also painted pictures of rustic scenes and winter landscapes.

Burger, Johann (1773—1842), p. 34, 35

Professor of agriculture at Klagenfurt, wrote several agricultural textbooks, including some on maize cultivation.

Charlemagne, King of the Franks and Roman Emperor (724—814 A.D.), p. 9, 205

During his 45 year reign he waged several wars and decreed many laws and orders (capitularies). To promote agricultural production, the Farming Estates Order was enacted around 800 for the imperial estates and landlordism was introduced with the socage farm constitution. The landlord holds domain over ground and soil, farming is carried on against payment of rent or through the employment of free or unfree workers. Farming was carried on according to the three crop rotation with winter cereal, spring cereal and fallowing. Charlemagne (Charles I, the Great) was the first ruler of the west which was made up of Roman and Germanic peoples with Christian ideas.

Columella, L. Junius Moderatus (1st century A.D.), p. 16

Roman farmer, in his work De re rustica (On farming) comprising twelve books written around 60 A.D., he gives descriptions of farming and animal husbandry in the Roman age.

Darwin, Charles Robert (1809—1882), p. 207

English naturalist, after education as a theologian travelled throughout the world as a naturalist. Through his observations and reflections on his expeditions he came to realize that present-day organisms are the result of a long evolutionary or developmental history, whose most important mechanism he recognized as being selection. In 1859 his celebrated major work "On the Origin of Species . . ." was published and in 1868 followed "Variation in Animals and Plants under Domestication". From 1842 he lived for forty years on his estate in Down where he dedicated himself to his scientific studies, which included an investigation of the importance of the earthworm for soil fertility.

Davy, Sir Humphrey (1778—1829), p. 102

English chemist, from 1802 held lectures on agricultural chemistry and originated the term "agrochemistry". He discovered, among other things, (1807—1808) the elements sodium, potassium, calcium, strontium, barium and magnesium.

Dioskorides, Pedanius (1st century A.D.), p. 180

Greek physician, composed a work on medicines in five books which retained its importance as a textbook of pharmacology and pharmacy for more than 1500 years up to the modern era.

Döring, Wilhelm Ludwig (19th century), p. 130

General medical practitioner in Remscheid, member of the Imperial Leopoldian = Carolingian Academy of Natural Scientists, produced numerous medical and scientific works, pre-eminent among which is his book "On the Queen among Flowers or the Higher Significance of the Rose"

Ezekiel (6th century B.C.), p. 10

Old Testament prophet.

Fabre, Jean Henri (1823—1915), p. 210

French entomologist and scientific writer, professor of sciences and natural history in Avignon etc., experimental investigations in biology, including the instincts of insects. He summarized his zoological observations and research results, including those on natural history, with great literary talent in numerous publications, particulary in his major work "Souvenirs entomologiques", which was published in ten volumes from 1879 to 1907. He was proposed for the Nobel prize for literature in 1910.

Fraile, E. Morales y (20th century), p. 11

Qualified agricultural engineer, Spanish member of the Central Committee of the International Research Association of Agricultural Broadcasting (Rome), at the XVII. International Agricultural Congress held from 6—12.6.1939 in Dresden, on knowledge so far acquired regarding the significance of broadcasting for agriculture.

Frederick II, the Great, King of Prussia (1712—1786), p. 43, 134, 139—143, 206

Promoted agriculture by means of extensive soil improvement programmes (dredging of the swamps between Warta and Notec rivers), settlement of 57,000 families and division of public land. On demesnes, liberation of the peasant class was commenced and yield capacity improved through the introduction of the English crop rotation. Played a major role in introducing the potato as a staple food. The Edict on Locust Control reproduced on pages 140—143 shows how important securing of harvests was at this time to guarantee food supplies for the population.

Fuchs, Leonhard (1502—1566), p. 63

Professor in Tübingen, published a book of herbs with illustrations which was printed in Latin in 1542 and in German in 1543 in Basle. He describes more than 500 species of plants, including cultivated plants and weeds. The plant genus fuchsia, indigenous to America and New Zealand, was named after him. The fuchsias now cultivated here as ornamentals are mainly hybrid varieties.

Gilbert, Joseph Henry (1817—1901), p. 102

English agricultural chemist (cf. Lawes, p. 235)

Goethe, Johann Wolfgang von (1749—1832), p. 128, 200

Lawyer, statesman, writer and natural scientist, Germany's greatest poet. After completing his study of jurisprudence, admitted to advocacy in Frankfurt a. M., practised at Supreme Reich Court of Justice in Wetzlar, entered the service of the Duke of Sachsen-Weimar as Privy Legation Councellor, 1776, 1779 Privy Councellor, 1782 ennoblement and appointment as President of the Chamber of Finance, 1804 Working Privy Councellor, 1815 Minister of State. In addition to his duties as statesman and extensive artistic activities, from his time in Weimar Goethe was concerned primarily with research into the natural sciences; in 1803 he also assumed the directorship of the scientific institutes of the university in Jena. His many scientific writings which in the large Weimar edition comprise 14 volumes, commence in 1782 with the essay "Nature" published in the Tiefurt Journal. With his work "The Metamorphosis of Plants" published in 1790, he became the founder of plant morphology. In addition to works on viniculture, hops, the metamorphosis of animals and meteorology, his essay "The Experiment as Mediator of Subject and Object" has particular topicality. The promotion of agriculture in the dukedom of Saxony-Weimar took the form of the establishment of model farms and the introduction of fruit cultivation. In 1826, The Agricultural Institute of the University of Jena was established. In 1798, Goethe acquired his own agricultural enterprise, Roßla freehold estate near Weimar, which however had to be sold in 1803 because of management difficulties.

Haber, Fritz (1868—1934), p. 103

Chemist, 1911—1933 director of the Kaiser-Wilhelm Institute of Physical Chemistry in Berlin. In 1933 he emigrated to the University of Cambridge. In addition to numerous other chemical researches, the reactions of nitrogen became his main field of investigation. He received the Nobel prize for chemistry (cf. also Bosch) in 1918 for his success in synthesizing ammonia from atmospheric nitrogen in 1908.

## Heresbach, Konrad (1496—1576), p. 11, 12, 13, 17, 18

Lawyer, statesman, multi-talented scholar (humanist) and practical farmer, was born on 2.8.1496 at Heresbach farm in Mettmann-Hahnenfurth. This farm with its original buildings still exists and is run by the descendants of the Heresbach family. From 1503 he attended the abbey school in Werden an der Ruhr, also in Hamm and from 1510 the cathedral school in Münster. In 1512 he commenced his studies in the liberal arts faculty of the University of Cologne where he received the degree of magister artium in 1515; this was followed by two years' study of jurisprudence in Cologne and two years at French universities, 1521 at the recommendation of Erasmus of Rotterdam, professor of Greek science in Freiburg, 1522 received the degree of doctor of civil law at the University of Ferrara. On 1.9.1523 he assumed the position at the ducal court of Cleves of tutor to hereditary prince Wilhelm who, as future lord of the dukedom of Cleves, Jülich, Berg and the counties of Mark and Ravensberg, entered the history books as Wilhelm "the Rich" and in 1545 founded the "Gymnasium Illustre" in Düsseldorf as the forerunner of the present university. At the same time he became adviser to the ruling duke Johann III (The Peaceful). In 1535 he was appointed "Privy Councillor to the Dukedom of Cleves", in 1536 he married Mechelt von Dunen who brought with her as dowry from her mother's side Lorward farm situated on an island on the Rhine near Wesel. Heresbach immediately took up residence at Lorward farm, built a new dwelling there in 1538 and managed this farm until his death there on 14.10.1576, that is for a period of 40 years. He transformed this farm into a model estate and described his agricultural experience and knowledge in his celebrated agricultural work "Rei rusticae libri quatuor" (Four Books on Agriculture) which was printed in Latin in Cologne in 1570, was published by Johannes Birckmann of Cologne and which two years later was translated into English but not into German. By 1606, seven editions of the Latin version of this first German book on domestic agriculture had appeared, and by 1631 a total of ten editions of the English translation. A German translation of the first book appeared in 1970, a reprint of the English edition in 1971 and a Handbook of Thereutics (hunting, fowling, fishery) in 1977.

Heresbach, who also produced extremely varied legal, pedagogical and religious writings and who possessed a substantial library of 2,000 volumes on his Lorward estate, was also particularly prominent as a humanist and religious conciliator during the Reformation period. After his death, he was buried in the transept of Heresbach chapel of the protestant Willibrordi Cathedral in Wesel, where he is still commemorated by a tombstone. The Heresbach Study Foundation for the advancement of gifted and diligent scholars and students from the neighbourhood or from the cities of Wesel, Kalkar, Nijmegen, Düsseldorf, Hamm and Werder has existed for more than 400 years.

It should be noted that the island of Lorward no longer exists after a change in the course of the Rhine but is now part of the village of Mehr of the community Haffen-Mehr in Rees rural district. The Heresbach estate of Lorward was later divided up into Ryswickshof (60 hectares) and Hagenshof (40 hectares). The former existed until 1968 after its last owner, farmer Heinz Heicks, had sold Ryswickshof for gravel quarrying, leaving a lake from the flooded workings in its place. A new dwelling house was built on its banks. Into this house have been incorporated three commemorative stone slabs with inscriptions which originate from the Heresbach farmhouse.

## Herodotus (484—424 B.C.), p. 13

Founder of Greek historiography, travelled through Egypt, Babylon, the Black Sea, Italy and North Africa, describing the countries and peoples of the then known world in his historical works.

## Homer (8th century B.C.), p. 10

Greek poet of the Iliad and Odyssey epics comprising 28,000 verses. The Iliad describes an episode from the ten-year siege of Troy, and the Odyssey relates the adventures of Odysseus, King of Ithaca, during a sea journey following the conquest of Troy over the ten years of his delayed return to Ithaca.

## Joel (4th century B.C.), p. 125

Old Testament prophet. The book of Joel refers to disasters caused by pests during this period. He interpreted droughts and plagues of locusts as presaging the end of the world.

Kant, Immanuel (1724—1804), p. 215

Philosopher and professor at the University of Königsberg founded in 1544, one of the greatest thinkers of the western world. In his major work "Critique of Pure Reason" published in 1781, he writes: "Reason must approach nature with its principles in one hand and experiment in the other, not as a pupil who allows himself to be taught, but as a judge who requires the witnesses to answer his questions." His work "Perpetual Peace", written in 1795, served as the foundation for the League of Nations after the first World War and of UNO after the Second World War. In this treatise he writes that wars are irreconcilable with reason and demanded a peace confederation of all the peoples: Whereas a peace treaty brings only one war to an end, this peace confederation was to seek the end of all wars for all time.

Immanuel Kant never left Königsberg during his lifetime and, because of his weak constitution, followed a strictly regulated daily routine so that he would be able to complete the extensive works he had planned.

Keyserlingk, Carl Graf von (1868—1928), p. 202

Estate Director and Member of the Board of Management of Vom Rath, Schöller & Skene AG, Klettendorf near Breslau, which operated a large sugar refinery in Klettendorf with 18 associated estates totalling 7,500 hectares. Under the aegis of the Anthroposophical Society, when a "Limited Company for the Promotion of Economic and Spiritual Values", referred to as the "Coming Day", was founded in 1920, he assumed as an additional activity the management of the "Coming Day" estates in Württemberg, which were to be farmed according to anthroposophic principles. At his behest, an "agricultural course" was held by Dr Rudolf Steiner at Whitsun 1924 at his residence Koberwitz estate (485 hectares) near Breslau, in which he propounded his views on the reorganization of agriculture on anthroposophic lines. In his talks, Dr Steiner explains that, as regards nutrition for humans, animals and plants, it was less the chemical-material relationships that were important than cosmic and dynamic forces. With the aid of biological-dynamic products acting as "accumulators", powerful forces could be brought to bear upon earth and plants and thereby on animals and man. This biological-dynamic mode of operation would, it was claimed, eliminate the need for mineral fertilizers and crop protection products. Many farmers who adopted these methods in the hope of reducing their expenditure on fertilizers and crop protectants only fell deeper into debt when their productivity slumped by 25 to 50 per cent. Since this new farming method could not be introduced on the estates of Rath, Schöller and Skeene, Count Keyserlingk left the company and purchased the agricultural enterprise Sasterhausen (318 hectares) on which he hoped to put the "Koberwitz impulse" into practice, but this soon had to be abandoned because of management difficulties. Koberwitz was renamed Rößlingen in 1933 (cf. also Steiner).

Kokoschka, Oskar (1886—1980), p. 107

Painter, graphic artist and poet, one of the major artists of German Expressionism.

Lawes, Sir John Bennet (1814—1900), p. 102

British landowner and chemist who established a superphosphate factory on his hereditary estate of Rothamsted in 1843, in which crude phosphates were processed with sulphuric acid into phosporous fertilizers and who, also in 1843, in cooperation with the chemist J.H. Gilbert, conducted the celebrated long-term fertilization trials in cereals and other species of crop plants, which have meanwhile been evaluated over a period of 140 years for the yield pattern in relation to fertilization, soil cultivation and weather variations. Rothamsted, now a foundation, is the oldest agricultural experimental station which has been continuously in existence from that time.

Leibniz, Gottfried Wilhelm Freiherr von (1646—1716), p. 209

Lawyer, mathematician and philosopher. The first German thinker of European status in modern times, founder of modern German philosophy, constructed the first calculating machine and in 1700 founded the Prussian Academy of Sciences. From 1667 he was Privy Councillor of Justice in the service of the Duke of Brunswick-Lüneburg.

Le Nôtre, Andre (1613—1700), p. 179

French garden designer. After studying painting and architecture, this scion of a gardening family in the service of the royal household was appointed director of the Tuileries gardens. He is regarded as the original creator of French garden landscaping of the Baroque, reflected in many of his castle gardens and particularly in Versailles.

Leonardo da Vinci (1452—1519), p. 200

Italian artist, engineer and naturalist of the highest universality and European rank. Among his last artistic creations are the plans of Chambord castle and its parks for the French king and his drawings of the end of the world.

Leontief, Wassily (* 1906), p. 198

American political economist, professor at Harvard University, 1973 Nobel prize for economic science, known for the input-output analysis he developed; in the context of the technological revolution in the computer age, he demands that national economic policy should provide for a more just distribution of work and income, without thereby directly or indirectly hindering technical progress.

Liebig, Justus von (1803—1873), p. 102, 199, 200, 201

Chemist. After studies in Bonn, Erlangen and Paris, at the age of 21 appointed professor of chemistry in Gießen in 1824, in Munich in 1852. His scientific work was concerned mainly with plants and animal nutrition and provided the scientific basis for mineral fertilization. His chief work on agrochemistry, published in 1840 "Organic Chemistry as Applied to Agriculture and Physiology" appeared in nine, and "Chemical Letters" in six editions up to 1876.

Louis XIV, King of France (1638—1715), p. 179

King of France for 72 years. During his reign, Le Nôtre created the gardens of Versailles and of numerous other French castles.

Malpighi, Marcello (1628—1694), p. 102

Italian naturalist, 1662—1691 professor of medicine in Bologna, Pisa and Messina. He was the first to use the microscope systematically for the investigation of plant and animal tissue and is regarded as the founder of microscopy.

Malthus, Thomas Robert (1766—1834), p. 209

Malthus was trained as a clergyman and from 1805 was professor of history and political economy in England. In his "An Essay on the Principle of Population", first published in 1798, he propounded a basically pessimistic view. The population principle he elaborated states that the multiplication of man occurs in geometric manner and that of food production in arithmetic progression or growth. The slow development of the yield increase in food was essentially a consequence of the law of the decreasing yield growth of the soil. The book attracted considerable controversy. After extensive studies and journeys throughout Europe, the second edition of the work appeared in 1803, in which he confirmed his theses and the German version of which appeared as early as 1807.

Maria Theresia, Queen of Hungaria and Bohemia, Archduchess of Austria and German Empress (1717—1780), p. 134

As a result of the reforms she introduced, the serfdom of peasants and the performance of socage labour was moderated and the development of agriculture encouraged.

Mariotte, Edme (1620—1684), p. 102

French physicist.

McLean, Gordon (mid 20th century), p. 98

Practical fruit grower in Kingston (Berkshire/Great Britain), who developed the "pillar system" in apple cultivation, a system of dense plantation in which the trees are grown in pillar arrangement designed to achieve an earlier start of yield and thus a more rapid return on investment. Dense plantings were also established at the start of the 20th century.

Mendel, Gregor Johann (1822—1884), p. 180, 207

Theologian (abbot) and scientist, 1843 entered the Augustinian foundation of Brünn, on conclusion of his theological and scientific studies teacher of natural history and physics in Brünn. From 1856—1863 cross-fertilization experiments in a total of 19,000 pea plants on 250 square metres in the monastery garden at Brünn, which led to the discovery of the laws of inheritance, known as "Mendel's Laws". The laws elaborated by Mendel were at first ignored and only rediscovered in 1900. He is regarded as the theoretical and practical founder of genetics and in particular of plant breeding.

Mill, John Stuart (1806—1873), p. 209

English philosopher and political economist. Chief proponent of classical political economy.

Montadon, R. (20th century), p. 212

French geographer of the University of Paris who in 1923 at the Revue Intern. de la Croix-Rouge presented an exhibition showing the importance and geographical distribution of disasters caused by earthquakes, volcanos, hurricanes, floods, famines and pests.

Müller, Hans and Rusch, H.P. (20th century), p. 203

Dr Hans Müller and the biologist Hans Peter Rusch are the founders of the organic-biological farming method.

Pliny, Gaius P. Secundus, the Elder (23—79 A.D.), p. 13, 14

Roman writer who died in the eruption of Vesuvius. He travelled throughout Gaul, Germania, Spain and Africa. Of his numerous writings, his Natural History (Historia Naturalis) in 37 books has been preserved, this being the first work to include all natural phenomena in an ordered, encyclopedic manner (cosmology, geography, botany, zoology, medicine, mineralogy etc.).

Prentice, Ezra Parmelee (20th century), p. 9

American writer.

Ramses III, King of Egypt (1188—1157 B.C.), p. 26

Egyptian king of the 20th dynasty, under whose reign (1184—1153 B.C.) the country experienced a great flowering.

Raphael (Santi, Raffaello) (1483—1520), p. 179

Italian painter and architect.

Rigo, D. (16th century), p. 12

It was with Rigo that Konrad Heresbach held his didactic conversations on farming which were published in 1570 as a four-volume work by Birckmann in Cologne. This is the first book dealing with German agriculture.

Schrader, Gerhard (*1903), p. 208

Chemist, from 1934 over a period of more than four decades synthesized numerous insecticides from organic fluorine and phosphorus compounds, including particularly the systemic insecticides, which are taken up by roots and leaves and translocated within the plants to the site of action.

Smith, Adam (1723—1790), p. 38

Philosopher and political economist of Scottish birth, from 1751 professor in Glasgow, regarded as the founder of classical political economics.

Sörgel, Hermann (20th century), p. 213

Engineer and writer (Atlantropa).

Solomon, King of Israel and Judah (10th century B.C.), p. 10

His reign (circa 965—926 B.C.) was the golden age because of his great wisdom. In oriental tradition, Solomon is the ideal of a wise and powerful ruler. Many texts in the Old Testament are attributed to him (cf. Proverbs of Solomon). The "Judgement of Solomon" was depicted artistically by Raphael on a ceiling fresco.

Sprengel, Carl (1787—1859), p. 102

Farmer and chemist, professor of agriculture at Braunschweig, founder and director of the Institute of Advanced Agricultural Teaching at Regenwalde. He applied chemical knowledge to agricultural soil science, including fertilizer science, and elaborated the theory of minerals which states that soil nutrients depleted by harvested crops must be replaced by mineral fertilization.

Steiner, Rudolf (1861—1925), p. 202

Philosopher and scientist, after studying mathematics and science in Vienna from 1882—1897, participated in editing Goethe's scientific writings, the Sophien edition, and was active at the Goethe and Schiller archive in Weimar, 1891 received his doctoral degree (Dr phil) in Rostock with his thesis on "Truth and Science", 1899—1904 taught at the Berlin School for the Education of Workers, 1901 lectured at the Theosophical Society, 1913 founded the Anthroposophical Society, 1919 proclaimed the idea of the "tripartite social organism" with the demand that economic life should be completely independent of the state; in 1920, to put these principles into practice, founded a "Limited Company for the Promotion of Economic and Spiritual Values" also known as "The Coming Day", 1920 start of the first anthroposophical university level course in the Goetheanum in Dornach (Switzerland), 1923 relaunching of the Anthroposophical Society, 1924 at Whitsun "Agricultural Course" at Koberwitz estate (Silesia) at the initiative of Count Keyserlingk, where Rudolf Steiner expounded his thoughts as an agricultural layman on the reorganization of agriculture from the anthroposophic perspective.

Whereas the scientific ideas of Goethe, based on thorough studies over several decades, concerning for instance the dispute with Newton on the theory of colour, today have a largely historical dimension, the amateurish agricultural ideas of the Goethian Rudolf Steiner are currently enjoying a revival. After the first wave of enthusiasm as a consequence of the First World War with its economic crisis and inflation and the second wave in which they were promoted as "farming in accordance with the laws of nature" by the ideologists of National Socialism (1933—1945), his ideas, in a climate of fear for survival and concern for the environment, are now again being propagated as an ecological refuge and a return to the "good old days", often with considerable commercial skill.

Strabo (63 B.C.—23 A.D.), p. 16

Greek geographer who traveled extensively and also visited Egypt. His work "Geographika" which was published in 17 books, most of which have survived, is of great importance for our knowledge of the world of antiquity.

Sylvaticus, Matthaeus (1277—1342), p. 180

Italian botanist, cultivated and observed rare plants in his botanical garden in Salerno, since in the Middle Ages Salerno possessed a celebrated medical school. Author of a botanical encyclopedia on several thousands of plant species, stating their medicinal uses. Important source for pharmacology.

Thaer, Albrecht Daniel (1752—1828), p. 102, 200

Physician and farmer, first practised in Celle as a doctor and agricultural teacher, in 1807 as Prussian Councillor of State in Möglin (Oderbruch), at the behest of the Prussian King founded an agricultural teaching institute with experimental farm, which in 1824 was given the status of royal academy of agriculture. Thaer was also a professor of agriculture at the University of Berlin. His achievement consists in using scientific knowledge in agriculture and applying in Germany the agricultural advances achieved in England.

Theophrastus (372—287 B.C.), p. 137

Greek philosopher and most important pupil of Aristotle. His numerous writing include a systematic presentation of botany in which he describes 500 plant species, which is of particular interest as a source from antiquity.

Thünen, Johann Heinrich von (1783—1850), p. 200, 206, 215

Agriculturalist and political economist, who established a model farm on his Tellow estate in Mecklenburg and who, on the basis of his managerial analysis of yields, labour economy and expenditure, developed his celebrated theory of location. In his theoretical model "The Isolated State" circles are drawn around an isolated city marking concentric zones of agricultural production which differ in intensity depending on the proximity or distance of the market.

Tillet, Mathieu (1714—1791), p. 201

Director of the Mint in Troyes (France), basing on work performed for a prize competition of the Academy at Bordeaux held in 1750 on the subject "On the Causes of Smut on Cereal and the Means of its Control", Tillet succeeded in comprehensive experiments over several years in proving the transmissibility of stinking smut of wheat by infection.

Varro, Marcus Terentius (116—27 B.C.), p. 12, 13

Prominent Roman writer, appointed senior librarian of the Empire by Caesar in 47 B.C. Only a small number of his 70 works have survived in their entirety. His late work on farming (Rerum rusticarum libri III) composed in dialogue form in 37 B.C. was used by Konrad Heresbach as a source for his work on farming which was published in Cologne in 1570.

Vergil, Publius Vergilius Maro (70—19 B.C.), p. 105

Roman poet, his four-part didactic poem "Georgica" (On Farming) written between 37 and 29 B.C. deals with I. arable farming, II. fruit growing and viniculture, III. animal husbandry and IV. beekeeping. The Georgica is not intended to give instruction in the manner of a farmer's almanac, but to keep alive love of the country and respect for the peaceful and natural work of countrymen.

Vulpius, Christiane (1765—1816), p. 128

Wife of the poet Johann Wolfgang von Goethe (cf. p. 233)

Wehnelt, Bruno (1902—1945), p. 6

Botanist, after receiving his doctorate in 1927 for his work on the subject of the necrohormone of plants ("Wehnelt Test"), five years as an assistant at the University of Erlangen, followed by employment at the Reich Biological Research Centre. In 1934 for political reasons entered employment with I.G. Farbenindustrie Aktiengesellschaft as head of the growth hormone laboratory in Leverkusen. Also wrote historical works on Johann Rudolf Glauber, Mathieu Tillet and plant pathology of the German Romantic Period. In recognition of his paper on Tillet, the Academy of Bordeaux appointed him its corresponding member in 1938. 1943 scientific director of Höfchen experimental farm in Burscheid, 1944 qualified as university lecturer at the University of Cologne, at the same time being appointed lecturer in botany. Conscripted into the Wehrmacht in autumn 1944 and executed py partisans on 7 May 1945 near Pilsen after the capitulation. Professor Weyland, then commercial director of the botanical institute of the University of Cologne, paid the following tribute in an obituary: "That this democrat by idealistic conviction should finally fall victim to the ideas of a collapsed political system which were so foreign to his instincts, and that fulfillment should so be denied him in a time so abundant in tragedy, is a misfortune which will always be painful to those who knew him."

The words of Bruno Wehnelt which provide the introduction to this book are taken from a historical work on "Grain Weevil Control in the Ancient Orient" dating from 1934. The edition of the "Information on Pest Control", already printed as Issue 2/1934, was reprinted without Wehnelt's article for political reasons. A facsimile was printed in 1979 in Issue 3 of Volume 32 (50) of Pflanzenschutz-Nachrichten Bayer as a tribute to his scientific achievements.

Xenophon (430—354 B.C.), p. 13

Greek chronicler, who produced both historical and political works and writings concerning public finances and property and estate management.